DEGRADATION OF FILLED POLYMERS
High Temperature and
Thermal-oxidative Processes

Ellis Horwood Series in
POLYMER SCIENCE AND TECHNOLOGY
Series Editors: T. J. KEMP, University of Warwick
J. F. KENNEDY, University of Birmingham

This series, which covers both natural and synthetic macromolecules, reflects knowledge and experience
from research, development and manufacture within both industry and academia. It deals with the general
characterization and properties of materials from chemical and engineering viewpoints and will include
monographs highlighting polymers of wide economic and industrial significance as well as of particular
fields of application.

DEGRADATION OF FILLED POLYMERS
High Temperature and Thermal-oxidative Processes

M. T. BRYK Dr.Sci
Institute of Colloidal Chemistry
Ukranian Academy of Sciences, Kiev, USSR

Translator
K. A. BABUTKINA
Naukova Dumka Publishers
Ukranian Academy of Sciences, Kiev, USSR

Translation Editor
T. J. KEMP
Department of Chemistry, University of Warwick

ELLIS HORWOOD
NEW YORK   LONDON   TORONTO   SYDNEY   TOKYO   SINGAPORE

This English edition first published in 1991 by
ELLIS HORWOOD LIMITED
Market Cross House, Cooper Street,
Chichester, West Sussex, PO19 1EB, England

A division of
Simon & Schuster International Group
A Paramount Communications Company

This English edition is translated from the original Russian edition *Destruktsiia napolnenykh polimerov*, published in 1989 by Khimiya, Moscow, © the copyright holders
© English Edition, Ellis Horwood 1991

Typeset in Times by Ellis Horwood Limited
Printed and bound in Great Britain
by Hartnolls Limited, Bodmin, Cornwall.

British Library Cataloguing in Publication Data

Bryk, M. T.
Degradation of filled polymers: High temperature and thermal-oxidative processes. —
(Ellis Horwood series in polymer science and technology)
I. Title   II. Series
620.1
ISBN 0–13–202490–X

Library of Congress Cataloging-in-Publication Data

Bryk, M. T. (Mikhail Teodorovich)
[Destruktsiia napolnenykh polimerov. English]
Degradation of filled polymers: high temperature and thermal-oxidative processes /
M. T. Bryk: translation editor T. J. Kemp.
p. cm. — (Ellis Horwood series in polymer science and technology)
Translation of: Destruktsiia napolnenykh polimerov.
Includes bibliographical references and index.
ISBN 0–13–202490–X
1. Polymeric composites — Thermal properties. 2. Polymeric composites — Deterioration.
3. Materials at high temperatures.
I. Title. II. Series.
TA418.9.C6B7313   1991
620.1′9217—dc20
91–19896
CIP

Contents

Preface

Polymers are rather heat-sensitive which presents problems, and considerable efforts are made to find ways of increasing their thermal stability. Both the thermal stability of polymers, defined as the limiting temperature which gives rise to chemical variations in a polymer affecting its properties, and the thermal and thermal–oxidative degradation processes of polymers have been studied in depth. However, at present the overwhelming majority of polymers are employed as composites. Until very recently the behaviour of polymer composites had been studied only to a limited extent, though the scientific and applied significance of such investigations is undoubtedly high.

The introduction of disperse mineral fillers into polymers induces substantial changes in their physicochemical and mechanical properties, which are caused by variation in the mobility of the macromolecules in boundary layers, the orientating influence of the filler surface, and different types of filler–polymer interaction as well as by the effect of fillers on the chemical composition and structure of polymers formed in their presence during the hardening and polymerization of monomers and oligomers. Indeed, the above factors have also a substantial influence on the thermal and thermal–oxidative degradation of filled polymers and, consequently, on their thermal stability. Accordingly, results and trends obtained during studies of the degradation of normal (unfilled) polymers do not necessarily apply to polymer composites.

Although in recent years the number of publications on the degradation of filled polymers has increased, systematic investigations on this problem are still few. Besides, the literature data on the degradation of filled polymers are in some cases contradictory, a problem associated with differences in the specific surface area of the fillers employed and in the methods used for their preparation and introduction into the polymers, as well as with the absence (or disregard) of data on the surface chemistry of disperse fillers.

Introduction into polymers of mineral fillers with definite surface-chemical properties may either accelerate or inhibit different stages of the degradation process, and also may change the mechanisms of these reactions. The diversity of disperse mineral fillers (differing essentially in their surface chemistry) and the different classes of polymers impedes a general approach to the thermal and thermal–oxidative degradation of filled polymers. It becomes more and more evident that disperse mineral fillers play the role of heterogeneous components in the high-temperature chemical processes of polymer degradation which proceed at the polymer–filler interface. It should be noted that disperse fillers, especially as regards their surface, undergo chemical changes due to the high-temperature surface reactions.

The author has made an attempt to generalize patterns in the thermal and thermal–oxidative degradation of filled polymers, noting that the surface chemistry of disperse mineral fillers substantially influences these processes and that fillers are directly involved in the high-temperature chemical reactions.

Taking into account the significance of experimental procedures in the study of polymer degradation, the author considers it necessary to present the methods, equipment and instruments employed for these purposes, with due regard for the special features of the degradation of filled polymers.

The thermal and thermal–oxidative degradation of filled polymers is considered with due regard to the effects of the chemical structure and composition of polymers as well as to surface chemistry and thermal properties of the disperse inorganic fillers.

ACKNOWLEDGEMENTS

The author wishes to thank Professor T. J. Kemp of the University of Warwick and co-editor of the Ellis Horwood Series Polymer Science & Technology for his constructive and most valuable help and guidance during the editing of this book.

1

Polymeric components of composites and their thermal stability

The dependence of the characteristic properties of polymers on their chemical structure and composition has always been one of the major problems in the synthesis and physical chemistry of high-molecular-mass compounds.

Many studies of the characteristic properties of polymers have shown that they are determined not only by the structure of the repeat unit but also by both the conformation of the macromolecular chains and the supramolecular organization of the polymer. These point to a rather complex relationship between the structure, composition and the many characteristic properties of polymers, including their thermal resistance or stability. The latter is understood as the limiting temperature giving rise to some change, normally degradation, in the polymer which influences its other properties.

The thermal stability of polymers is a characteristic rather sensitive not only to their structure and composition but, in line with other phenomena associated with chemical processes, to the action of environmental factors, especially the presence of chemically active components in the environment such as oxygen, additives and fillers.

Such an approach may also be adopted when considering the thermal degradation of polymers filled with those disperse inorganic fillers which are chemically active and are able to participate in high temperature chemical reactions with polymers. Any analysis of the thermal resistance of filled polymers and investigation of their degradation at elevated temperatures requires the chemical properties of the filler surface, and their dependence on temperature and the nature of the polymer to be taken into account. Also of importance are those chemical and structural phase changes which may occur with the fillers on heating the filled polymer. Thus, making due allowance for the filler as a component of the chemical processes, induced on heating filled polymers, may help to clarify those difficulties and contradictions which appear when studying the thermal stability of composite polymer systems. The situation becomes more complicated if the degradation processes of filled polymers are studied in the presence of oxygen, since in this case a multicomponent system (polymer, filler, oxygen, thermal–oxidative degradation products) is involved, whose composition and properties change rapidly at high temperatures.

Taking into account the complexity of the chemical processes occurring on degradation of filled polymers, and the significance of the thermal behaviour of certain components in understanding these, we shall consider the thermal stability of the principal components of polymer composites (polymers and inorganic fillers) and the influence of the structure and composition of both the polymers and fillers upon it.

1.1   INFLUENCE OF CHEMICAL STRUCTURE AND COMPOSITION OF POLYMERS ON THEIR THERMAL AND THERMAL–OXIDATIVE STABILITY

The chemical classification of high-molecular-mass compounds suggested by Korshak [1], based on the structure of the main chain of the macromolecule, has been used to consider their thermal and thermal–oxidative stability. According to this scheme, all polymers are divided into two basic groups: carbochain or carbocyclochain and heterochain or heterocyclochain polymers; the latter also includes elemento-organic and silicon–organic polymers.

1.1.1   Carbochain and carbocyclochain polymers
Polyalkenes (polyethylene, polypropylene, polyisobutylene, etc.)
The action of heat on polymers, including polyalkenes, initially induces degradation, i.e. the break-up of macromolecular chains and the formation of low-molecular-mass products. Simultaneously there is the opposite effect, i.e. the cross-linking of the macromolecules. It is customary to designate the whole complex of chemical processes proceeding under the influence of heat as thermal degradation, and this problem has been thoroughly covered in monographs [2–4]. In this book the mechanisms of the reactions of degradation and cross-linking of polymers are considered to a degree enabling the role of fillers in these processes to be understood.

A mechanism [5] involving two equilibrium stages, i.e. the formation of free radicals and abstraction of hydrogen atoms by these radicals, has been suggested for the thermal degradation of alkanes and polyalkenes. The initiation of polyalkene degradation consists of the cleavage of the carbon–carbon bond of the macromolecules to form free radicals:

$$\sim CH_2-CH_2-CH_2-CH_2\sim \longrightarrow \sim CH_2-\dot{C}H_2 + \dot{C}H_2-CH_2\sim \qquad (1.1)$$

Such cleavage occurs at the weakest bonds (the tertiary carbon atom in groups containing other atoms, etc.).

The scission of the chain, with the elimination of small amounts (1%) of monomer, occurs at its free-radical ends, a process which has been termed 'unzipping':

$$\sim CH_2-CH_2-CH_2-\dot{C}H_2 \longrightarrow \sim CH_2-\dot{C}H_2 + CH_2=CH_2 \qquad (1.2)$$

The chain transfer, in which the free radical abstracts a hydrogen atom, may proceed both intra- and intermolecularly. In this case both saturated and unsaturated groups are formed at the chain ends together with a new free radical:

$$\sim CH_2-\dot{C}H_2 + \sim CH_2-CH_2-CH_2-CH_2\sim \longrightarrow \sim CH_2-CH_3 +$$
$$\sim CH_2-CH_2-CH=CH_2 \text{ or } \sim CH_2-\dot{C}H-CH_2-CH_2\sim \qquad (1.3)$$

Chain scission occurs owing to the recombination of two free radicals with the formation of one linear or branched chain and, in some cases, of a cross-linked polymer. As is seen from the reaction schemes given, free radicals formed during polyalkene degradation are involved in two competing reactions: free radical transfer of a hydrogen atom and chain scission to form monomer. The number of hydrogen atoms in the chain determines which reaction will predominate. Since polyethylene is the polyalkene most saturated with hydrogen atoms, the chain transfer reaction predominates. The low yield of monomer during the thermal degradation of polyethylene may thus be associated with this mechanism.

If a fraction of the hydrogen atoms in the polyalkene chain are replaced by methyl or other small groups, then the hydrogen atom transfer process becomes difficult; this leads to the formation of free radicals which continue polymer degradation to produce monomer. For instance, during the thermal degradation of polyisobutylene, the cleavage of a fraction of the carbon–carbon bonds causes the formation of free radicals which promote chain scission to produce monomer (in up to 18% yield):

$$\sim CH_2-C(CH_3)_2-\dot{C}H_2 \longrightarrow \sim \dot{C}H_2 + C(CH_3)_2=CH_2 \qquad (1.4)$$

The thermal decomposition of polyalkenes may be presented as follows. In contrast to low-molecular-mass substances, for instance alkanes, macromolecules do not behave as a single kinetic unit: some of their elements may acquire greater amounts of energy, while the others may acquire less. At the same time all three types of motion of these elements of the macromolecule are limited by their being chemically bound to the remainder of the macromolecule with its large dimensions. The resultant fluctuation in tensions leads to the cleavage of chemical bonds occurring in different parts of the macromolecule. If, as in polyethylene, there are sufficient quantities of mobile hydrogen atoms in the chain, then such a macromolecular scission is accompanied by the abstraction of a hydrogen atom from the carbon atom nearest to the site of scission. However, when the hydrogen atom content is low, as in polyisobutylene and propylene, the occurrence of chain scission is *not* accompanied by the transfer of hydrogen atoms. Instead, the free radicals formed continue the process of chain cleavage to form monomer.

The thermal degradation reactions of polymers, including polyalkenes, proceed at temperatures considerably lower than those of thermal homolytic degradation. In some cases the features of oxidation can be observed at room temperature in polymers which have not been well-protected from the action of atmospheric oxygen. Thus, problems of the thermal–oxidative stability of polymers are of great practical importance as compared with normal thermal stability.

It is known [2] that three basic types of reaction proceed in polymers in the presence of oxygen:

(a) oxidation as a process of certain molecular reactions;
(b) oxidation via a chain mechanism;
(c) oxidation of polymer thermolysis products, the oxidized products being catalysts of the subsequent polymer decomposition.

Oxidation via a chain mechanism is the commonest process, which is properly considered to be analogous to the autoxidation of low-molecular-mass substances [6].

Most polymers, including polyalkenes, are oxidized at high temperatures by autoacceleration. Autoxidation is characterized by the presence of an induction period during which no noticeable transformation of the polymer is observed. After the induction period the oxidation rate grows sharply and may reach large values for a short time. Thus, for high-pressure polyethylene powder, the induction period at 413 K is 5 h (Fig. 1.1) [7]. During the induction period the temperature of the polymer gradually rises, and on its termination the temperature rises sharply. In the same period the rate of oxygen uptake by the polymer increases greatly.

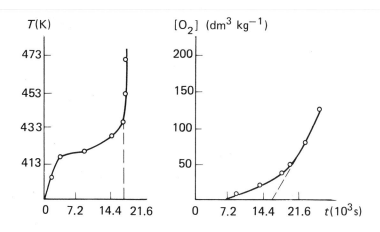

Fig. 1.1 — Kinetics of changes in the temperature and oxygen consumption by a polyethylene sample during thermal oxidation (thermostatted at 413 K) [7].

Studies on the mechanism of polyalkene oxidation have shown that hydroperoxides are its primary products, which then decompose to form other oxygen-containing compounds [6]. The oxidation of polyalkenes is described by a radical-chain scheme as follows. Initiation may occur with the formation of radicals $R\cdot$ or $RO_2\cdot$.

$$R-R \longrightarrow R\cdot + R\cdot \qquad R\cdot + O_2 \longrightarrow RO_2\cdot \tag{1.5}$$

but in the case of the developed oxidation process, initiation occurs owing to the decomposition of hydroperoxides with the formation of radicals by monomolecular or bimolecular reactions [15]:

$$ROOH \longrightarrow RO\cdot + \cdot OH \tag{1.6}$$
$$2ROOH \longrightarrow RO\cdot + RO_2\cdot + H_2O \tag{1.7}$$

The radicals formed attack the C−H groups of polyalkenes to produce hydroperoxides

$$RO_2\cdot + RH \longrightarrow ROOH + R\cdot \tag{1.8}$$

which, on decomposing, initiate new kinetic oxidation chains. Hydroperoxides, being thermally unstable primary products of the chain oxidation of polyalkenes, in addition to decomposing into radicals, may also decompose via a molecular mechanism to form stable oxygen-containing polymer and low-molecular-mass compounds.

The termination of the kinetic chain of oxidative degradation of polyalkenes is attributable to the reactions:

$$2R\cdot \longrightarrow R-R \tag{1.9}$$

$$R\cdot + RO_2\cdot \longrightarrow ROOR \tag{1.10}$$

$$2RO_2\cdot \longrightarrow ROOR + O_2 \tag{1.11}$$

For ideal polyethylene molecules (e.g. polymethylene) the susceptibility to attack by oxygen is the same for all methylene groups, whereas double bonds are especially vulnerable to oxygen via addition:

$$\sim CH=CH-CH_2\sim\cdot + O_2 \longrightarrow \sim CH-\overset{\centerdot}{C}H-CH_2\sim \tag{1.12}$$
$$\underset{\displaystyle O_2\cdot}{\vert}$$

However, the predominant oxidation of methylene groups in the β-position to double bonds may occur [2]:

$$\sim CH=CHCH_2\sim + O_2 \longrightarrow \sim CH=CH-\overset{\centerdot}{C}H\sim + HO_2\cdot \tag{1.13}$$

The biradical formed via reaction (1.12) may be completely or partially deactivated:

$$\sim CH-\overset{\cdot}{C}H-CH_2\sim \;+\; \sim CH=CH-CH_2\sim \;\longrightarrow$$
$$\qquad\quad |$$
$$\qquad\quad OO\cdot$$
$$\longrightarrow \sim CH-\overset{\cdot}{C}H-CH_2\sim \;+\; \sim CH=CH-\overset{\cdot}{C}H\sim$$
$$\qquad\quad |$$
$$\qquad\quad OOH$$

(1.14)

$$\sim CH-\overset{\cdot}{C}H-CH_2\sim \;+\; \sim CH=CH-CH_2\sim \;\longrightarrow$$
$$\qquad\quad |$$
$$\qquad\quad OOH$$
$$\longrightarrow \sim CH-CH_2-CH_2\sim \;+\; \sim CH=CH-\overset{\cdot}{C}H\sim$$
$$\qquad\quad |$$
$$\qquad\quad OOH$$

(1.15)

The numerous schemes suggested for this type of hydroperoxide decomposition are not always well substantiated. The chemical structure of the polyalkene, as well as the process conditions (presence of admixtures, additives, temperature, etc.) play a decisive role in realizing one or other mechanism of hydroperoxide decomposition.

Reactions with participation of hydroperoxide groups and radicals cause cleavage of the molecular chain, i.e. polymer degradation. Additionally, structural changes associated with branching, cross-linking and cyclization of macromolecules take place on autoxidation of polyalkenes. However, one should note that these processes are typical only of polymers with double bonds, whereas saturated macrochains, especially containing side-groups, are subject to degradation processes.

Polyethylene
It is known [2,3] that, in the absence of oxygen, polyethylene is thermally stable. The decomposition of this polymer begins above 560 K, and near to 630 K its thermal degradation proceeds rapidly with the elimination of considerable quantities of volatile materials [3]. The half-life temperature (i.e. that leading to 50% weight-loss on heating for 40–45 min) of polyethylene is 679 K [1,3]. Only 1% of monomer is formed during the thermal degradation of polyethylene, which indicates the absence of the chain depolymerization reaction of this polymer. Since all carbon–carbon bonds in polyethylene (except for those sited at the chain ends, at branching sites and at other side-groups) possess the same strength, then the probability of their degradation on heating is the same. Thus the pattern of thermal degradation of polyethylene macromolecules is random.

It has been found [3] that, on the thermal degradation of comparatively low-molecular-mass polyethylene *in vacuo* or in a nitrogen atmosphere under normal pressure, the volatile products of degradation consist of molecular fragments of polyethylene macromolecules. The viscosity-average molecular mass of the residue falls sharply on a 10-h exposure above 588 K (Fig. 1.2) [3]. Subsequent heating leads

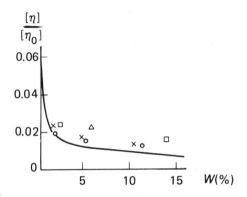

Fig. 1.2 — Variation in relative intrinsic viscosity of the residue from polymethylene decomposition (W is the degree of conversion) [3]: △ at 648 K; □ at 653 K; X at 663 K; ○ at 673 K; the solid curve is that calculated.

to a smoother decrease in the molecular mass of the polymer. The degradation of polyethylene in a nitrogen atmosphere results in growth of its unsaturation with the extent of its decomposition; this may be associated with the disproportionation of more low-molecular-mass macroradicals at their end-groups or with the transfer of hydrogen atoms from two neighbouring carbon atoms of the main chain.

Analysis of the degradation products of polyethylene produced *in vacuo* and under atmospheres of nitrogen and helium at different temperatures made it possible to establish that the higher the decomposition temperature, the lower the molecular mass of the decomposition products, and the larger the fraction of gaseous compounds [3]. Thus, the fraction of ethylene is 0% at 773 K, 5.5% at 1073 K and 26.4% at 1473 K. This may be explained by the fact that, at temperatures above 1073 K, both competing reactions proceed, i.e. the cleavage of chains into comparatively high-molecular-mass fragments with the transfer of hydrogen atoms, and the cleavage of free macroradicals via the chain mechanism to form monomer [2,3]. The rate and significance of the latter process increase at higher temperatures.

Studies on the thermal degradation of polyethylene samples with different molecular masses in the isothermal regime at different temperatures have shown that the kinetic curves have linear plots up to 70% weight loss (Fig. 1.3) [3], which point to a zero-order reaction. The activation energy of thermal degradation increases with the molecular mass of the polymer from 192.3 kJ mol^{-1} (molecular mass 11 000) up to 276.3 kJ mol^{-1} (molecular mass 23 000) [19].

A comparison of the decomposition processes of three polyethylene samples (commercial polyethylene having a molecular mass of 20 000, unbranched high-molecular-mass polymethylene and strongly branched polyethylene) differing in

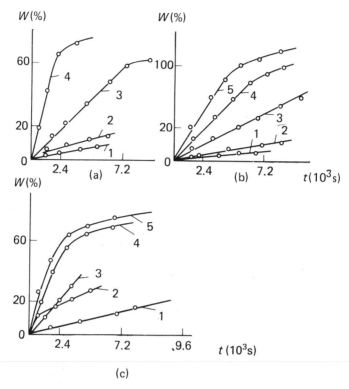

Fig. 1.3 — Kinetic curves of the thermal degradation of polyethylene with molecular mass 23 000 (a), 16 000 (b) and 11 000 (c) at different temperatures: (a) 1, 678 K; 2, 666.5 K; 3, 685 K; 4, 709 K; (b) 1, 650 K; 2, 649 K; 3, 661.6 K; 4, 676 K; 5, 685 K; (c) 1, 647 K; 2, 666 K; 3, 683 K; 4, 693 K; 5, 669 K.

structure and molecular mass [3] has enabled the characterization of substantial differences in their thermal degradation.

The dependence of the degradation rate upon the extent of degradation was calculated from weight-loss curves of commercial polyethylene (Fig. 1.4) [3]. It was found that in its initial stage (up to 10–40%) the rate of the process is very high, but then it is sharply reduced and transforms into a virtually linear dependence, which is extrapolated to zero at 100% decomposition. Such a kinetic pattern derives from two main factors: (i) the polydisperse nature of the polymer, whose low-molecular-mass fractions are easily removed in the initial degradation stages and (ii) the presence of weak bonds in the main polymer chain caused by the presence of hydroperoxide and other groups. The weak links lead to the splitting of carbon–carbon bonds and other reactions in the initial stages of the process. These particular factors diminish in significance over the course of degradation, and the rate of the process decreases sharply.

Studies on the rate of thermal degradation of unbranched high-molecular-mass polyethylene (polymethylene) have shown that the process follows almost ideal first-order kinetics. The rate of thermal degradation is directly proportional to the

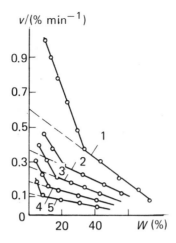

Fig. 1.4—Dependence of the rate of thermal degradation (v) of commercial PE with molecular mass 20 000 on the degree of decomposition at temperatures 1, 665 K; 2, 660 K; 3, 655 K; 4, 650 K; 5, 645 K [3].

temperature of the process. The dependences of the rate of elimination of volatiles on their quantity show complex behaviour. The rate curves pass through a maximum at degrees of decomposition from 2 to 10%, and then become gradually straight, finally falling to zero at 100% decomposition of the polymer.

As regards the thermal degradation of branched polyethylene, as in the case of low-molecular-mass commercial polyethylene, high rates of decomposition are observed in the initial stages of the process. After 15–30% decomposition of the polymer, the rate falls sharply.

A comparison of the rates of degradation of three types of polyethylene sample has established (Table 1.1) [3] that they are approximately equal at the same temperatures, but the activation energy is higher for polymethylene than for low-molecular-mass and branched polyethylenes.

The thermal stability of polyethylene decreases sharply in the presence of oxygen. This effect is clearly observed at elevated temperatures, which promote rapid development of the oxidative processes that essentially decrease the mechanical properties of polyethylene. Thus, low-pressure polyethylene (0.93 g cm^{-3}) completely loses its mechanical strength after exposure at 373 K for 48 h in air; the impact viscosity of such a material is only 7% of its initial value [2].

The oxidation process is complex, not only from the chemical but also from the physicochemical viewpoint which is owing to the uneven course of the process in the bulk of the polyethylene. It has been shown, in particular, that the amorphous zones of polyethylene, being more accessible to oxygen molecules than the densely packed crystalline regions, are oxidized at first. The amorphous zones of polyethylene act as a buffer, which protects the crystalline regions from attack during thermal degradation. Thus the increase in crystallinity results in an increase in sensitivity of the mechanical properties of ethylene to oxidation, though its oxidation rate is lower [2].

Table 1.1 — Thermal degradation of polyethylene (*in vacuo*) [3]

Decomposition temperature (K)	Duration of heating (h)	Total quantity of volatiles (% by mass)	Initial rate of degradation (% min^{-1})	Activation energy (kJ mol^{-1})
Commercial polyethylene (molecular mass 20 000)				
633	31	52	0.051	
645	8.5	49	0.160	
650	7.5	58	0.225	
655	7.2	70	0.340	263.3
660	4.6	71	0.480	
665	4.5	87	0.745	
Branched polyethylene				
623.9	54.5	39.6	0.0160	
628.4	3.1	38.6	0.022	
636.2	31.0	54.7	0.0430	267.5
645.6	25.0	75.3	0.0950	
Unbranched high-molecular-mass polyethylene (polymethylene)				
618	55.0	21.0	0.0080	
627.4	51.0	47.6	0.022	
635.4	37.8	60.6	0.0424	
639	9.0	28.4	0.053	300.9
644	8.0	38.1	0.109	
649	7.5	54.1	0.178	
659	6.5	78.2	0.413	
669	5.1	92.0	0.860	

Infrared (IR) spectroscopic study of the thermal oxidation of polyethylene under different temperature regimes established [8] that mainly ketone and aldehyde groups are formed in the oxidized polyethylene. Ester and anhydride groups are not present in the polymer.

Absorption bands typical of hydroperoxide groups are found in the spectra of oxidized polyethylene [3,8]. When the polyethylene melt is heated in air for 40 min the content of these groups increases and then becomes constant, a result most likely due to establishment of a dynamic equilibrium between the formation and decomposition of hydroperoxide groups.

Polypropylene and polyisobutylene
Since in the polypropylene macrochain every second carbon atom is tertiary and in polyisobutylene is quaternary, then the strength of the carbon–carbon bonds falls in going from polyethylene through polypropylene to polyisobutylene. This is clearly

confirmed by the data on the thermal degradation of propylene and polyisobutylene
in vacuo (Table 1.2) [3]. Comparison of the number of volatile products released at
corresponding temperatures has shown that polyisobutylene is less thermally stable
than polypropylene; thus the polypropylene half-life temperature is 660 K, while that
of polyisobutylene is 621 K [3].

Table 1.2 — Thermal degradation of polypropylene and polyisobutylene (0.5 h
in vacuo) [3]

Polypropylene		Polyisobutylene	
Decomposition temperature (K)	Quantity of volatiles (%)	Decomposition temperature (K)	Quantity of volatiles (%)
601	8.2	561	2.8
647	28.6	609	35.7
653	41.5	626	79.3
657	46.1	649	99.2
666	63.2	663	99.7
668	70.8	698	100.0
673	86.8	773	99.4
683	96.4	1073	96.6
1073	100.0		

Mass-spectroscopic analysis of the volatile fractions released by polypropylene
during its half-life at 653–683 K has shown [3] that propylene, butene, pentene,
hexene, butane, pentane and hexane are the main products of decomposition.

In propylene the tertiary hydrogen atom is more reactive, undergoing scission
more readily than the secondary hydrogen atom. Accordingly, bond cleavage in the
polymer chain occurs mainly with the transfer of a hydrogen atom:

$$\underset{\displaystyle \sim CH_2-CH-CH_2 \dashv CH-CH_2\sim}{\overset{\displaystyle \overset{\textstyle CH_3}{|} \qquad \overset{\textstyle CH_3}{|}}{}} \longrightarrow CH_2-C(CH_3)=CH_2 + \overset{\textstyle CH_3}{\overset{|}{CH_2-CH_2\sim}}$$

$$(1.16)$$

The cleavage of carbon–carbon bonds with the formation of free radicals and the
subsequent elimination of monomer molecules is more frequent than for
polyethylene.

The presence of two methyl groups at every second carbon atom of the
polyisobutylene chain causes steric difficulties for cleavage followed by transfer of a

hydrogen atom. This results in a considerable increase in the number of chain breaks with the formation of free radicals which, on decomposing by a chain mechanism, produce monomer:

$$\sim C(CH_3)_2-CH_2-C(CH_3)_2\overset{|}{\underset{|}{\cancel{}}}CH_2-C(CH_3)_2-CH_2\sim \longrightarrow C(CH_3)_2$$
$$-CH_2-\dot{C}(CH_3)_2 + \dot{C}H_2-C(CH_3)_2-CH_2\sim \tag{1.17}$$

$$\sim C(CH_3)_2\overset{|}{\underset{|}{\cancel{}}}CH_2-\dot{C}(CH_3)_2 \longrightarrow \sim\dot{C}(CH_3)_2 + CH_2{=}C(CH_3)_2 \tag{1.18}$$

Simultaneously a significant number of $C-C$ scissions occur with the transfer of hydrogen atoms, leading to the formation of compounds with saturated and unsaturated groups at the chain ends.

Studies on the rate of thermal degradation of polypropylene and polyisobutylene have shown that the reaction order determined over the linear sections of the kinetic curves is 1, and the activation energies for the degradation of polypropylene and polyisobutylene are 242.4 and 204.8 kJ mol^{-1} respectively [3].

The results of studies on the influence of molecular mass and molecular mass distribution of polyisobutylene on the kinetics of its thermal degradation are of interest as regards the effect of chemical structure on the thermal stability of the polymer. Several high- and low-molecular-mass fractions and non-fractionated samples of polyisobutylene with high and low molecular masses have been used in these studies. It has been found that the molecular mass of polyisobutylene sharply decreases from about 2×10^6 to about 25 000 in the initial period (10% of weight loss) of polymer degradation *in vacuo* at 573 K. Thereafter the decrease in molecular mass of the polymer decelerates.

In their initial stages of decomposition, the pattern of the dependence of the rate on the degree of decomposition differs for low-molecular and high-molecular-mass samples of polyisobutylene (Fig. 1.5) [3]. While a drastic decrease in the degradation

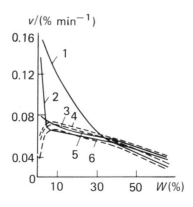

Fig. 1.5 — Dependence of the rate of thermal degradation on the degree of decomposition of polyisobutylene with different molecular masses [3]: 1, 23 400; 2, 49 000; 3, 440 000; 4, 100 000; 5, 198 000; 6, 700 000.

rate is typical of low-molecular-mass fractions (Fig. 1.5, curves 1–3), the occurrence of maxima in the rate curves within the same range of polymer degradation (10–20%) is typical of high-molecular-mass samples of polyisobutylene.

The high values of the initial rate of degradation of low-molecular-mass polyisobutylene are probably associated with the presence of very short chains, leading to formation of monomer which volatilizes.

At later stages of the process, the decomposition curves (Fig. 1.5) reveal that the initial values of the molecular mass of the polymer and its distribution have no critical influence on the rate of thermal degradation. This is explained by the fact that even in the initial stages of decomposition, the molecular mass of even high-molecular-mass polyisobutylene is sharply reduced through cleavages of the carbon–carbon bonds of the main chain to form low-molecular-mass (about 25 000) polymer and monomer.

The oxidation of polypropylene in the presence of oxygen occurs more rapidly than that of polyethylene. On oxidation, polyethylene becomes fragile and brief heating of polypropylene film at 373 K leads to its complete degradation [2]. Polyisoprene itself behaves in the same way. The presence of weak carbon–carbon bonds at the tertiary and quaternary carbon atoms promotes oxidation of these polymers to yield hydroperoxide groups [9]:

$$\sim CH_2-CH(CH_3)\sim \xrightarrow{O_2} \sim CH_2-\overset{\displaystyle OOH}{\overset{\displaystyle |}{C}}(CH_3)\sim \qquad (1.19)$$

as well as the oxidative decomposition by reactions (1.6)–(1.15). A trimolecular reaction of polypropylene with oxygen leading to primary initiation of the kinetic chains of oxidation has been proposed [10]. Here the influence of oxygen is shown not only on the decomposition process but also on the cross-linking of the polypropylene macromolecules.

Polybutadiene, polyisoprene and natural rubber

Studies on the thermal degradation *in vacuo* of reprecipitated polybutadiene at 653–668 K indicate [3] that the initial rate of the process (up to around 20% decomposition) is rather high (Fig. 1.6) [3], but later on it falls gradually, with a linear dependence on the quantity of volatile products. The activation energy of the thermal degradation of polybutadiene, calculated from its initial rates, is 259.2 kJ mol^{-1}. The temperature of the polybutadiene half-life is 680 K [9].

The molecular mass of the wax-like compounds which are volatile at the decomposition temperatures and comprise the basic mass (82–97%) of the products of the thermal degradation of polybutadiene is 739. The average yield of monomer on degradation of polybutadiene does not exceed 1.5% mass of the total quantity of volatile compounds, a result which may be associated with both the partial polymerization of the monomer produced, which is kept at room temperature, and the formation of vinylcyclohexane, reaction (1.20):

$v/(\% \ min^{-1})$

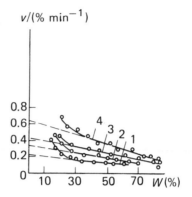

Fig. 1.6 — Dependence of the rate of thermal degradation of polybutadiene on the degree of decomposition at temperatures 1, 653 K; 2, 658 K; 3, 663 K; 4, 668 K [3].

$$(1.20)$$

It is possible to associate the small yield of monomer with the fact that most $C-C$ bonds scissions are accompanied by the transfer of hydrogen atoms. The formation of monomer is possible via cleavage of the carbon–carbon bonds located at the β-position relative to the double bond, which are the weakest, without transfer of a hydrogen atom [3]:

$$\sim H_2C-CH=CH-CH_2 \vdots CH_2-CH=CH-CH_2\sim \longrightarrow \sim CH_2-CH=$$
$$=CH-\dot{C}H_2 + \dot{C}H_2-CH=CH-CH_2\sim \qquad (1.21)$$

Studies on the thermal stability of polyisoprene, natural rubber (*cis*-polyisoprene) and gutta-percha (*trans*-polyisoprene) have been conducted virtually from the beginning of the chemistry of high-molecular-mass compounds [3]. However, any systematic study of their thermal stability has been performed only fairly recently. Of particular interest are comparative studies on the thermal degradation of polyisoprene, natural rubber and gutta-percha. They have the same chemical composition, but differ in that in natural rubber the isoprene links are coupled 'head to tail' and the *cis*-configuration predominates, whereas the *trans*-configuration is typical of gutta-percha and the irregular alternation of *cis*- and *trans*-configurations is observed in synthetic polyisoprene.

The decomposition of natural rubber, gutta-percha and synthetic polyisoprene *in vacuo* at 560–640 K has shown [3] that the thermal behaviour of these polymers has much in common (Fig. 1.7). It should be noted that the decomposition of natural rubber is initiated at comparatively low temperatures at a considerable rate, whereas its decomposition rate at higher temperatures (above 600 K) is to some extent slower than that of gutta-percha and polyisoprene.

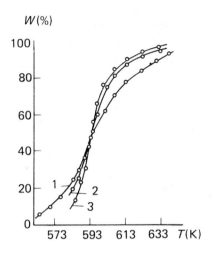

Fig. 1.7 — Dependence of the degree of thermal degradation of natural rubber (*cis*-polyisoprene) (1), gutta-percha (*trans*-polyisoprene) (2) and polyisoprene (3) on temperature [3].

The half-life temperature for synthetic polyisoprene is 596 K [26].

The formation of monomer and dimer (dipentene), due to the thermal degradation of polyisoprenes of different structure, may be explained on the basis of cleavage of carbon–carbon bonds along the main chain. Cleavage of the polymer chain may proceed when *two* adjacent single bonds are present, being in the positions α and β to the double bond; the α-bonds, being at the tertiary carbon atom, are weaker and break more readily. Two types of carbon–carbon cleavage are possible, i.e. with and without hydrogen-atom transfer:

$$
\begin{aligned}
&\sim CH_2-CH=C(CH_3)-\overset{\downarrow}{C}H_2\!\!\dashv\!\!CH_2-CH=C(CH_3)-CH_2\sim \longrightarrow \\
&\longrightarrow CH_2-CH=C(CH_3)-CH_3 + CH_2=C=C(CH_3)-CH_2\sim \\
&CH_2-CH=C(CH_3)-CH_2-CH_2-CH=C(CH_3)-CH_2-CH_2-CH= \\
&\qquad =C(CH_3)-CH_2\sim \longrightarrow \\
&\longrightarrow \sim CH_2-CH=C(CH_3)-CH_2-CH_2-CH= \\
&\qquad =C(CH_3)-\dot{C}H_2 + \dot{C}H_2-CH=C(CH_3)-CH_2\sim \\
&\sim CH_2-CH=C(CH_3)-CH_2\!\!\dashv\!\!CH_2-CH=C(CH_3)-\dot{C}H_2 \longrightarrow
\end{aligned}
\tag{1.22}
$$

$$\longrightarrow \sim CH_2-CH=C(CH_3)-\dot{C}H_2 + CH_2=CH-C(CH_3)=CH_2, \text{ etc. } (1.23)$$

The formation of dimer during the decomposition of the macroradical chain occurs due to the uncoupling of fragments consisting of two elementary links, and their subsequent cyclization to dipentene. The dimer may also be formed owing to the dimerization of the monomer. Based on quantitative data on the decomposition products of synthetic polyisoprene, natural rubber and gutta-percha, one may surmise that regularity in the arrangement of monomeric links in the polymer chain favours the formation of dipentene [3].

The oxidation of diene rubbers proceeds under the influence of atmospheric oxygen even at room temperature, and results in the hardening and fragility of the surface layer. In its initial stages, the oxidative degradation of natural rubber is characterized by softening of the material and the appearance of stickiness, the rubber elasticity then decreases and it cracks. Non-vulcanized synthetic polyisoprene is oxidized extensively even at room temperature [2]. The oxidation of rubber proceeds both at its double bonds and at the single bond α to the tertiary carbon atom.

The oxidation of rubbers and low-molecular-mass alkenes is most probably realized by the same mechanism, which involves degradation and structurization simultaneously. Structurization plays the key role in the isoprene-based rubbers [2].

Vinyl polymers
We shall consider the results of investigations on the degradation of such key polymers as polystyrene, polyacrylonitrile, poly(methyl methacrylate), etc.

Polystyrene and poly(α-methylstyrene)
According to the experimental data the most probable mechanism of the thermal degradation of polystyrene is as follows [3]. In polystyrene of any molecular mass above 40 000–60 000, the initial stage of the thermal degradation (5–10% weight loss) is marked by a sharp decrease in the molecular mass (Fig. 1.8) [3] to 40 000–60 000, and at these values the process becomes stabilized. Fig. 1.8 shows that values of the 'stable' molecular mass is virtually independent of both its intial value and the molecular-mass distribution of the polymer.

The drastic decrease in the molecular mass of polystyrene in the initial stage of the process is evidently associated with the cleavage of weak bonds in the polymer chain. This continues until these breakages reach an equilibrium at the expense of the chain decomposition of lower-molecular-mass chains yielding monomer. Monomer formation occurs when free macroradicals decompose via a chain mechanism without hydrogen-atom transfer. The half-life temperature for polystyrene is 637 K [9]. The thermal degradation products consist mainly of monomer, dimer and trimer.

The thermal degradation of polystyrene may proceed in the following ways [3].

1. Decomposition without hydrogen-atom transfer and with formation of monomeric products

$$\sim CH-CH_2-CH-CH_2 \vdots CH-CH_2-CH-CH_2 \sim \longrightarrow$$

$$\underset{C_6H_5}{|} \qquad \underset{C_6H_5}{|} \qquad \underset{C_6H_5}{|} \qquad \underset{C_6H_5}{|}$$

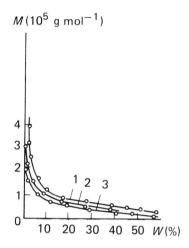

Fig. 1.8 — Dependence of the molecular mass (M) of polystyrene on its degree of thermal degradation (initial molecular mass 1, 2, 2×10^6; 3, 23×10^4) [3].

$$\longrightarrow \sim\!CH\!-\!CH_2\!-\!CH\!-\!\dot{C}H_2 + \dot{C}H\!-\!CH_2\!-\!CH\!-\!CH_2\!\sim$$
$$\qquad\quad \underset{C_6H_5}{|} \qquad \underset{C_6H_5}{|} \qquad \underset{C_6H_5}{|} \qquad \underset{C_6H_5}{|} \qquad\qquad (1.24)$$

$$\sim\!CH\!-\!CH_2\!-\!CH\!-\!\dot{C}H_2 \longrightarrow \sim\!CH\!-\!\dot{C}H_2 + CH\!=\!CH_2$$
$$\underset{C_6H_5}{|} \qquad \underset{C_6H_5}{|} \qquad\qquad \underset{C_6H_5}{|} \qquad \underset{C_6H_5}{|} \qquad (1.25)$$

2. Decomposition with hydrogen-atom transfer:

$$\sim\!CH\!-\!CH_2\!-\!CH\!-\!CH_2\!-\!CH\!\vdots\!CH_2\!-\!CH\!-\!CH_2\!-\!CH\!-\!CH_2\!\sim$$
$$\underset{C_6H_5}{|} \qquad \underset{C_6H_5}{|} \qquad \underset{C_6H_5}{|} \qquad \underset{C_6H_5}{|} \qquad \underset{C_6H_5}{|}$$
$$\longrightarrow \sim\!CH\!-\!CH_2\!-\!CH\!-\!CH_2\!-\!CH_2 + CH_2\!=\!C\!-\!CH_2\!-\!CH\!-\!CH_2\!\sim$$
$$\underset{C_6H_5}{|} \qquad \underset{C_6H_5}{|} \qquad \underset{C_6H_5}{|} \qquad \underset{C_6H_5}{|} \quad \underset{C_6H_5}{|} \qquad (1.26)$$

or

$$\sim\!CH_2\!-\!CH\!-\!\dot{C}H_2 + \;\sim\!CH\!-\!CH_2\!-\!CH\!\vdots\!CH_2\!-\!CH\!-\!CH_2\!\sim \longrightarrow$$
$$\underset{C_6H_5}{|} \qquad\qquad \underset{C_6H_5}{|} \qquad \underset{C_6H_5}{|} \qquad \underset{C_6H_5}{|}$$

$$\longrightarrow \sim CH_2-\underset{\underset{C_6H_5}{|}}{CH}-CH_3 + \sim\underset{\underset{C_6H_5}{|}}{CH}-CH_2-\overset{\cdot}{\underset{\underset{C_6H_5}{|}}{CH}} + CH_2=\underset{\underset{C_6H_5}{|}}{C}-CH_2\sim \qquad (1.27)$$

The formation of chain fragments of a size greater than that of monomer (dimer, trimer) occurs according to the following scheme:

$$\sim CH_2-\underset{\underset{C_6H_5}{|}}{CH}-CH_2-\underset{\underset{C_6H_5}{|}}{CH}-CH_2-\underset{\underset{C_6H_5}{|}}{CH}-CH_2\overset{\ulcorner}{|}\underset{\underset{C_6H_5}{|}}{CH}-$$

$$CH_2-\underset{\underset{C_6H_5}{|}}{CH}-CH_2-\underset{\underset{C_6H_5}{|}}{CH}-CH_2\sim \longrightarrow$$

$$\longrightarrow \sim CH_2-\underset{\underset{C_6H_5}{|}}{C}=CH_2 + CH_2-CH_2-\underset{\underset{C_6H_5}{|}}{C}=CH_2 +$$

$$CH_2-CH_2-\underset{\underset{C_6H_5}{|}}{C}=CH_2 + CH_2-CH_2\sim$$
$$\underset{\underset{C_6H_5}{|}}{}\qquad\underset{\underset{C_6H_5}{|}}{}\qquad\underset{\underset{C_6H_5}{|}}{} \qquad (1.28)$$

The formation of trimer and tetramer proceeds by an analogous mechanism.

There are also oligomeric compounds with an average molecular mass of about 2000 produced on the thermal decomposition of polystyrene. The ratio between the oligomeric and monomeric fractions is in the range 1.4–1.6 [3].

If the degradation of polystyrene occurs *in vacuo* at temperatures up to about 800 K, then the monomer is the main product of its degradation. However, increasing the temperature to 1100–1500 K leads to a decrease in the monomer yield and release of C_2H_2, C_2H_4 and C_6H_6 in considerable quantities. Benzene may be formed either as a result of transfer of the hydrogen atom located at the neighbouring carbon atom of the chain to the phenyl group with concomitant elimination from the main chain, or as a result of the phenyl group being eliminated as a free radical which abstracts a hydrogen atom from neighbouring chains, thus instigating the subsequent thermal decomposition of the main polymer chain; C_2H_2 and C_2H_4 may form owing to extensive decomposition of both the monomer and the main chain [3].

There have been quite extensive and systematic studies concerning the rate of thermal degradation of polystyrene samples having different molecular masses and molecular-mass distributions [3,11]. One group [12] considers that the thermal degradation of polystyrene up to levels of 15–80% yield proceeds as a zero-order reaction, whereas other data [3,33] indicate that a first-order reaction is involved (Fig. 1.9). The dependences of the reaction rates on the quantity of volatile materials are of complex character (Fig. 1.10) [3], showing a maximum at 35–40% weight loss. Now zero-order reaction kinetics should feature straight lines which are parallel to the abscissa while first order reactions should display straight lines with a definite and constant angle of slope. Fig. 1.10 shows that a fall in temperature leads to the

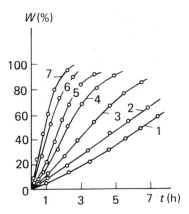

Fig. 1.9 — Kinetic curves of the thermal degradation of polystyrene (molecular mass 230 000) at different temperatures: 1, 591 K; 2, 596 K; 3, 601 K; 4, 606 K; 5, 611 K; 6, 616 K; 7, 621 K.

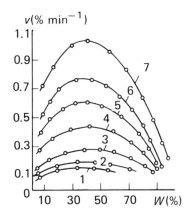

Fig. 1.10 — Dependence of the rate of thermal degradation of polystyrene (molecular mass 230 000) on its decomposition temperature: 1, 591 K; 2, 596 K; 3, 601 K; 4, 606 K; 5, 611 K; 6, 616 K; 7, 721 K.

appearance of a plateau in the curves, and at the lower temperature (591 K) the part of the curve corresponding to 30–55% weight loss is almost the straight line parallel to the abscissa. The formation of the plateau in these curves is explained by the mechanism of thermal degradation of polystyrene. Random breaks in the main chain in the initial stages of the degradation lead to the formation of three types of terminal group: saturated and free radical. Most volatile substances are formed by the cleavage of monomer (and a certain quantity of dimers) via a chain mechanism from chain ends existing as free radicals. These products make up 60% of the total amount of volatile materials.

The random cleavage of chains and the scission of monomer molecules from free-radical ends of the chain take place at different rates. The total rate of weight loss for polymers is mainly determined by the number of chains with free radicals at their ends, which are always present during the thermal degradation of polymers. After the initial stage of the process, the rate of random scission sharply decreases, the molecular mass of the polymer becoming stabilized. At rather low decomposition temperatures the rate of formation of new terminal groups equates with the rate of disappearance of such groups owing to the complete decomposition of fragments. Therefore a plateau appears in the curves from which the reaction constant is determined and, consequently, the apparent order of the reaction is zero. At higher pyrolysis temperatures, the equilibrium between these two reactions exists over a narrow range of decomposition and for a shorter period, and therefore maxima are observed in the rate curves (Fig. 1.10).

At higher temperatures the degradation of the polymer may also proceed by a first-order process. The activation energy of the thermal degradation of polystyrene of different molecular masses calculated from the reaction rate constants is 230 kJ mol^{-1} [3].

The replacement of the hydrogen atom in the α-position by a methyl group (α-methylstyrene) leads to a substantial effect on the thermal properties of poly(α-methylstyrene). Thus whilst about 40% of monomer is produced during the thermal degradation of polystyrene *in vacuo* at temperatures of 500–800 K, poly(α-methyl-styrene) yields up to 95–100% monomer under analogous conditions [3]. This is due to the presence of the quaternary carbon atom which weakens the neighbouring $C-C$ bond. The presence of C_6H_5 and CH_3 groups in the α-position virtually blocks the transfer of a hydrogen atom during pyrolysis at temperatures up to 800 K. Fragments terminating in radical sites, formed as a result of chain cleavage, easily decompose to monomer via a chain mechanism. The half-life temperature of poly(α-methylstyrene) is 560 K [9].

If the pyrolysis of poly(α-methylstyrene) is conducted at around 1100 or 1500 K, then considerable quantities of fractions with a molecular mass exceeding that of the monomer are formed. This is a result of the volatilization of chain fragments produced during pyrolysis of the polymer from the high-temperature zone before chain decay to monomer can take place. At temperatures of 1100–1500 K a definite quantity of small molecules such as H_2, CH_4, C_2H_5, C_2H_4 and C_6H_6 is formed as products of the secondary, more extensive decomposition of monomer.

The rate of degradation of poly(α-methylstyrene) increases linearly over time up to about 80% decomposition, after which it is sharply reduced [12]. This linear dependence implies the reaction is of zero order. The activation energy of the thermal degradation of poly(α-methylstyrene) is 187.3 kJ mol^{-1}.

Comparison of these data with those obtained in [3] reveals that the thermal degradation of poly(α-methylstyrene) is undoubtedly a first-order reaction with an activation energy of 271.7 kJ mol^{-1}. The first-order kinetics are explained in terms of a mechanism of chain decay of the polymer proceeding randomly, which leads to the formation of free radicals. Then follows a rapid chain decay of chains having terminal free radicals to form monomer molecules. Since the rate of random cleavage of the chain is essentially lower than that of chain decay, the former predetermines the reaction rate as a whole which therefore displays first-order behaviour.

In the presence of oxygen both polystyrene and poly(α-methylstyrene) decompose at higher rates than *in vacuo* or in an inert medium [2,13]. When heated in air for 200 h at 373 K polystyrene films display brittleness without changing in colour or solubility; under the same conditions but at 398 K the polymer becomes yellow. The thermal degradation processes are accompanied by the production of peroxide and hydroperoxide groups at the sites of cleavage of carbon–carbon bonds and the abstraction of hydrogen atoms from the tertiary carbon atom [13]. On decomposing by a chain mechanism, the peroxide and hydroperoxide groups initiate the subsequent degradation of the polymer.

The thermal oxidative stability of poly(α-methylstyrene) is substantially lower than that of polystyrene, as a result of the presence of weak bonds at the quaternary carbon atom, which readily decompose under the attack of oxygen at elevated temperatures.

Polyacrylonitrile

Heating polyacrylonitrile up to 473 K induces no noticeable changes in its chemical composition. However, the polymer becomes firstly yellow, then red-brown and, finally, blue-black. According to IR spectroscopic data the coloration of the polymer is associated with the cyclization of nitrile groups:

$$(1.29)$$

Accumulation of these polyconjugated structures during pyrolysis of the polymer *in vacuo* is characterized by a symmetrical electron paramagnetic resonance (EPR) signal of width 2.3 mT [14].

Study of the thermal degradation of polyacrylonitrile of molecular mass 40 000 at temperatures of 523–1073 K have shown that ammonia and hydrogen cyanide, as well as mixtures of liquid products which readily repolymerize during storage, are eliminated [3]. The quantities of hydrogen cyanide, acrylonitrile and vinyl acetonitrile in the fraction of volatile products condensing at temperatures of about 298 K are 2.9; 5.2 and 3.7% (of the initial weight of polymer), respectively. The average molecular mass of the wax-like fraction of the degradation products is 330 [3]. After degradation, the polymer residue is a black insoluble powder.

It should be noted that the decomposition of polyacrylonitrile at temperatures up to 1073 K induces self-stabilization, i.e. the quantity and the rate of elimination of volatile products gradually *decrease*. This is most probably associated with the production of the highly thermally resistant polymer with cyclized nitrile groups.

Curves of the rate of thermal degradation of polyacrylonitrile *in vacuo* at different temperatures have maxima as shown in Fig. 1.11 [11]. The shape of the curves indicates that the process of thermal degradation most probably occurs in two stages. Initially, hydrogen cyanide, acrylonitrile and acetonitrile are released at a high rate, then the rate gradually lowers and approaches zero, the total release of volatiles being comparatively low (10–25%). The activation energy for the thermal degradation of polyacrylonitrile calculated from the maximal values of the reaction rate is 129.6 kJ mol^{-1}.

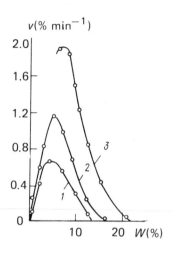

Fig. 1.11 — Dependence of the rate of thermal degradation of polyacrylonitrile on its degree of decomposition at 523 K (1), 533 K (2) and 543 K (3).

On heating polyacrylonitrile in air, the same substances are released as on heating it *in vacuo* and under inert gases [3]. Simultaneously an intense, narrow structureless line appears in the EPR spectrum [14]. This line is considered to comprise two superimposed EPR lines of widths 2.3 mT (due to thermal degradation) and 1.7 mT (due to thermal–oxidative degradation) when polyacrylonitrile is heated in air. Stabilization of polyconjugated structures of the polyimine type with the formation of an *N*-oxide occurs in the atmospheric environment. Subsequent heating may lead to the stabilization of polyacrylonitrile at the expense of conjugated bonds of the polyene type which are formed.

Poly(vinyl acetate) and poly(vinyl alcohol)
These polymers possess rather low thermal stability. Thus, at temperatures above 463 K poly(vinyl acetate) readily decomposes *in vacuo* to release acetic acid. Grassie [4] has explained the formation of acetic acid by a chain reaction which is initiated via the scission of the acetic acid molecule at the end of the polymer and the formation of a double bond. This reaction leads to the formation of mainly two substances: polyacetylene and acetic acid. However, the chain reaction leading to

the formation of acetic acid may proceed via the cleavage of the ester bond. These bonds are less strong than the carbon–carbon bonds and, during pyrolysis of the polymer, should decompose in the first place. Such cleavages of the ester bond should proceed randomly at any site in the polymer chain. The removal of the acetate radical is accompanied by the abstraction of a hydrogen atom from the neighbouring carbon atom to form acetic acid, and in this case the double bond appears in the polymer chain [3], i.e. acetic acid is produced as a result of the intramolecular transformation:

$$\sim CH - CH - CH - CH_2 - CH\sim \rightarrow$$

(1.30)

$$\rightarrow \sim CH - CH = CH - CH_2 - CH\sim \quad + \quad \underset{CH_3}{\overset{HO}{\underset{|}{\overset{}{C}}}}\!\!=\!\!O$$

Since in this case the ester bond is in the β-position relative to the double bond, it splits more readily than the other C–O bonds and the process of acetic acid cleavage proceeds via a chain mechanism. In the event of abstraction of a hydrogen atom from another polymer molecule, cross-linking of the degraded poly(vinyl acetate) takes place. The process of thermal degradation of poly(vinyl alcohol) also proceeds via the same mechanism. It occurs at low temperatures (up to 470 K) via a chain mechanism with the release of water [3]. After double-bond formation in the polymer chain (due to the OH group and the abstraction of a hydrogen atom from the neighbouring carbon atom) the strength of the C–OH bond, which is in the β-position relative to it, decreases. This essentially facilitates the thermal degradation of the polymer to form polyene chains, cross-linked polymer (via the abstraction of a hydrogen atom from another molecule) and water. The production of cross-linked polymer and polyene structures during the thermal degradation of poly(vinyl acetate) and poly(vinyl alcohol) enables the production of carbonized materials based on the above compounds at elevated temperatures (above 1150 K). The degradation of these polymers at high temperatures is accompanied by release of H_2, CO, CH_4, C_2H_4, C_2H_6, CO_2 as products of the secondary decomposition of the degradation products [3].

Poly(methyl methacrylate)
The thermal degradation of poly(methyl methacrylate) (PMMA) over the temperature range 420–770 K gives virtually 100% yield of monomer. Having studied the thermal degradation of PMMA Grassie [4] concluded that the complete decomposition of PMMA to monomer cannot be accounted for by the

theory of random breaks. Studies on the manner of variation in the molecular mass of PMMA during its thermal degradation made it possible to establish an important relation [4]: the lower the molecular mass of the initial polymer, the greater the degree of decomposition of polymer before its molecular mass begins to decrease. Thus, PMMA having an initial molecular mass of 443 000 displays noticeable loss of relative molecular mass only after 65% elimination of volatiles (Fig. 1.12).

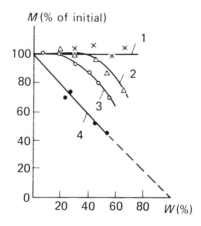

Fig. 1.12 — Dependence of the molecular mass of PMMA on its degree of decomposition 1, 444 300; 2, 94 000; 3, 179 000; 4, 725 000.

The molecular mass of PMMA samples with initial molecular masses of 94 000 and 179 000 remains virtually constant after only up to 30% and 20% weight loss, respectively. The dependence of the molecular mass of residual PMMA (with an initial molecular mass of 725 000) on the degree of decomposition of the polymer is linear.

According to [4] the thermal degradation behaviour of PMMA with different molecular masses indicates that depolymerization of free-radical fragments follows random cleavage via the chain mechanism. The chain scissions of the polymer are not accompanied by hydrogen-atom transfer owing to the steric difficulties resulting from the presence of CH_3 and $COOCH_3$ groups at every alternate carbon atom, which is quaternary. The free radicals formed during scission easily eliminate monomer:

$$\sim C(CH_3)-CH_2-C(CH_3) \dashv CH_2-C(CH_3)-CH_2\sim \longrightarrow$$
$$\underset{\displaystyle COOCH_3}{|} \qquad \underset{\displaystyle COOCH_3}{|} \qquad \underset{\displaystyle COOCH_3}{|}$$

$$\longrightarrow \sim C(CH_3)-CH_2-\dot{C}(CH_3) + \dot{C}H_2-C(CH_3)-CH_2\sim$$
$$\underset{\displaystyle COOCH_3}{|} \qquad \underset{\displaystyle COOCH_3}{|} \qquad \underset{\displaystyle COOCH_3}{|} \qquad (1.31)$$

$$\underset{\substack{| \\ COOCH_3}}{\sim C(CH_3)} - CH_2 - \underset{\substack{| \\ COOCH_3}}{\dot{C}(CH_3)} \longrightarrow \underset{\substack{| \\ COOCH_3}}{\sim \dot{C}(CH_3)} + CH_2 = \underset{\substack{| \\ COOCH_3}}{C(CH_3)} \qquad (1.32)$$

The higher the initial molecular mass of PMMA, the more sharply its decrease takes place. This is well-illustrated by the data presented below on the dependence of the thermal stability of PMMA on the initial molecular mass (up to 50% decomposition at 593 K) [4]:

Initial RMM	RMM solid residue	RMM solid residue/initial RMM (%)
44 000	44 000	100
94 000	92 000	98
150 000	102 000	77
179 000	143 000	80
650 000	293 000	45
725 000	326 000	45
5 100 000	402 000	8

RMM, relative molecular mass.

It has been revealed [4] that the activation energy of the thermal degradation of PMMA increases with the extent of polymer degradation, being 133.7, 140.8, 150.5, 158.0 and 165.1 kJ mol^{-1} at levels of polymer decomposition of 0, 2, 4, 6 and 8% respectively. This effect is associated with the cleavage of weaker bonds in the initial stages of degradation, whose existence is caused by the presence of oxygen in the polymer chain (derived from an initiator, the formation of peroxide compounds, etc.). The strongest carbon–carbon bonds remain in the molecular chains after cleavage of the weaker bonds.

The half-life temperature of PMMA having a molecular mass of 150 000 is 556 K, while that of PMMA having a molecular mass of 5 100 000 is 600 K [9].

When determining the thermal degradation rate for PMMA, the sample should be thoroughly purified from contaminants particularly from monomer. For this purpose the PMMA samples are initially allowed to stand for 2–3 h *in vacuo* at 423 K. The thermal degradation rate of PMMA in the initial stages [3] is rather high, as a result of the cleavage of weak bonds, and only at 20–25% conversion is it possible to determine variations in the mass of samples reliably. After this, the dependence of the rate of decomposition of PMMA on the extent of the process acquires a linear character (Fig. 1.13) [3]. The initial rate of thermal degradation of PMMA may be

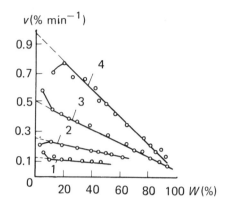

Fig. 1.13 — Dependence of the rate of liberation of volatile products in the thermal degradation of PMMA (molecular mass 5 100 000) on its degree of decomposition at 1, 569 K; 2, 574 K, 3, 579 K; 4, 584 K.

easily found by extrapolation of the linear parts of the curves to the intersection with the ordinate (Fig. 1.13). The shapes of the curves illustrating the dependence of the rate of decomposition on the quantity of liberated volatiles shows that this is a first-order reaction (excluding the initial stages).

The thermal degradation of PMMA is accompanied by two reactions (random break of the C−C bonds and depolymerization via a chain mechanism). The former reaction is thought to proceed with a lower rate and thus to determine both the rate of the whole process and the reaction order.

Halogen-containing polymers

Among the halogen-containing carbon-chain polymers, the fluorine-containing polymers [1] are characterized by the highest thermal stability, which is due to the high strength of the C−F bond of 485 kJ mol^{-1}, as compared with the C−C, C−H and C−Cl bond strengths of 347 405.5 and 334.4 kJ mol^{-1} respectively [1].

Poly(vinyl chloride) and poly(vinylidene chloride)

A considerable number of publications [3,15] are devoted to the production processes and properties (including the thermal and thermal–oxidative stability) of poly(vinyl chloride) (PVC) and poly(vinylidene chloride). This is associated both with their commercial significance and with the necessity of finding ways to stabilize them.

A striking influence has been found of the method of production on the thermal stability of PVC over a temperature range up to 613 K [3]. Thus PVC obtained as a result of γ-irradiation and benzoyl peroxide (BP) initiation has approximately the same stability, while PVC obtained by initiation with azo-bis-isobutyronitrile (AZBN) is noticeably less thermally stable over the temperature range of 493–543 K. However, stabilization towards further thermal degradation of all PVC samples tested is observed at about 60% weight loss, possibly due to the considerable dehydrochlorination of the polymer to form polyene and cross-linked structures.

HCl (96–99% (mol.)) is the main volatile product of the pyrolysis of PVC, while benzene (0.2–2.7% (mol)), toluene (0.1% (mol.)) and other hydrocarbons

(0.2–0.9% (mol.)) are minor volatiles; HCl begins to be released even at temperatures as low as 400–430 K.

The further heating of PVC previously pyrolysed at temperatures up to 620 K at 673 K for 0.5 h causes further release of 32–62% (mol.) HCl, sizeable amounts of alkenes (ethylene 16.2–19.1% (mol.), propylene 3.4–15.1% (mol.), butene 11.1% (mol.), hexane 2.3–5.6% (mol.), etc.), alkanes (ethane 7.6–9.9% (mol.), propane 5.3–7.0% (mol.), butane 0.7–5.8% (mol.), pentane 3.2%, hexane 2.1–3.5% (mol.), etc.) and aromatic hydrocarbons (benzene 8.4–16.6% (mol.), toluene 8.1–9.4 (mol.), xylenes 3.4–4.5% (mol.), etc.), as well as of small quantities of dienes, vinyl monomers, other saturated and unsaturated organic substances, hydrogen and carbon monoxide. The quantity of substances released varies according to the method of production of PVC.

The thermal degradation of PVC, being essentially a dehydrochlorination up to about 550 K, has a reaction order of 1.5 and follows the equation

$$C^{-1/2} = C_0^{-1/2} + 1/2 \, kt,$$

where C is the quantity of HCl retained in the polymer after pyrolysis, C_0 is the initial quantity of HCl in the polymer (which is equal to 1), k is the rate constant of the reaction and t is time.

Determination of the rate of dehydrochlorination of PVC manufactured by different methods has shown that the rate constants of PVC synthesized using AZBN initiator are 3 to 5 times those of PVC produced using γ-ray initiation or BP initiator. The activation energies of the process also differ noticeably, i.e. 133.7 (γ-ray initiation), 125.4 (BP) and 108.7 kJ mol^{-1} (AZBN).

These differences are obviously connected with the influence of these conditions of preparation on the chemical structure of the polymer chains (their degree of branching, the presence of oxygen atoms and unsaturation).

The dehydrochlorination of PVC proceeds via a radical chain reaction accompanied by the heterolytic splitting of HCl [3,16]. The C–Cl bond is the weakest in the PVC macromolecules and, on heating, initiates degradation of the polymer. Then the abstraction of hydrogen from the adjacent carbon atom may take place together with the formation of a double bond in the backbone:

$$\sim CH_2-CH-CH_2-CH-CH_2-CH\sim \longrightarrow$$
$$\qquad\quad | \qquad\quad | \qquad\quad |$$
$$\qquad\quad Cl \qquad\quad Cl \qquad\quad Cl$$

$$\sim CH_2-CH-CH_2-CH=CH-CH\sim$$
$$\qquad\quad | \qquad\qquad\qquad |$$
$$\qquad\quad Cl \qquad\qquad\qquad Cl \qquad\qquad\qquad (1.33)$$

A chlorine atom located at the β-position to the double bond is split more readily than other chlorine atoms.

The initiation of dehydrochlorination via formation of free Cl· atoms, which are capable of interacting with any atom in the chain, is hardly possible, since the release of chlorine due to chain termination by the reaction $Cl\cdot + Cl\cdot \longrightarrow Cl_2$ should also be expected. However, chlorine is not observed in the products of the thermal degradation of PVC over a wide temperature range [3].

Poly(vinylidene chloride) resembles PVC in its thermal degradation, thus a rapid weight loss occurs over the range 498–548 K on heating in an inert atmosphere. Analysis of the volatile products shows that weight loss occurs mainly owing to elimination of HCl [3].

The formation of highly conjugated systems, with their associated colouring, on the thermal and thermal–oxidative degradation of PVC is conveniently followed by EPR and ultraviolet (UV) spectroscopy [16].

As a rule, the presence of oxygen increases the concentration of free radicals produced during polymer degradation; it either increases the initiation rate of degradation due to random scission or increases the quantity of gel in the polymer residue due to interchain cross-linking. In a number of cases the degradation of chlorine-containing polymers leads to the formation of noticeable quantities of polyconjugated systems, which are characterized by the coloration of samples and the formation of paramagnetic centres [16]. The latter are formed via the local cleavage of π-bonds in the long conjugated chain and the production of excited triplet states.

Heating PVC films in atmospheres of argon and air results in different behaviour in their UV spectra. On prolonged heating and with increasing temperature, the intensity of the UV spectral maximum increases and a hypsochromic shift is observed. The rate of formation of the conjugated system during the thermal degradation of PVC is higher than that during thermal oxidation. This may be caused by cleavage of the long conjugated chains due to oxygen. Additionally, the presence of oxygen inhibits the formation of polyconjugated systems.

It is believed [16] that, under vacuum, the polyconjugated chains grow at the expense of PVC dehydrochlorination, the concentration of polyene radicals determined by EPR remaining unchanged. Since in the presence of oxygen the polyenyl radicals are destroyed, their concentration and, consequently, that of the polyene molecules in the PVC sample may be determined by reaction with oxygen [17]. It has been established [17] that the introduction of oxygen decreases the intensity of the 291- and 330-nm bands in the UV spectrum of PVC, while the bands at wavelengths greater than 400 nm are unchanged. Presumably, the 291- and 330-nm bands may be attributed to polyene radicals produced during the thermal oxidative degradation of PVC via the cleavage of long polyconjugated chains.

Polytetrafluoroethylene and polytrifluorochloroethylene
The perfluorohydrocarbon polymers are among the most thermally resistant organic polymers. Polytetrafluoroethylene, polytrifluoroethylene and various copolymers of fluorine-containing monomers are the most important among them.

Fluoropolymers are arranged in the following order according to their thermal stability [1]:

$$(-CF_2-CF_2-)_n > (-CH_2-CF_2-)_n > (-CF_2-CHF-)_n >$$
$$> (CH_2-CH_2-)_n > (CH_2-CHF)_n$$

thus polytetrafluoroethylene (PTFE) has the highest thermal stability of this group, its thermal degradation *in vacuo* proceeding over the temperature range 746–806 K [1]. The half-life temperature for PTFE is 782 K [9].

The incomplete substitution of hydrogen atoms, as exemplified by poly(vinylidene fluoride) ($T_{50} = 718$ K) as well as the presence of chlorine atoms as in polytrifluorochloroethylene ($T_{50} = 686$ K) reduces their thermal stability. Poly(vinyl fluoride) ($T_{50} = 662$ K) proves to be the least thermally stable [9], even less so than polyethylene.

Studies on the thermal stability of PTFE, including the nature of the degradation products, and the rate and activation energy of the depolymerization process have been conducted over the temperature range 670–1500 K [3]. The thermal degradation products are mostly monomer (86.8–96.8% (mol.)) and C_3F_6 (3.0–6.4% (mol.)) [3]; the other minor products (SiF_4, CO, CO_2) are formed via the interaction of fluorinated compounds with vessel walls (glass and quartz) in the presence of traces of moisture. The rate of degradation shows a linear dependence on the degree of conversion of PTFE over the temperature range 753–783 K (Fig. 1.14) [3]. These

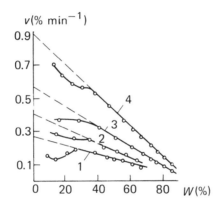

Fig. 1.14 — Dependence of the rate of thermal degradation of PTFE on its degree of decomposition at 1, 753 K; 2, 763 K; 3, 773 K; 4, 783 K.

results are in good agreement with the formula [16]:

$$\frac{1}{w_0} \cdot \frac{dw_2}{dt} = k_{\text{eff}} - k_{\text{eff}} \frac{w_2}{w_0},$$

where w_0 is the initial mass of the sample, w_2 is the mass of volatiles liberated over the period of time t, k_{eff} is the effective rate constant for the destruction of the macroradical and $k_{\text{eff}} = A_{\text{eff}} \exp(-E_{\text{eff}}/RT)$ (A_{eff} is the corresponding pre-exponential term, and E_{eff} is the corresponding activation energy).

Calculations on the thermal degradation of PTFE [42] produce a value of $k_{\text{eff}} = 10^{19} \exp(347\,500\,(\text{J})/RT)$ which agrees well with the experimental data. The above equation is derived from a hypothetical simplified model, the cell effect being taken into account. The model is based on the following premises: the initiation of the thermal degradation occurs randomly; the primary macroradicals may migrate from a cell with a probability rapidly decreasing with increase in the viscosity of the system; the macroradicals which have been transported from the cell decompose completely to form monomer, which evaporates without reacting; the primary radicals may recombine before leaving the cell; and the sample density remains constant during polymer degradation.

The satisfactory agreement between the calculated k_{eff} and the experimental results makes it possible to conclude that the cell effect plays a key role in the thermal degradation of PTFE. However, it should be noted that, although the simplified model is of importance in elucidating the kinetic pecularities of the thermal degradation of the polymer, the results obtained from it should be treated cautiously. In particular, the model predicts that the rate of the process should be proportional either to the degree of polymerization or to the molecular mass of PFTE. It has been shown experimentally, however, that the degradation rate of PFTE in the molecular mass range 3×10^5 to 4×10^7 is constant [16].

Since the C−F bond is considerably stronger than C−H, no transfer of the fluorine atom occurs during chain cleavage. Thus, chain scission of the polymer during thermal degradation of PTFE leads to the formation of two macroradicals capable of unzipping to produce monomer [16]:

$$\sim CF_2-CF_2-CF_2-CF_2\sim \longrightarrow \sim CF_2-\dot{C}F_2 + \dot{C}F_2-CF_2\sim \qquad (1.34)$$

$$\sim CF_2-CF_2-CF_2-\dot{C}F_2 \longrightarrow CF_2 = CF_2 + \sim CF_2-\dot{C}F_2, \text{ etc.} \qquad (1.35)$$

Since the C−C bonds remote from the chain ends are weaker than the terminal bonds, C−C bond cleavage during initiation occurs randomly, mainly at the expense of the thermal mobility of the macromolecules. Of the two successive reactions, i.e. polymer chain cleavage and macroradical chain cleavage, the former proceeds with a lower rate and is rate-limiting as regards the thermal degradation of PTFE, which thus proceeds as a first-order reaction.

The chain transfer and disproportionation reactions of fluoroalkyl radicals proceed via C−F bond cleavage and fluorine-atom transfer:

$$\sim CF-CF_2-\dot{C}F_2\sim + \dot{C}F_2-CF_2\sim \longrightarrow$$
$$--|--$$
$$F$$
$$\longrightarrow \sim CF_2-\dot{C}F-CF_2\sim + CF_3-CF_2\sim \qquad (1.36)$$

$$\sim CF_2{-}\underset{\substack{| \\ F}}{C}F{-}\dot{C}F_2 + \dot{C}F_2{-}CF_2\sim \longrightarrow$$

$$\longrightarrow \sim CF_2{-}CF{=}CF_2 + CF_3{-}CF_2\sim \qquad (1.37)$$

Since C–F bonds are very strong and highly polarized, and since the atomic mass of fluorine is 19 times that of hydrogen, the activation energies of reactions (1.36) and (1.37) are substantially greater than for their polyethylene analogues and, hence, they can be neglected in the thermal degradation of PTFE.

Chain scission in PTFE of a different degree of crystallinity proceeds by second-order kinetics [16]. The termination rate of the macroradicals also depends on their spatial distribution in the bulk of the polymer and the structure of the polymer matrix.

Taking into account the high viscosity of PTFE, one may presume that, during its thermal degradation, the recombination of the macroradicals involves the monomer as a chain-transfer agent in a relay mechanism [42,50], which is due to migration of the radical centre in a chain process:

$$P_nX + \dot{R}_m \longrightarrow \dot{R}_n + P_mX \qquad (1.38)$$

$$P_mX + \dot{R}_n \longrightarrow \dot{R}_m + P_nX, \text{ etc.} \qquad (1.39)$$

The activation energy of this process is equal to 126 kJ mol^{-1} for amorphous PTFE and 270 kJ mol^{-1} for partially crystalline (46%) PTFE [50]. The activation energy of the thermal degradation of PTFE calculated from the temperature dependence of k_{eff} is 338 kJ mol^{-1} [3,16].

Since there is one chlorine atom in the repeat unit of the polytrifluorochloroethylene macromolecule, it is less thermally stable ($T_{50} = 653$ K) [9] than PTFE and its degradation occurs by the other mechanism. In particular, the yield of monomer reaches only 25% [3], while oligomeric compounds with an average molecular mass of about 900 are more significant [3]. Thus one may consider that, during the degradation of polytrifluorochlorethylene, some of the polymer chain scissions give rise to macroradicals which decompose via a chain mechanism to form monomer:

$$\sim CFCl{-}CF_2{-}CFCl{-}CF_2{-}CFCl{-}CF_2\sim \longrightarrow$$

$$\longrightarrow \sim CFCl{-}CF_2{-}\dot{C}FCl + \dot{C}F_2{-}CFCl{-}CF_2\sim$$

$$\sim CF_2{-}CFCl{-}\dot{C}F_2 \longrightarrow \sim \dot{C}F_2 + CFCl{=}CF_2 \qquad (1.40)$$

The other chain scissions are accompanied by chlorine-atom transfer to the break site to form two fragments (by disproportionation) of lower molecular mass than the original polymer:

$$\overset{\displaystyle \overset{\text{r------Cl}}{\underset{\downarrow}{}}}{\sim\text{CFCl}-\text{CF}_2-\overset{|}{\text{CFCl}}-\text{CF}_2\dashv\text{CF}-\text{CF}_2} \longrightarrow$$

$$\longrightarrow \sim\text{CFCl}-\text{CF}_2-\text{CFCl}_2 + \text{CF}_2=\text{CF}-\text{CF}_2\sim \qquad (1.41)$$

The activation energy of the thermal degradation of polytrifluorochloroethylene from the temperature dependence of its initial rate is 234 kJ mol^{-1} [3].

The thermal degradation of other fluorine-containing polymers (poly(vinyl fluoride), poly(vinyldene fluoride), polytrifluorethylene) have been studied to a limited extent.

It should be noted that the relative thermal stability of the fluorine-containing polymers is determined by heating them *in vacuo* for 2 h at different temperatures (Fig. 1.15) [9]. The figure shows that trifluoronitrosomethane copolymers are the least thermally stable. Trifluorochloroethylene copolymers occupy an intermediate position, while poly(vinylidene fluoride) and polytetrafluoroethylene are the most thermally stable.

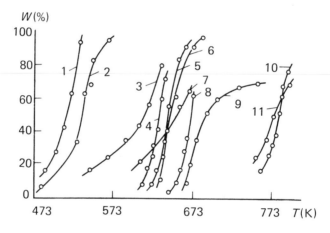

Fig. 1.15 — Thermal degradation of different fluorine-containing polymers after heating *in vacuo* for 2 h at different temperatures: 1, copolymer of trifluoronitrosomethane and trifluoroethylene; 2, copolymer of trifluoronitrosomethane and tetrafluoroethylene; 3, poly-hexafluoropentene adipate; 4, polytrifluorochloroethylene; 5, copolymer of vinylidene fluoride (36%) and trifluorochloroethylene (64%); 6, copolymer of vinylidene fluoride (55%) and trifluoroethylene (45%); 7, copolymer of vinylidene fluoride (77%) and trifluorochlorethylene (23%); 8, copolymer of octafluorocyclohexa-1,3-diene and butadiene; 9, copolymer of vinyli-dene fluoride and hexafluoropropylene; 10, poly(vinylidene fluoride); 11, copolymer of tetrafluoroethylene and hexafluoropropylene.

Studies on the rate of degradation of PTFE in air at 673, 698 and 723 K have shown [3] that the quantity of the volatile decomposition products is approximately the same as *in vacuo*. The thermal–oxidative degradation of PTFE at 743 K leads to volatile products to a somewhat greater extent than thermal degradation *in vacuo*.

The degradation of PTFE at 623–653 K in the presence of oxygen leads to the appearance of considerable quantities of carbon monoxide (18% (mol.)) and carbon dioxide (63% (mol.)) among the volatile products [3], indicating defluorination.

One might predict the accelerating action of oxygen during the degradation of PTFE to be insignificant, because the production of hydroperoxides in this polymer is impossible. Clearly, the following reactions are the basic ones in the thermal degradation of PTFE [52]:

$$\sim CF_2-\dot{C}F_2 + O_2 \longrightarrow \sim CF_2-CF_2OO\cdot \tag{1.42}$$

$$\sim CF_2-\dot{C}F-CF_2\sim + O_2\sim \longrightarrow \underset{\underset{OO\cdot}{|}}{CF_2-CF-CF_2\sim} \tag{1.43}$$

$$\sim CF_2-CF_2OO\cdot + \underset{\underset{OO\cdot}{|}}{\sim CF_2-CF-CF_2\sim} \longrightarrow$$
$$\longrightarrow \sim CF_2-CF_2O\cdot + O_2 + \underset{\underset{O\cdot}{|}}{\sim CF_2-CF-CF_2} \tag{1.44}$$

$$\sim CF_2-CF_2O\cdot \longrightarrow \sim\dot{C}F_2 + CF_2O \tag{1.45}$$

$$\underset{\underset{O\cdot}{|}}{\sim CF_2-CF-CF_2\sim} \begin{cases} \longrightarrow \sim\dot{C}F_2 + \underset{\overset{\|}{O}}{CF-CF_2\sim} \\ \\ \longrightarrow \sim\dot{C}F_2 + CF_2O + CF_2{=}CF-CF_2\sim \end{cases} \tag{1.46}$$

$$\underset{\underset{OO\cdot}{|}}{\sim CF_2-CF-CF_2\sim} \longrightarrow \sim CF_2-\dot{C}F-O-O-CF_2\sim \longrightarrow \tag{1.47}$$

$$\longrightarrow \underset{\overset{\|}{O}}{\sim CF_2-CF} + \dot{O}-CF_2\sim$$

The reactions (1.42)–(1.47) show that oxygen promotes recombination of the macroradicals and, consequently, the rate of chain scission increases in its presence. This would enable structurization of the involatile residue from PTFE. However, reactions (1.45)–(1.47) show that the recombination of the secondary peroxide radicals results in the formation of radicals which readily isomerize with cleavage of the macromolecules. For this reason structurization of the final residue of PTFE is observed only at the late stages of its thermal oxidation.

Carbocyclic polymers
Among these compounds containing benzene, naphthalene, anthracene and other aromatic compounds are of particular interest.

The backbone of polycyclic molecules may involve either only rings (polyphenylenes) or, additionally, aliphatic groups, e.g. (poly(p-xylylene)).

The carbocyclic polymers include condensed systems (polycyclopentadiene or polybutadiene) [1]. While of interest in a number of their properties, in particular their thermal stability, these polymers have yet to be studied in detail. Poly(p-xylylene) [1] (which may be produced from p-xylylene formed on heating p-xylene up to 1273 K) and also polyphenyl (produced on heating benzoyl chloride at 373 K in the presence of an iron oxide catalyst) are representatives of this class of compounds [3]. Studies on the thermal degradation of these two polymers have shown that they have almost the same thermal stability (T_{50} of polyphenyl is 703 K, while T_{50} of poly(p-xylylene) is 705 K) and they decompose completely over the temperature range 683–743 K. The mass spectroscopic analysis of volatile products of the degradation of polyphenyl demonstrates the presence of toluene (5.9% (mass)), benzene (1.4% (mass)) and xylene (0.1% (mass)) [3]. The thermal degradation of poly(p-xylene) results in the liberation of such products as xylene (2.83% (mass)), toluene (0.29% (mass)), methylethylbenzene (0.28% (mass)), methylstyrene (0.14% (mass)) and benzene (0.06% (mass)) [3]. The absence of monomer, i.e. p-xylyene, in the volatile products is probably associated with its high reactivity and ability undergo polymerization on leaving the heating zone.

The methylene bonds are the weakest in the poly(p-xylene) macrochain. The cleavage of such bonds causes the formation of two macroradicals which should decompose via a chain mechanism to yield monomer:

$$\sim CH_2-\langle\bigcirc\rangle-CH_2 \!\mid\! CH_2-\langle\bigcirc\rangle-CH_2\sim \longrightarrow$$

$$\longrightarrow \sim CH_2-\langle\bigcirc\rangle-\dot{C}H_2 + \dot{C}H_2-\langle\bigcirc\rangle-CH_2\sim \longrightarrow \qquad (1.48)$$

$$\longrightarrow CH_2{=}\langle\bigcirc\rangle{=}CH_2 \text{ , etc.}$$

The activation energy of the thermal degradation of polyphenyl and poly(p-xylylene) as determined by their maximal decomposition rates are 209 and 305.1 kJ mol^{-1}, respectively [3].

It has been established [1] that polyacenaphthylene

$$\sim CH\!-\!CH_2\sim$$

which is produced on polymerization of the monomer (398 K) begins to decompose at temperatures above 570 K to form the initial monomer.

Polyarylenequinones produced by the action of *p*-benzoquinone on different bis-dinitrogenated aromatic diamines are stable in an inert atmosphere up to 970 K and in air to 623 K [54]. The copolymer of anthracene and styrene which at 578 K loses only 5.5% of its initial mass after 4 h is also a thermally resistant polymer [1].

The above data demonstrate that the introduction of benzene rings into the vinyl polymer chain increases its thermal stability. The nature of the bridging groups which connect the aryl groups in polymers also plays a key role in their thermal stability. The thermal stability of polymers containing various bridging groups between the aromatic rings decreases as follows $CO > CH_2 > O > O_2$ [9].

Phenol-formaldehyde polymers
These are widely used in industry and, consequently, studies on their thermal properties are of great technical importance. Phenol–formaldehyde polymers heated for 1 h up to 570, 703, and 1100 K lose 7%, 10% and 50% of their mass respectively [1].

The thermogravimetric analysis (TGA) of solidified phenol–formaldehyde resins has shown that the ratio of the initial components influences the thermal stability of the polymers produced: the most thermally resistant polymers were obtained with a phenol:formaldehyde ratio of 0.5 [1].

During the thermal decomposition of phenol–formaldehyde resins, considerable quantities of volatiles (up to 50% of initial mass) having a rather diverse composition are liberated. At temperatures up to 630 K one may observe release of considerable quantities of propanols (up to 11% mass), acetone (6.7% (mass)), propylene (4.0% (mass) and butanols (3.0% (mass)) [3]; the involatile products of decomposition temperature to 770 K causes an increase in the quantity of acetone (17.6% (mass)) while methane, CO_2 and CO which are the major products of decomposition also begin to be released. The quantity of involatile pyrolysis products (of molecular mass about 350) is gradually reduced to about 37% (mass) at elevated temperatures [3].

In the involatile residue, the concentration of hydrogen and oxygen gradually decreases as the temperature increases, while at 1473 K virtually only carbon remains in it (99.2% (mass)) [3]. The data presented suggest that cleavage of polymer chains occurs at the bond $-CH_2-C_6H_4OH-$.

The activation energy of the thermal degradation of phenol–formaldehyde polymers is 75.2 kJ mol^{-1} [3].

In the presence of oxygen, the process of degradation of phenol–formaldehyde resins becomes enhanced owing to the formation of hydroperoxide and peroxide groups at the expense of oxidation, methylene groups being attacked at first.

1.1.2   Heterochain and heterocyclochain polymers

Heterochain and heterocyclochain polymers cover a large group of compounds, exhibiting widely varying thermal stability. They include polyethers and polyesters, polyamines, polyimides, polyhydrazides, polyorganosiloxanes, polyorganoelementosiloxanes and others [1].

Polyethers

This class of compounds embraces different polymers in the backbone of which certain links are bound via an ether oxygen atom: saturated and unsaturated aliphatic polyethers, poly(phenylene oxides), polyacetals, epoxide polymers, cellulose and its esters, etc.

Poly(alkylene oxides)

The introduction of oxygen into the hydrocarbon chain of polymers reduces their thermal stability; this trend is nicely illustrated by the examples of polyformaldehyde (T_{50} = 443 K), poly(ethylene oxide) (T_{50} = 618 K), isotactic poly(propylene oxide) (T_{50} = 585 K) and atactic poly(propylene oxide) (T_{50} = 568 K); here thermal resistances are lower than those in the corresponding hydrocarbon polymers, namely polyethylene (T_{50} = 679 K) and polypropylene (T_{50} = 660 K) [9].

The differential thermogravimetric analysis (DTGA) curves in Fig. 1.16 show that for polyformaldehyde decomposition in an inert atmosphere at 443 K, its maximal rate is achieved at 473 K, while its second maximum is at 542 K. Acetylation

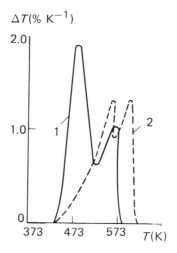

Fig. 1.16 — DTGA curves of polyformaldehyde (1) and acetylated polyformaldehyde (2) during decomposition in a nitrogen atmosphere.

of polyformaldehyde enhances its thermal stability: the first maximum on the DTGA curves is now at 523 K, while the second is at 558 K. This effect is associated with the fact that polyformaldehyde readily decomposes to monomer owing to the presence of polar $C-O$ bonds and OH groups:

$$\sim CH_2-O-CH_2-OH \longrightarrow [\sim CH_2-O \; ... \; H] \longrightarrow \sim CH_2-OH + CH_2O$$
$$\begin{array}{cc} | & | \\ H_2C & \!\!\!\!-\!\!\!\!- O \end{array}$$
$$(1.49)$$

In the case of acetylated polyformaldehyde, the transfer of the larger acetyl group is more difficult than that of the hydrogen atom of the OH-group in polyformaldehyde:

$$\sim CH_2-O-CH_2-O-CO-CH_3 \longrightarrow \sim CH_2-O----CO-CH_3 \longrightarrow$$
$$\begin{array}{cc} | & | \\ H_2C & \!\!\!\!-\!\!\!\!- O \end{array}$$
$$\longrightarrow \sim CH_2-O-CO-CH_3 + CH_2O \qquad\qquad (1.50)$$

However, the acetylation procedure is less effective as regards stabilization of polyformaldehyde against thermal–oxidative degradation; in this case the polymer begins to degrade at 423 K, with maxima on the DTGA curves at 453 K and at about 520 K. This is associated with the ready oxidation of the terminal acetyl group via a radical mechanism.

Studies on the thermal stability of poly(ethylene oxide) and poly(propylene oxide) have confirmed, as shown above, that incorporation of oxygen causes a decrease in the thermal stability of these polymers; indeed, the higher the oxygen content, or number of tertiary and quaternary carbon atoms in the chains of polyalkylene oxides, the lower is their thermal stability [3].

The thermal degradation *in vacuo* of poly(ethylene oxide) with a molecular mass of 10 000, atactic poly(propylene oxide) with a molecular mass of 16 000 and isotactic poly(propylene oxide) with a molecular mass of 215 000 has shown that, along with many low-molecular-mass organic compounds, thermal degradation products involve monomers: ethylene oxide (3.9% (mass)) and propylene oxide (0.01–1.16% (mass)). The molecular masses of oligomer fragments, being volatiles at the decomposition temperature, were 675 for poly(ethylene oxide) and 606 for isotactic poly(propylene oxide) [3].

It has been established that the thermal degradation of poly(alkylene oxides) increases with molecular mass. Thus, the thermal stability of polymer with a molecular mass of 100 000 is considerably higher than that of the same polymer with a molecular mass of 50 000. However, if the molecular mass of poly(alkylene oxides) exceeds 10^5, the differences in molecular masses do not produce much effect on their thermal stability.

The formation of monomers during the thermal degradation of high-molecular-mass poly(alkylene oxides) evidently proceeds along the same mechanism as that of polyalkenes. The presence of terminal OH groups, the significance of which is substantial in the low-molecular-mass polymers, favours decomposition, with the formation of monomer via the mechanism indicated above for polyformaldehyde. It should also be noted that the greater the number of oxygen atoms (and hence the fewer the hydrogen atoms) in the polymer, which are capable of participating in the transfer of the intramolecular chain during bond cleavage, the higher is the yield of monomers during the thermal degradation of poly(alkylene oxides) [3].

Poly(phenylene oxides)
The complexity of the chemical structure of heterocyclic polymers, including poly(phenylene oxides) (PPOs) which are very strong, thermally stable polymers, makes the study of their thermal and thermal–oxidative degradation difficult. The schemes suggested for their thermal degradation are in many cases only hypotheti-cal; however, the available experimental data make it possible to delineate the major factors determining the thermal stability of these polymers [9,18,19].

Of the PPOs, poly(2,6-dimethyl-*p*-phenylene oxide), the thermal decomposition of which begins at 723 K, is of immense practical significance [1,9]. Poly(methylene diphenylene oxide) which at 523 K is stable for 3000 h, is also thermally resistant on short-term heating up to 573 K [1,26]. According to [18], the basic weight loss of PPO occurs at 800–900 K. Water, CO and H_2 are the main gaseous degradation products at temperatures up to 723 K, while CH_4, CO_2 and benzene appear at higher temperatures. In the first stage of pyrolysis (up to 723 K) phenols are also released, the polymeric residue being a strongly cross-linked product (with a gel content above 70%). At the second stage (above 723 K) a gradual process of carbonization takes place, accompanied by release of rather small quantities of CH_4, CO and H_2. The carbon content of the final residue increases considerably with temperature, while the quantity of oxygen and hydrogen decreases.

Based on data for the thermal degradation products of PPO, the following scheme is suggested [18]:

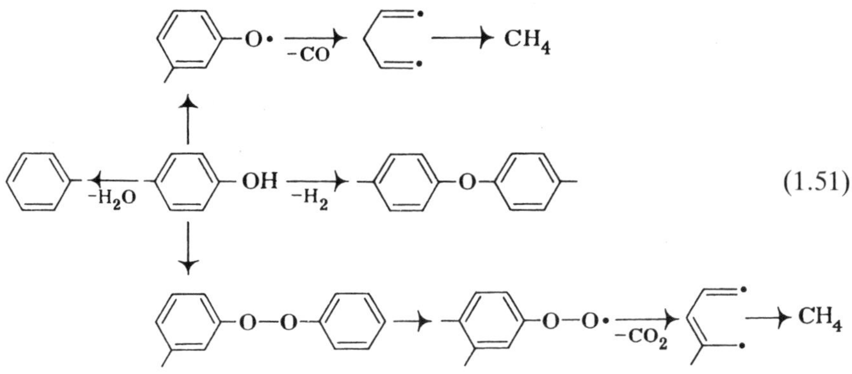

(1.51)

The following characteristic of the thermal degradation of PPO has been observed: in its initial stages, the products form in great quantities owing to the decomposition of the bridging and side-groups, while at deeper oxidation levels, the appearance of volatiles is associated with the decomposition of aromatic nuclei.

It has been established [1,9,18] that the degradation of PPOs based on phenol, o-cresol and 2,6-dimethylphenol depends on both the structure of the repeat unit and the molecular mass. The thermal degradation of these PPOs *in vacuo* proceeds with the release of both gaseous (H_2, CO, CO_2, CH_4, CH_3Cl, C_2H_6) and involatile products which are aromatic compounds of the type $Ar-O-Ar$. It has been suggested [1,9,18] that the thermal degradation of PPOs may proceed with the formation of benzyl radicals, namely:

$$Ph-CH_3 + Ph-O\cdot \longrightarrow Ph\dot{C}H_2 + PhOH \qquad (1.52)$$

This results in cleavage of the chain at the ester bond closest to the free radical, with the formation of an *O*-quinomethide and a substituted phenyl radical:

$$(1.53)$$

The free radical formed may continue the kinetic chain of thermal degradation of the PPO.

The data obtained show that the thermal stability of PPO is determined by two factors: the strength of the backbone, mainly of its (weakest) ether bonds, and the ability of alkyl and aryl groups to decompose at comparatively high temperatures.

If the thermal stability of the ether bonds is very low, then their decomposition occurs at temperatures which are insufficiently high for the subsequent thermal degradation of the polymer. After the decomposition of all the weak bonds, the polymer acquires a thermally stable structure. Higher temperatures lead to the degradation of the newly formed structure, followed by the release of comparatively high-molecular-mass oligomers, cross-linking and the thermal decomposition of aromatic nuclei. Such a scheme for the thermal degradation of PPOs depends on data on the chemical structure of the initial PPO, and the volatile and final solid products of this process at different temperatures. These data enable determination of the direction of thermal degradation, but are insufficient to prove the elementary steps of the reactions, the formation of free-radical centres and the intermediate degradation products.

Studies on the characteristics of the thermal degradation of PPOs have prompted the suggestion [18] of a radical mechanism for the thermal decomposition of the bridging groups and aromatic nuclei. In examples concerning PPOs containing aliphatic fragments, the experimental data confirm this mechanism. However, there is no direct experimental proof of the radical decomposition of the $Ph-O$ bonds in PPO.

The formation of a gel-fraction and release of CO_2 are the main processes during the oxidation of PPO, and are caused by hydroxide groups in the polymer decomposing to form benzylic groups, the subsequent condensation of which leads to the release of water:

$$2 \quad \text{(aryl)} \overset{CH_3}{\underset{CH_2O^{\bullet}}{}} -O\sim \longrightarrow \text{(aryl)} \overset{CH_3}{\underset{CH=O}{}} -O\sim + \text{(aryl)} \overset{CH_3}{\underset{CH_2OH}{}} -O\sim \qquad (1.54)$$

$$2 \quad \text{(aryl)} \overset{CH_3}{\underset{CH_2OH}{}} -O\sim \xrightarrow{-H_2O} \text{(aryl)} \overset{CH_3}{\underset{CH_2-O-CH_2}{}} -O\sim \quad \text{(aryl)} \overset{}{\underset{CH_3}{}} -O\sim \qquad (1.55)$$

The thermal–oxidative degradation of unsubstituted oligophenylene oxides of *meta-* and *para-*structure reveals a sharp rise in viscosity of these compounds. It is believed that initiation occurs through the addition of oxygen to oligophenylene oxides in the middle or at the ends of macromolecules, with the formation and subsequent decomposition of hydroperoxides.

The characteristics of the thermal–oxidative degradation of PPOs are as follows: oxygen enhances the decomposition of the bridging groups at considerably lower temperatures, whereas the aromatic segments of the chain are virtually unchanged. The radical-chain oxidation of aromatic segments of the chain predominates at the second, high-temperature stage of the thermal degradation of PPOs [18,19].

Epoxide polymers
Epoxide polymers have found wide applications as binders for glass-reinforced plastics, adhesives, impregnating materials, plotting compounds, etc., and therefore the study of their thermal stability, including epoxy-based composites is of great practical interest.

During the thermal decomposition of viscous epoxide oligomers, mainly phenols are released. These processes proceed via homolytic and heterolytic mechanisms followed by the splitting of the bis-phenol link to form phenol and isopropylphenol. Thermal conversions leading to the cyclization and formation of benzopyran structures are also possible, but of minor importance.

A comparison of the thermal stability of different epoxide polymers made it possible to conclude that it increases with the introduction into the chain of multinuclear phenols or bis-epoxides [9]. It has been established that the thermal stability of epoxide polymers is linearly dependent on the content of benzene rings in the repeat unit and the carbon content of the polymer [9].

Data on the thermal stability (i.e. the temperature at which 10% of the mass is lost) of epoxide polymers obtained on the basis of epichlorohydrin and multinuclear phenols, with the use of maleic anhydride as a curing agent, are presented below [1, 9]:

Dioxydiphenylpropane	493
Phenolphthalein	—
Rosolic acid	643
4,4-Dioxydiphenyl	623
Eosin	623
Fluorescein	553

Cellulose and its derivatives

Studies on the thermal and thermal–oxidative degradation of cellulose and its derivatives are significant in elucidating the mechanism and kinetics of their degradation. Since cellulose and its derivatives are widely used for the production of various materials, which are composites in many cases, the problem of their thermal degradation is also important from the practical point of view.

During the thermal decomposition of cotton cellulose and cellulose hydrate, the volatile products mainly consist of water, CO, CO_2 and minute quantities of acetaldehyde [3]. Analysis of the resinous products formed on pyrolysis of different types of cellulose materials has shown that they incorporate levoglucosans and carbonyl compounds. The yield of resinous products increases, and that of H_2O and CO_2 decreases, with increasing temperature and degree of degradation, the CO_2 yield in all cases remaining low.

On heating, the oxidized cellulose loses mass at a high rate in the initial stages of degradation, when the temperature is comparatively low. The subsequent increase in temperature results in inhibition of the degradation rate. H_2O, CO_2 and CO are the main products of the thermal decomposition of oxidized cellulose, the rather small yield of resinous products having an average molecular mass around 160 [3].

During the thermal degradation of cellulose triacetate the principal volatile is acetic acid, formed together with H_2, CO, CO_2, CH_3OH, resinous products, etc. Water is absent, which indicates the complete acetylation of cellulose.

The mechanism of the thermal decomposition of cellulose incorporates two basic stages: dehydration and subsequent cleavage of the $C-O$ bonds between and in the rings. The cleavage of $C-O$ bonds in the rings occurs with the release of CO_2, CO and H_2O, and the cleavage of $C-O$ bonds which are not in the rings leads to the formation of levoglucosan and hydroxyl-containing fragments. The view has been advanced [3] that chain fragments containing more than one cellulose ring are thermally unstable. Therefore, during the cleavage of bonds which are one ring distant from the levoglucosan or hydroxyl end of the chain, monomer is released only in the form of levoglucosan.

The production of acetic acid, CO_2, CO, etc., during the decomposition of cellulose triacetate is caused by the cleavage of $C-O$ bonds either within or external to the cellulose ring. The absence of monomeric compounds among the degradation products presumably depends on the fact that the primary alcohol participating in the production of levoglucosan exists in the form of an ester. The production of acetic acid occurs with the abstraction of an acetate group and a hydrogen atom.

The oxidation of the primary alcohol group in oxidized cellulose leads to a weakening of the ring and emergence of steric interaction between C-1 and C-6. This results in rapid thermal decomposition at low temperatures of the oxidized cellulose molecules.

The presence of water in cellulose may induce cleavage of glucoside bonds in the chain as well as the opening of the glucose rings to form aldehyde groups, which readily decompose with release of CO [16]. An increase in the degradation rate and changes in the dependence of the rate of this process on the degree of conversion after preliminary treatment of cotton cellulose samples with soda solution indicates the important role of water in the thermal decomposition of cellulosic materials [3].

Studies on the thermal degradation rate made it possible to establish that its dependence on the degree of conversion shows a common trend for different cellulose materials: in all cases it increases at first (up to 18–25% decomposition) and then gradually decreases towards zero at 70% mass loss, which characterizes the end point of carbonization of cellulose materials.

The rate constants of the initiation of thermal degradation for cellulose hydrate k_i (Table 1.3) are determined from the maxima of kinetic curves of the dependence of rate on the degree of decomposition. The values of the pre-exponential factors (10^5 s^{-1}) and of the activation energy of the process proved to be rather low compared with hydrocarbons. This indicates that the calculated constants for the initiation of the pyrolysis of cellulosic materials are effective values. The low values of the activation energy are associated both with the comparatively weak strength of $C-O$ bonds in the chain and, evidently, with the contribution of hydrolytic reactions.

Table 1.3 — The rate and activation energy of the thermal degradation of cellulose [3,16]

T (K)	W_{max} (10^5 s^{-1})	k_i (10^5 s^{-1})	E (kJ mol^{-1})
544	2.8	5.6	209.0 (cotton cellulose)
			196.5 (hydrate cellulose)
554	5.4	10.8	204.8 (viscose silk)
564	11.2	22.4	188.1 (cellulose triace-tate)

Though the decomposition of cellulose materials proceeds in an oxidizing medium with a higher rate [2] than *in vacuo*, it has no influence on the composition of the volatile products [3].

Polyesters

Poly(ethylene terephthalate) and polycarbonates are of key practical and scientific interest among the polyesters, becoming the focus of attention as regards their thermal and thermal–oxidative degradation [1–3,9,16,18,19].

Poly(ethylene terephthalate)
Poly(ethylene terephthalate) (PETP) is a typical representative of comparatively thermally resistant aryl aliphatic polyesters: its thermal decomposition begins at temperatures above 623 K [18,9].

The thermal degradation of PETP (553–593 K) in an inert atmosphere leads to CO_2, acetaldehyde and methane, benzene, acetylene, 2-methyldioxane and water as the basic gaseous products, and these are released in considerable amounts. Terephthalic acid and oligomeric products (dimers, trimers, cyclic tetra- and pentamers) are found among the poorly volatile products of the thermal degradation of PETP [3,18,19]. The half-life temperature for PETP is 723 K [9].

Studies on the thermal degradation of low-molecular-mass compounds (benzyl benzoate, ethylene glycol benzoate) modelling fragments of the backbone and intermediate products of the thermal degradation of PETP made it possible to propose the following scheme for this process [18, 19]:

$$\sim C_6H_4COOCH_2CH_2OCOC_6H_4\sim \longrightarrow \sim C_6H_4COOCH=CH_2 +$$
$$+ \sim C_6H_4COOH \rightleftharpoons \sim C_6H_4COOCHOCOC_6H_4\sim$$
$$|$$
$$CH_3 \qquad\qquad (1.56)$$

$$\sim C_6H_4COOCH=CH_2 \longrightarrow \sim C_6H_4COOCHCH_2CHCH_2\sim \longrightarrow$$
$$|$$
$$OCOC_6H_4$$
$$\longrightarrow \sim C_6H_4COOCHCH_2CH=CH_2 + \sim C_6H_4COOH \qquad (1.57)$$

$$\sim C_6H_4COOC(CH_3)HOCOC_6H_4\sim \longrightarrow \sim C_6H_4COOC_6H_4\sim +$$
$$+ CH_3CHO \quad (1.58)$$

The thermal conversions of the vinyl ester end-groups proceed at 673–773 K by the following schemes:

$$C_6H_4COOCH=CH_2 - \begin{cases} \rightarrow \sim C_6H_4COOH + CH\equiv CH \\ \rightarrow \sim C_6H_4CH=CH_2 + CO_2 \\ \rightarrow \sim C_6H_4COCH_2CHO \end{cases} \qquad (1.59)$$

The above schemes make it possible to elucidate the formation routes for acetylene, ketones and CO_2 detected among the thermal degradation products of PETP.

The thermal degradation rate of PETP has been determined by the change in the characteristic melt viscosity, by the concentration of end COOH and OH groups as well as by the rate of release of acetaldehyde [3]. The data obtained show that the process proceeds by first-order kinetics and by random chain scission. The activation energy calculated for the thermal degradation of PETP by changes in the intrinsic visocity is 260.4 kJ mol^{-1}, by the content of the terminal COOH groups is 156.3 kJ mol^{-1}; by the content of terminal OH groups is 94.0 kJ mol^{-1} and by acetaldehyde is 157.6 kJ mol^{-1} [3].

The random thermal degradation of PETP proceeds via the preliminary formation of a six-membered activated complex with its subsequent decomposition into products containing terminal carboxyl and vinyl ester groups [16].

$$\sim COC_6H_4 - C \underset{O-CH_2}{\overset{O \cdots H}{<}} CH-OCOC_6H_4-CO\sim \longrightarrow$$

$$\longrightarrow \ \sim COC_6H_4-C \overset{OH}{\underset{O}{<}} \ + \ CH_2{=}CH-O-COC_6H_4-CO\sim$$

(1.60)

A detailed study of the mechanism of thermal degradation of PETP at different temperatures indicates that the primary scission of the ester bonds is a reaction of ionic or molecular type, and radical processes may play a definite role in the secondary reactions [18].

Macroradicals produced in the thermal degradation of PETP are destroyed at temperatures above 250 K by a second-order reaction [16,18].

Generally, the processes in the thermal degradation of PETP have not been studied in detail. The degradation at 553–598 K in nitrogen–oxygen mixtures increases with the oxygen content [18], the molecular mass of the polymer decreasing substantially. Among the products of the thermal–oxidative degradation of PETP there are those which are also observed in the process of thermal degradation, but in considerably greater quantities. Only carbon oxide is not found during the thermal degradation of PETP.

On heating PETP in atmospheres of air, oxygen and water vapour, the concentration of COOH groups increases considerably. The view has been put [20] that the decomposition of PETP under oxidation conditions proceeds mainly through ester bonds via their hydrolysis with water formed from the decomposition of hydroperoxides. Such a scission of the polymer chain leads to the appearance of one COOH and one OH group from one ester group. In addition, carboxyl groups may be formed from oxidation of terminal ethylene glycol groups, both those initially present and those appearing during the cleavage of ester bonds.

The formation of new end-carboxyl groups leads to the additional production of CO_2 as a result of decarboxylation. Vinyl ester groups readily decompose to produce radicals:

$$\sim COC_6H_4COOCH{=}CH_2\sim \longrightarrow \sim COC_6H_4\dot{C}O + O{=}CH\dot{C}H_2 \quad (1.61)$$

After abstracting a secondary hydrogen atom, radicals initiate the reaction via a chain mechanism. In this case a benzaldehyde end-group and acetaldehyde are produced:

$$\sim\!COC_6H_4\dot{C}O + \sim\!C_6H_4COOCH_2CH_2\!\sim \longrightarrow \sim\!COC_6H_4CHO + \\ \sim\!C_6H_4COO\dot{C}HCH_2 \quad (1.62)$$

$$O=CH\dot{C}H_2 + \sim\!C_6H_4COOCH_2CH_2\!\sim \longrightarrow O=CHCH_3 \\ + \sim\!C_6H_4COO\dot{C}HCH_2\!\sim \quad (1.63)$$

On decomposition of the alkyl radical, terminal benzyl and acetaldehyde radicals are formed:

$$\sim\!C_6H_4COO\dot{C}HCH_2OOCC_6H_4\!\sim \longrightarrow \sim\!C_6H_4\dot{C}O + \\ O=CHCH_2OOCC_6H_4\!\sim \quad (1.64)$$

The formation of formaldehyde is evidently associated with C−C bond cleavage in the glycol link and subsequent decomposition of the radicals:

$$\sim\!C_6H_4COO\dot{C}H_2 \longrightarrow \sim\!C_6H_4\dot{C}O + CH_2O \quad (1.65)$$

Since the compositions of the products of the thermal and thermal–oxidative degradation of PETP are the same, the mechanism of initiation of these processes is identical. In this case addition of oxygen to the radicals produced promotes the development of degenerate branching.

All investigations on the mechanism of the thermal–oxidative degradation of PETP presuppose [18] that this process has a radical-chain character which proceeds by the formation and decomposition of peroxides and hydroperoxides. Simultaneously with the oxidation of aliphatic links, resulting in the formation of H_2O, CO_2, CO, aldehydes, etc., and in the appearance of new carboxyl and phenyl groups, there are also changes in the aromatic links of the chain associated with the formation of biphenyl structures and cross-linking of the polymer.

Polycarbonates
Among polycarbonates (PCs) which generally exhibit comparatively high thermal stability, the PC

$$\sim\!O-\!\!\!\left\langle\!\!\bigcirc\!\!\right\rangle\!\!-C(CH_3)_2-\!\!\!\left\langle\!\!\bigcirc\!\!\right\rangle\!\!-OCO\!\sim$$

has found wide application. This PC is a product of either phosgenation or transesterification of 2,2-di(4′-oxyphenyl)propane (diphenylpropane of bisphenol A) [21]. It has been established that the thermal degradation of PCs *in vacuo* in the range 573–673 K occurs with the random cleavage of ester bonds and elimination of carbon oxides.

Increasing the temperature above 673 K may lead not only to the decomposition of carbonate groups but also to the degradation of isopropylene groups. In this case CO and CO_2, together with methane, ethane, ethylene, propylene and considerable quantities of ethylphenol, isopropenyl phenol, isopropyl phenol and cresol, are found among the gaseous products [18,21].

Decarboxylation is the main pyrolysis reaction of PCs at temperatures above 723 K. It is supposed that CO_2 elimination occurs according to the scheme:

$$\text{(structure)} \quad C=O \longrightarrow CO_2 + \text{(diphenyl ether structure)} \tag{1.66}$$

Large quantities of bisphenol A eliminated during the decomposition of PCs at about 700 K may be formed in the thermal degradation of the polymer chain or be due to hydrolysis (alcoholysis) by phenolic compounds of the terminal carbonate group:

$$\text{(structure)} \xrightarrow{H_2O} \text{(structure)}\text{—OH} + $$

$$+ CO_2 + HO\text{—}\text{(bisphenol A structure)}\text{—OH} \tag{1.67}$$

$$\text{(structure)} \xrightarrow{ROH} \text{(structure)}\text{—OCOR} + $$

$$+ HO\text{—}\text{(bisphenol A structure)}\text{—OH} \tag{1.68}$$

The high-temperature decomposition of PCs at 973–1373 K results in the elimination of CO_2, CO, CH_4 and H_2, as well as in the formation of terminal phenol groups, which is explained by the following radical process:

$$(1.69)$$

$$(1.70)$$

The IR spectroscopic and NMR analysis of the solid residue from the pyrolysis of PCs at 773 K indicates [18] not only the ester group content, but also the methyl group content decreases, while that of the phenyl groups increases.

The activation energy of the thermal degradation of PCs *in vacuo* calculated by kinetic curves for the elimination of volatile products at 573–673 K is 117 kJ mol^{-1} [18,21]. Very similar values (107 kJ mol^{-1}) of the activation energy are found for the thermal degradation of PCs as investigated by the thermogravimetric method over the same temperature range, which may be associated with the strong contribution of the processes of thermal degradation during the thermal oxidation of PCs.

CO, CO_2, acetaldehyde, formaldehyde, methanol and water are found in the thermal–oxidation products of PCs. Their formation is explained by the isomerization and decomposition of peroxide and hydroperoxide radicals, with aldehyde and hydroxyl groups being accumulated in the solid polymer residue.

Studies on the mechanism of formation of the main gaseous products of the thermal degradation of PCs (CO, CO_2) have established [18] that CO forms exclusively via the oxidation of CH_3 groups, whereas CO_2 arises from the decomposition of ester groups and the oxidation of CH_3 groups.

Polyarylates

As polyesters based on various dicarboxylic acids and dihydroxybenzenes, the polyarylates (PAr) are thermally resistant compounds with a wide range of physicochemical and mechanical properties [1,9]. Most known PAr begin to decompose in an inert atmosphere at rather high temperatures (650–740 K), and at 773 K the mass loss by these polymers is 13.3–43.8% (mass) depending on the chemical nature of the repeat groups [1].

Based on analysis of the thermal-degradation products of PAr using various chemical and physicochemical methods, a mechanism for the thermal degradation of these polymers has been suggested in several publications [22–24]. All PAr feature a common mechanism independent of their chemical struture, i.e. structurization dominates at lower temperatures, while thermal degradation dominates at higher ones [24]. The thermal decomposition of ester links causes the formation of unstable radicals which decompose to eliminate CO and CO_2:

$$\tag{1.71}$$

Radicals may form either phenols or quinones. Triphenylmethane, fluorene, biphenyl, etc., are formed during recombination of radicals of different types. The formation of phenol and benzene in the products of the thermal degradation of PAr is obviously associated with hydrolytic decomposition. Consequently, consideration of the ratio of CO, CO_2 and phenol enables one to conclude about the predominance of either the radical or hydrolysis mechanisms for the primary decomposition of PAr macrochains.

The low-temperature initiation of the decomposition processes in PAr is caused by hydrolysis of the ester groups with subsequent scission of CO_2 via a radical mechanism. The replacement of this decomposition mechanism of PAr by the completely radical one occurs at temperatures above 670 K [9,19]. Over the temperature range to 720 K, intensive removal of oxygen and hydrogen from PAr takes place, whereas the relative quantity of carbon increases, i.e. a process of coke formation develops at the expense of cross-linked polyphenylene structures.

Increasing the temperature up to 900 K leads to thermal degradation of the polyphenyl structures with the formation of a graphite-like system and elimination of H_2 and CH_4 as volatiles [60].

Sulphur-containing polymers

Currently the group of sulphur-containing polymers is comparatively small, their synthesis having only recently attracted wide interest. Nonetheless, rather thermally resistant sulphur-containing polymers are now available which are finding wide application.

Aliphatic and aromatic polythioesters (polysulphides) ~S−R~ and ~S−Ar~, polysulphones ~SO_2−Ar~ and polysulphonates ~SO_2−O−Ar~ are representative of sulphur-containing polymers [1].

Studies on the thermal degradation of polysulphones and polysulphonates indicate a general similarity between their processes of decomposition and those of

(PPOs). Decomposition products of the bridging and side-groups form in consider-able quantities in the initial stage, while decomposition products of the aromatic nuclei predominate at more extensive conversions.

SO_2 is virtually the sole product of the thermal degradation of polysulphonate at temperatures up to 623 K (Table 1.4) [18] and when this temperature is reached there is eventually no sulphur left in the polymer. After complete removal of sulphur at 670 K, the polymer acquires the structure typical of PPO.

Table 1.4 — Products of the thermal degradation of polysulphonate [18]

Temperature (K)	Volatile products (% (mol.))					Mass of volatiles, (% of initial mass)	Loss of mass (% of initial mass)
	H_2	CO	H_2	CO_2	SO_2		
293–523	0.2	1.8	0.2	1.0	87.2	10.0	10.0
523–623	0.2	1.5	0.2	0.8	93.1	22.0	27.5
623–723	10.4	33.3	20.1	5.6	14.3	3.0	17.5

During the degradation of polysulphones of various structures a rapid loss of mass is observed in any medium over the range 770–820 K [18,19]. Mass-spectro-scopic investigations of the gaseous products have shown that SO_2 is the main volatile product, with lesser amounts of methane, phenol, benzene, toluene, H_2, CO and H_2S. The chromatographic mass spectroscopy of liquid and solid products of the thermal degradation of polysulphone has demonstrated [18, 19] that they are chiefly a mixture of phenols and esters. The quantity of phenol groups in the solid polymer residue increases linearly with the pyrolysis time. Heating of the polysulphone over 3 h at 650 K causes gelling, i.e. a three-dimensional structure is produced.

The following mechanism for the thermal degradation of polysulphones is suggested on the basis of the available experimental data. C−S bond scission is the primary process, followed by elimination of SO_2 and the formation of two phenyl radicals, which add to the phenylene rings of the chain [25]:

$$(1.72)$$

Subsequently, the degradation may proceed in two directions: abstraction of a hydrogen atom from the cyclohexadienyl-type radical and cleavage of the Ar−O bond [25]:

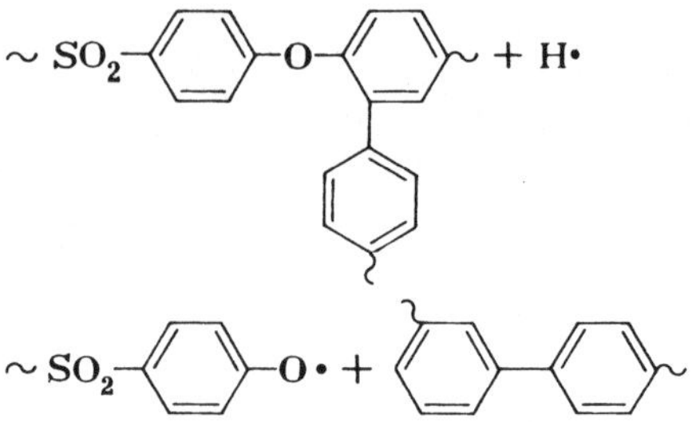

$$\sim SO_2 \text{—}\underset{}{\bigcirc}\text{—}O\text{—}\underset{}{\bigcirc}\sim \; + \; H\bullet \tag{1.73}$$

$$\tag{1.74}$$

$$\sim SO_2 \text{—}\underset{}{\bigcirc}\text{—}O\bullet \; + \; \underset{}{\bigcirc}\text{—}\underset{}{\bigcirc}\sim$$

Both reactions (1.73) and (1.74) cause the cross-linking of polymer chains.

The thermal-oxidative degradation of sulphur-containing polymers develops via a radical-chain mechanism which is similar to that of benzene oxidation at high temperatures [6]. It has been shown [26] that kinetic curves of oxygen uptake by a polysulphone based on 4,4'-dioxydiphenylsulphone and 4,4'-dichlorodiphenylsulphone are S-shaped and characterized by autoacceleration in the region 600–670 K. The thermally unstable product formed at initial stages of polysulphone oxidation is considered [26] to be responsible for autocatalysis.

Nitrogen-containing polymers
This group of polymers embraces chain aliphatic and aromatic polyamides, polyamines, polyhydrazides, polyhydrazones, polyurethanes, etc., as well as cyclochain polyimides, polybenzoxazoles, polybenzimidazoles, polypyrazoles, etc. [1]. Of the numerous polymers of this group, the polyamides, polyurethanes, polyimides and polybenzoxazoles are widely used and have been investigated quite extensively. Their physicochemical properties, including their thermal and thermal–oxidative stability have been studied in some detail [1,3,9,16,18,19,27].

Aliphatic and aromatic polyamides
The characteristics of the thermal degradation have been studied most fully for aliphatic polyamides [3,9,16,18], from which cyclic monomers are split rather readily. Thus, of the volatile products of the thermal degradation of polycaproamide at temperatures above 573 K, mainly ε-caprolactam is observed in a dry inert atmosphere. Simultaneously the molecular mass of the polycaproamide (PCA) decreases. The monomer is supposed to be released via a depolymerization reaction proceeding from terminal COOH groups:

intramolecular acidolysis

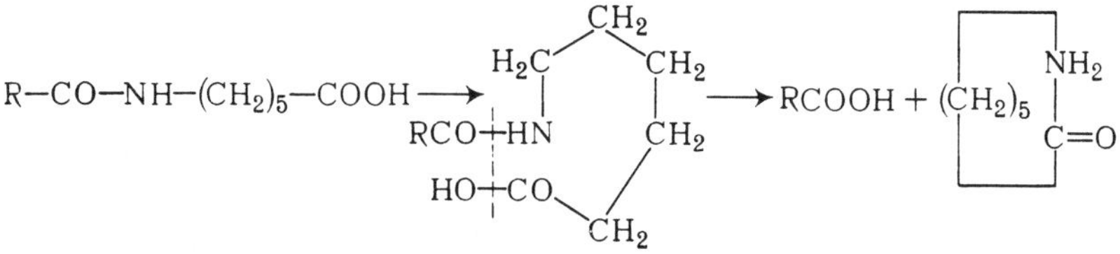

$$R\text{—}CO\text{—}NH\text{—}(CH_2)_5\text{—}COOH \longrightarrow \quad \longrightarrow RCOOH + (CH_2)_5 \begin{array}{c} NH_2 \\ | \\ C{=}O \end{array} \tag{1.75}$$

intramolecular aminolysis

$$R-NH-CO-(CH_2)_5-NH_2 \longrightarrow R-NH+OC \underset{H+HN}{\overset{H_2C}{\underset{\diagdown}{\diagup}}} \underset{CH_2}{\overset{CH_2}{\underset{\diagup}{\diagdown}}} \underset{CH_2}{\overset{CH_2}{\underset{}{}}} \longrightarrow$$

$$(1.76)$$

$$\longrightarrow RNH_2 + (CH_2)_5 \underset{C=O}{\overset{NH}{|}}$$

Since the fraction of terminal groups decreases as the molecular mass of PCA increases, the quantity of caprolactam eliminated during thermal degradation becomes lower (Fig. 1.17) [28,29]. The intermolecular acidolysis and aminolysis reactions exert a more substantial effect on changes in the molecular mass and thermal resistance of aliphatic polyamides. These reactions lead to the elimination of ε-aminocaproic acid which condenses to produce caprolactam and water, and to form higher molecular-mass polymer owing to the interaction of the macrochains between themselves (in the event of removal of water from the system). If water is *not* removed, then the macrochains are subjected to random hydrolysis with the reduction of the terminal COOH and NH_2 groups.

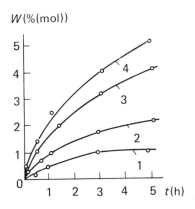

Fig. 1.17 — Kinetic curves of the yield of caprolactam in the thermal degradation of polycaproamide of different initial relative viscosity [28,29]: 1, 0.786; 2, 0.612; 3, 0.450; 4, 0.400.

In addition to caprolactam and water, considerable quantities of CO_2, NH_3, CO, CH_4, etc. are released via secondary reactions during the thermal degradation of aliphatic polyamides. Thus decarboxylation of the terminal COOH groups of polyamides results in release of CO_2. Ammonia forms owing to the self-interaction of terminal amino groups [16, 30]

$$\sim CO-NH-R-NH_2 + NH_2-R-NH-CO\sim \longrightarrow$$
$$\longrightarrow NH_3 + \sim CO-NH-R-NH-R-NH-CO\sim \qquad (1.77)$$

or owing to the interaction of this end-group and any other amino group in the chain:

$$\sim CO-NH-R-NH_2 + \overset{\displaystyle \nearrow R-NH-CO\sim}{\underset{\displaystyle \searrow R-NH-CO\sim}{N}H} \longrightarrow NH_3 +$$

$$+ \sim CO-NH-R-N \overset{\displaystyle \nearrow R-NH-CO\sim}{\underset{\displaystyle \searrow R-NH-CO\sim}{}} \qquad (1.78)$$

The latter reaction (1.78) may lead to branching and cross-linking of the polymer chains.

The rate of thermal degradation of aliphatic polyamides depends critically on the degree of conversion (Fig. 1.18) [3]. The maximal rate is observed with the

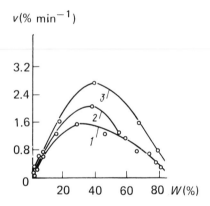

Fig. 1.18—Dependence of the rate of liberation of volatile products in the thermal degradation of PCA (molecular mass 60 000) on the quantity of volatiles at 1, 569 K; 2, 574 K; 3, 579 K.

release of 20–40% of volatiles; the rate and activation constants for degradation calculated from the maximal rates of the process are given below [3,16]:

	569 K	574 K	579 K
W_{max} (10^{-5} s^{-1})	28.1	37.3	49.4
k_d (10^{-5} s^{-1})	56.2	74.6	99.8
E_a (kJ mol^{-1})		113	

The low values of the activation energy for the thermal degradation of PCA (of molecular mass 30 000) are typical of hydrolysis reactions in the liquid phase, which points to the essential role of hydrolysis during polyamide degradation.

The thermal stability of aromatic polyamides is determined by the positions of the COOH and NH_2 groups in the aromatic ring. In terms of their thermal stability, these polymers are arranged in the sequence [19]: *ortho–ortho* < *ortho–meta* < *ortho–para* < *meta–meta* < *meta–para* < *para–para*.

Among the gaseous products of the thermal degradation of aromatic polyamides, it was possible to identify CO_2, H_2O, CH_4, NH_3, H_2, benzene and toluene as well as bennzonitrile [19]. It has been shown in several studies [19,31] that the amide group, which at comparatively low temperatures breaks down via a heterolytic mechanism (hydrolysis) and at high temperatures via homolysis, is the weak link in the polyamide chain. Experimental data on the temperature-dependence of the degradation rate constant have demonstrated the presence of two independent decomposition processes for aromatic polyamides: hydrolytic (of activation energy 63–70 kJ mol^{-1}) and homolytic (of activation energy 170–250 kJ mol^{-1}) processes.

The production of CO_2, H_2O and benzene among the decomposition products of aromatic polyamides indicates the hydrolysis of amide bonds with subsequent decarboxylation of carboxyl groups, by analogy with aliphatic polyamides. The production of benzonitrile is most probably connected with the following process

$$\sim NHC_6H_4NHCOC_6H_4COOH \xrightarrow[-NH_3]{}$$

$$\xrightarrow{} \sim NHC_6H_4NHCOC_6H_4-COONH_4 \xrightarrow[-H_2O]{}$$

$$\xrightarrow{} \sim HNC_6H_4NHCOC_6H_4CONH_2 \xrightarrow[-H_2O]{}$$

$$\xrightarrow{} \sim HNC_6H_4NHCOC_6H_4C\equiv N \xrightarrow{H_2O}$$

$$\xrightarrow{} C_6H_4C\equiv N + \sim HNC_6H_4COOH + NH_3 \qquad (1.79)$$

The increase in molecular mass on the subsequent structurization of aromatic polyamides during pyrolysis may be attributed to the interaction of amino groups with the release of ammonia, or to interaction of the terminal amino group with carboxyl groups, with the release of water [19].

On heating aliphatic polyamides in air at 433–473 K the molecular mass is reduced, with the simultaneous formation of a gel. The thermolysis of PCA at 623 K occurs with the formation of considerable quantities of monomer, as well as with reduction of the molecular mass with gel *not* being formed.

Heating PCA at comparatively low temperatures (about 370 K) in air causes the formation of peroxides which act as branching agents, leading to thermal oxidation via a degenerate branched chain mechanism. No peroxide compounds are found in PCA at higher temperatures.

Mass-spectroscopic studies on the thermal degradation products of aromatic polyamides have established that oxygen is completely consumed in forming CO_2 and H_2O. Oxygen is not an initiator for the decomposition of aromatic polyamides but only participates in secondary oxidation reactions of the decomposition products [32]. Oxygen promotes the amido–iminol rearrangement and the iminol groups formed readily engage in intermolecular condensation to produce cross-linked polymer, releasing water which hydrolyses the amide bonds. Thus, the amide bond is the weakest link in aliphatic and aromatic polyamides of different chemical structure. In both thermal and thermal–oxidative degradation this bond is subjected to decomposition via homolytic and heterolytic mechanisms leading to the decomposition of polymer chains, their cross-linking and to isomerization.

Polyurethanes
This important class of polymers is widely employed in different branches of engineering. Polyurethanes (PUs) possess a wide range of physicochemical and mechanical properties that, to a considerable extent, are associated with the vast diversity in their chemical structure and composition [1]. However, few examples exhibiting appreciable thermal stability are known among the PUs [9,33], mainly because the PU group readily decomposes at temperatures above 470 K.

Data on the thermal properties of PUs obtained by means of DTGA and TGA have shown that these polymers are stable up to their melting temperatures following which their thermal–oxidative degradation and depolymerization takes place at high temperatures (above 600 K). Thus it has been established that the thermal–oxidative degradation of PUs based on an ether 4,4'-diisocyanatodiphenylmethane, and an aliphatic diamine begins at 550 K, while at 598 K partial thermal degradation occurs at the expense of isocyanate decomposition. Depolymerization of this PU takes place at temperatures above 670 K. The oxidation of PUs based on an ester, diphenylmethane diisocyanate and an aromatic diamine begins at 583 K, while at 638 K their thermal degradation occurs at the expense of isocyanate decomposition followed by depolymerization at temperatures above 670 K. PUs based on esters, toluylene diisoocyanate and an aromatic diamine possess thermal properties similar to those mentioned above.

Large quantities of volatiles (CO_2, NH_3, CO, CH_4, etc.) produced either via secondary reactions of radicals or decomposition of terminal and side-groups, are apparent during the thermal degradation of PUs [30], which may proceed in two mains ways as follows:

$$\sim RCH_2-OCO-NHR'- \begin{cases} \longrightarrow \sim RCH_2OH + HCONHR' \sim & (1.80) \\ \longrightarrow \sim R{=}CH_2 + CO_2 + H_2NR' \sim & (1.81) \end{cases}$$

The first pathway (1.80) is characteristic, for instance, for PUs based on toluylene diisocyanate and ethylene glycol on heating to 440 K. The second pathway (1.81) proceeds at temperatures about 470 K on heating PUs based on hexamethylene diisocyanate and ethylene glycol.

The thermal degradation of PUs based on 4,4'-diisocyanatodiphenylmethane occurs at about 700 K and is a two-stage process, whereas that of PUs based on toluylene diisocyanate begins at temperatures below 670 K and is a one-stage process. The thermal and thermal–oxidative stability of cross-linked PUs which possess the highest thermal stability, have barely been examined.

It has been found [34] that, in the temperature range 643–650 K, the quantity of paramagnetic species produced in the decomposition of PUs increases sharply in atmospheres of helium and air, the maximal content of paramagnetic species correlating with the maximal rate of PU degradation.

Polyimides
Among the organic polymers of great thermal stability, polyimides (PIs) containing a cyclic imide group in a chain condensed with aromatic rings are those most widely used in industry. All polymers of this class are distinguished by their high thermal stability [1,9,18,27].

Studies over the last decade have led to the accumulation of a large body of evidence concerning the thermal and thermal–oxidative stability of PUs and have enabled development of a mechanism for their thermal and thermal–oxidative degradation [18,27].

The thermal stability of PIs depends essentially on their chemical structure. According to which temperature initiates their degradation, PIs are arranged in the following sequence depending on the diamine skeletal structure [9,27]:

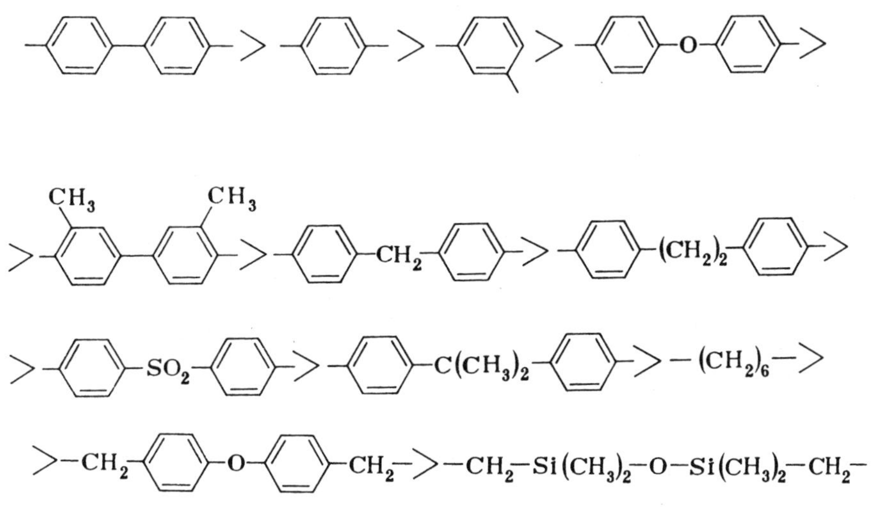

As seen from the above series, the thermal stability of PIs is reduced on going from rigid rod-like structures to flexible structures possessing oxymethylene or aliphatic groups as bridging groups.

PIs based on 4,4′-diaminodiphenyl esters and dianhydrides are arranged according to their thermal stability in the following sequence (in terms of the dianhydride radicals) [27]:

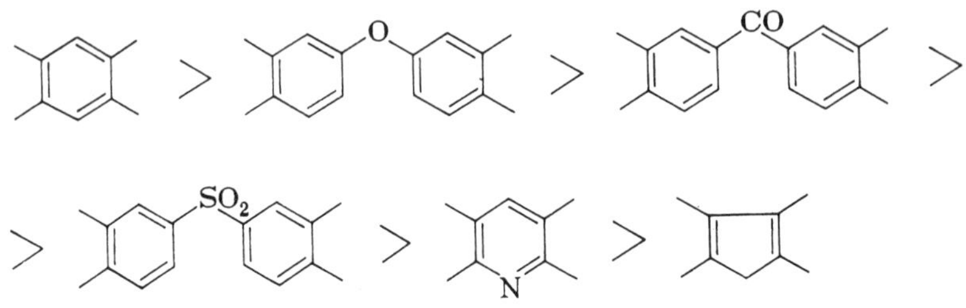

In PIs the imide bond is initially subject to thermal conversions. The presence in the chain not only of the imide bond but also of a definite number of amide bonds, the existence of which is caused by the kinetic arrest of the cyclodehydration reaction of polyamide acids in the solid phase, impedes the analysis of PI degradation [27]. Therefore, the role of each type of bond during the pyrolysis of PIs should be estimated by thorough analysis of the composition and properties of the decomposition products of PIs, polyamides, polyamidoimides and model compounds. Numerous studies concerning PI degradation provide the basis for several schemes which are based principally on a comparison of the structure of the repeat unit and the degradation products rather than on kinetic data. As a result a mechanism for the thermal degradation of PIs is suggested which proceeds in two directions:

(1) the decomposition of the imide ring with elimination of CO;
(2) thermal isomerization of the imide ring into the isoimide structure with subsequent elimination of CO_2.

In the first route, in addition to CO are produced benzene, fluorene and the anilide of phthalic acid, while in the second besides CO_2 are found benzene, biphenyl and fluorene [35].

The fact that, of the volatile products of PI pyrolysis (at 973 K) with ^{14}C-labelled carbonyl groups, only the carbon oxides appear to be labelled proves that carbon monoxide is a product of homolytic decomposition of the bridging group [18,27]. The absence of any label in CH_4 demonstrates its origin from the aromatic rings.

The high yield of CO_2 may be explained by the decomposition of non-cyclic amide links: this occurs by hydrolysis of the imide ring into its isoimide isomer, with subsequent decomposition of the latter as well as by condensation of the NCO groups formed via radical decomposition of the imide ring [18,27].

The source of water required for hydrolysis of the imide groups is considered to be (i) adsorbed water, (ii) water formed from the final cyclization of amidoacetic groups, and (iii) water formed from the interaction of terminal amine groups with the carbonyl group of the imide ring [18,35]. Thus release of sufficient water (0.5–7% (mol.)) in the pyrolysis of PIs does not exclude the possibility of hydrolytic reactions. The low activation energies of degradation (40–80 kJ mol^{-1}) and elimination of CO_2

($80\,kJ\,mol^{-1}$) in the low-temperature region [18,36] in contrast to $160\text{--}240\,kJ\,mol^{-1}$ in the high-temperature region of the homolytic decomposition of polymers confirm the possibility of PI hydrolysis [18].

The copious elimination of H_2 and CH_4, as well as the production of oligomeric degradation products, begins at 670–720 K. The cross-linking of aromatic rings also begins in this temperature range. The complete degradation of heterocycles at a rate still insufficient for polymer cross-linking may cause release of the degradation products of PIs as oligomers [18].

The cross-linking processes of PIs proceed most effectively in the high-temperature region of the pyrolysis. A large number of reaction schemes rationalizing formation of the three-dimensional network in PIs are found in the literature. The following principal schemes are considered in publications [18,27]:

(1) dehydrogenation-combination of diamine-component rings;
(2) interaction between adjacent imide rings;
(3) interaction of terminal amine or isocyanate groups with the imide ring;
(4) reaction between two amide groups in the tautomeric iminole form;
(5) formation of a bond between dianhydride and diamine components with opening of the imide ring;
(6) formation of intermolecular bonds which is, in principle, already a possibility during the synthesis of polyamido acids.

During the thermal–oxidative degradation of PIs the composition of the elimination products is approximately the same in pyrolysis but their rate of formation is considerably higher [27]. The similarity in the make-up of the degradation products makes it reasonable to suppose that homolytic cleavage of a bond in the polymer backbone is the primary act of both the thermal and the thermal–oxidative degradation. Oxygen is involved only in subsequent intermediate stages of decomposition by oxidizing products of pyrolysis [35].

However, differences in the shapes of the kinetic curves for the elimination of CO, CO_2 and H_2O during degradation of PIs in inert and oxidative media, which are associated with the presence of an autocatalytic effect in the thermal–oxidative degradation, prompted the authors of [18] to suppose that degradation during the thermal oxidation of PIs occurs with the direct participation of oxygen. This standpoint is confirmed by the substantial differences in activation energies for the degradation of PIs in air ($130\text{--}137\,kJ\,mol^{-1}$) and *in vacuo* ($310\,kJ\,mol^{-1}$) as well as by differences in the elemental composition of the solid polymer residues after decomposition.

According to [18] oxygen catalyses abstraction of a hydrogen atom from the benzene nucleus, and the resulting macroradical interacts with another oxygen molecule to form a peroxide radical. It has been established [18] that a greater fraction of CO_2, and a certain amount of CO, are formed at the expense of atmospheric oxygen during thermal oxidation of PIs.

The thermal–oxidative degradation of PIs is also possible at the expense of the benzene rings involved in the polymer chain. This is confirmed by the oxidation of these rings in an oxygen atmosphere at 613 K [37], and the introduction of substituents reduces considerably the thermal stability of the aromatic rings.

The abstraction of a hydrogen atom from the benzene ring during the oxidation of PIs may cause the formation of water, the presence of which promotes the development of autocatalytic random heterolytic processes of degradation of the polymer chain [27].

The occurrence of interchain cross-linking due to the interaction of two phenyl radicals is a further important indication of the abstraction of a hydrogen atom from the benzene ring. This is confirmed by the greater rate of polymer cross-linking in the presence of oxygen than in an inert atmosphere [27].

The manner of degradation of PIs in the solid phase has a number of peculiarities. In particular, it has been shown [38] that the decomposition rate of PIs in both inert and oxidative atmospheres decreases with increasing film thickness. These differences are considered to be associated with specific features in the supermolecular structure of thin and thick polyimide films.

Thus the thermal–oxidative degradation of PIs is a complex chemical process which proceeds in the solid phase and incorporates simultaneously thermal decomposition, oxidation and hydrolysis as well as condensation processes.

Polybenzoxazoles and polybenzimidazoles

This group of highly thermally resistant polymers embraces the compounds [1]

The thermal stability of aromatic polybenzoxazoles is high; on heating to 1200 K in a nitrogen atmosphere the loss of mass is about 27% and in air only 35% [1]. The thermal stability of aromatic and aliphatic polybenzoxazoles differs fundamentally. Initiation of the decomposition of aliphatic polybenzoxazoles in air begins at about 570 K, while the aromatic analogues start to decompose at 770 K. Polybenzoxazoles and polybenzimidazoles are of comparable thermal stability, although polybenzoxazoles are stable to hydrolysis, especially at higher temperatures.

The thermal decomposition of polybenzoxazoles starts with the fragmentation of heterocycles at about 670 K, as confirmed by the elimination of nitrogen, CO, CO_2, O_2, small quantities of H_2 and cyanogen. Isophthalodinitrile, isophthalic acid dihydrazide, traces of benzoic acid and benzonitrile are components of the liquid products of pyrolysis. The solid residue is a carbonizing agent. Based on the decomposition products, the most probable scheme for the thermal degradation of polybenzoxazoles is as follows:

$$\text{(1.82)}$$

The CO_2 output during thermal degradation of polybenzoxazoles is an order of magnitude more than that of CO in the temperature range up to 770 K. Since in the structure of the heterocycle there are no groups which could lead directly to CO_2, then, evidently, oxygen which is eliminated during pyrolysis instigates secondary oxidation reactions.

Mass-spectroscopic analysis of the decomposition products of polybenzimidazoles has shown that among them HCN, NH_3, H_2O and H_2 are the basic products, while CO, CO_2, CH_4 and phenol are eliminated in lesser quantities [9]. The activation energy for the formation of the main pyrolysis products of polybenzimidazoles is 108.7–225.7 kJ mol^{-1}, i.e. substantially lower than is required for the homolytic decomposition of any bonds present in polybenzimidazoles.

In this connection a view has been advanced about the possible thermohydrolytic decomposition of polybenzimidazoles in the initial stage of degradation [9,18]. Studies using $H_2^{18}O$ have been conducted to establish the role of hydrolysis of the benzimidazole structure. However discrepancies within the data obtained enable no unambiguous conclusion to be drawn [18].

The presence of oxygen increases the rate of both weight loss and elimination of gaseous products in the thermal degradation of both polybenzoxazoles and polybenzimidazoles [9,18]. These effects are related to a predominant attack by oxygen on the aromatic nuclei bearing nitrogen-containing functional groups.

On heating, polybenzimidazoles adsorb oxygen and from 570 K quinoid structures, which may initiate the decomposition of aromatic nuclei, accumulate:

$$(1.83)$$

Kinetic curves of weight loss, oxygen uptake and CO and CO_2 elimination in the thermal degradation of polybenzoxazoles and polybenzimidazoles are S-shaped; degradation is believed to occur via a radical-chain mechanism, similar to that of benzene oxidation at high temperatures. High values of the effective energy of these decompositions (142–159 kJ mol^{-1}) provide evidence for the radical-chain mechanism [18].

Polyorganosiloxanes and polyelementorganosiloxanes
Organosilicon and elementorganosilicon polymers embrace a number of thermally resistant polymers, being of interest for their physicochemical and mechanical properties, which have found wide application recently [1,9,39].

The thermal stability of polyorganosiloxanes containing aromatic groups is higher than that of their aliphatic analogues, increasing considerably on the introduction of phenylene groups into the backbone.

The nature of the side-group also has a considerable effect on the thermal stability of polyorganosiloxanes: polymers containing a CH_3-group are those most thermally stable, those with the *p*-dimethylaminophenyl group being thermally stable. Cross-linked and ladder organosilicon polymers are characterized by high thermal stability [39].

Liquid polydimethylsiloxanes are stable up to 450 K, while liquid polyphenyl-methylsiloxanes are so to 520 K. Polydimethylsiloxane (PDMS) decomposes *in vacuo* at 670 K to form the cyclic oligomers hexamethylcyclotrisiloxane and oxamethylcyclotetrasiloxane. This process occurs at lower temperatures in the presence of terminal Si−OH groups or additives of electrophilic or nucleophilic character. The terminal OH groups interact with the Si−O bond by the scheme:

$$(1.84)$$

where $n = 3,4$.

During the thermal degradation of polysiloxanes, the weaker Si−C bond is cleaved at random and then the radicals formed undergo a number of transformations:

$$\sim Si(CH_3)_2-O-Si(CH_3)_2-O\sim \longrightarrow \sim Si(CH_3)_2-O-\dot{S}i(CH_3)-O\sim + \dot{C}H_3\cdot$$
$$\longrightarrow \sim Si(CH_3)_2 + O=Si(CH_3)_2-O\sim$$

$$(1.85)$$

$$(1.86)$$

$$\begin{array}{c} \text{Si(CH}_3)_2 \\ \sim\!\text{O}-\text{Si(CH}_3)_2-\text{O} \diagup \diagdown \text{O} \\ \quad\quad\quad\quad (\text{CH}_3)_2\text{Si} \diagdown_{\text{O}} \diagup \text{Si(CH}_3)_2 \end{array} \quad\longrightarrow\quad \sim\!\text{O}-\text{Si(CH}_3)_2 + \big[\text{Si(CH}_3)_2\text{O}\big]_3 \qquad (1.87)$$

Thus it follows that a radical-chain process is the main mechanism for the thermal degradation of polyorganosiloxanes at comparatively low temperatures [16].

The thermal degradation of organosilicon polymers of cyclolinear structure is more complex. Based on results from mass spectroscopy, NMR, and gas–liquid chromatography (g.l.c) of the products of thermal degradation, it was possible to suggest an appropriate mechanism [19]. The data obtained suggest that all degradation products (cyclic and bicyclic organosiloxanes) are formed by the mechanism suggested for PDMS, according to which the decomposition begins, as shown above, with the formation of an intermediate four-centre complex followed by rearrangement of the siloxane sites of two linear segments of the polymer chain.

Besides cyclosiloxanes, products such as formaldehyde, formic acid, CH_3OH, H_2O, CO, CO_2, CH_4 and solid residue are formed during pyrolysis of polyorganosiloxanes [19].

The degree of acceleration observed during the decomposition of polyorganosiloxanes in the presence of oxygen is associated with the oxidation of side-groups, leading to the formation of Si−OH groups, which are active in the degradation. The following main schemes are suggested for the thermal oxidation of organic groups at The silicon atom of polyorganosiloxanes [19,39,40]:

(1) $2\equiv\!Si-CH_3 + O_2 \longrightarrow 2\equiv\!Si-\dot{C}H_2 + H_2O_2$

$\quad \equiv\!Si\dot{C}H_2 + O_2 \longrightarrow \equiv\!Si-CH_2O\dot{O} \longrightarrow \equiv\!Si-OO\dot{C}H_2 \longrightarrow \equiv\!Si-O\cdot + CH_2O$
$$\qquad\qquad\qquad\qquad\qquad\qquad\qquad\qquad\qquad\qquad\qquad\qquad \downarrow$$
$$\qquad\qquad\qquad\qquad\qquad\qquad\qquad\qquad\qquad\qquad\qquad\quad CO + H_2$$

$\quad \equiv\!Si-\dot{O} + H_3C-Si\equiv \longrightarrow \equiv\!Si-OH + \equiv\!Si-\dot{C}H_2 \qquad\qquad (1.88)$

(2) $\equiv\!Si-CH_3 + O_2 \longrightarrow \equiv\!Si-\dot{C}H_2OOH \longrightarrow \equiv\!\dot{S}i + CH_2O + \dot{O}H$
$\quad \equiv\!\dot{S}i + \dot{O}H \longrightarrow \equiv\!Si-OH \qquad\qquad\qquad\qquad\qquad\qquad (1.89)$

(3) $\equiv\!Si-CH_3 + O_2 \longrightarrow \equiv\!Si-\dot{C}H_2 + H\dot{O}_2$
$\quad \equiv Si-\dot{C}H_2 + O_2 \longrightarrow \equiv\!Si-CH_2O\dot{O}$
$\quad \equiv Si-CH_2O\dot{O} + H_3CSi\equiv \longrightarrow \equiv\!SiCH_2OOH + \equiv\!Si-\dot{C}H_2$
$\quad \equiv Si-CH_2OOH \longrightarrow \equiv\!Si-CH_2\dot{O} + \dot{O}H$
$\quad \equiv Si-CH_2\dot{O} \longrightarrow \equiv\!\dot{S}i + CH_2O \qquad\qquad\qquad\qquad\qquad (1.90)$

It has been established spectroscopically [40] that quartz-like structures are formed during the oxidation of PDMS at temperatures above 1300 K. The ordering of these structures becomes higher, the lower the rate of heating.

The introduction of Al, Co, Ni, Ti, Fe, etc., into the backbone chain of polyorganosiloxanes increases their thermal and thermal–oxidative stability owing both to termination of the kinetic chain of depolymerization and to the formation of cross-linked rigid structures in the initial stages of the process.

2

Disperse inorganic polymer fillers and their thermal properties

The introduction of fillers into polymers leads to the appearance of a wide range of interactions (from weak physical forces to chemical bonds) arising at the polymer–filler interface. The nature of these interactions depends to a considerable extent on the surface chemistry of the filler. The various types of interaction arising at the interface critically influence the mechanical and physicochemical (including thermal) properties of the polymer and the filled system as a whole. The surface chemistry of the disperse fillers is likely to be one of the most substantial factors influencing the pattern of interaction at the polymer–filler interface and, consequently, the properties of the polymer. The chemical properties of the surface of a filler and its composition are of paramount significance from the standpoint of its effect on the thermal properties of the polymer and filled polymer system.

2.1 SURFACE CHEMISTRY AND THERMAL PROPERTIES OF DISPERSE INORGANIC FILLERS

2.1.1 Metals

The virgin surface of disperse metals produced by any technique (mechanical, chemical, thermal, condensation, electrolytic, etc.) [41–44] readily oxidizes in air even to the point of self-ignition in the absence of a protective material [42]. Therefore highly disperse metals are always produced *in vacuo* or in an inert gaseous medium, with subsequent or simultaneous passivation of their surface by various protective materials such as hydrocarbons, alcohols, fatty acids, amines, PAS solutions, monomers and polymers and their solutions [42–44].

The surface of disperse metals produced in the presence of protective materials will contain adsorbed and chemisorbed molecules of protective [42–47] as well as M–OH, M–H and M–O groups (where M is the metal) which form on contact of the surface with the atmospheric environment. Most of these surface groups and compounds probably play an active role in the surface interaction with polymer molecules and exert a definite action on their thermal stability. In addition, many of these materials possess low thermal stability and at higher temperatures tend to undergo various conversions on the metal surface. Thus it is important to define the surface chemistry of disperse metals introduced into polymers, as well as the mechanism of interaction of different low-molecular-mass compounds with both the metal surface and the relevant polymer at elevated temperatures.

The hydride mechanism of interaction of metals with water and other hydrogen-containing compounds has been substantiated [47]. According to this mechanism a redistribution of the electrons of the entire system, with the formation of new chemical bonds, occurs at the intitial stage of reaction after orientation of the adsorbed molecules on the metal surface and mutual polarization of the surface molecular and atomic layers. Thus adsorption of water results in the formation on the clean metal surface of two new types of surface compounds, i.e. hydride and hydroxide, while ammonia adsorption leads to the formation of hydride and amide, all groups being identified by IR spectroscopy for a number of metals [41,47].

The adsorption of benzene on nickel and copper produces a wide absorption band in the IR spectrum in the region 3060–2760 cm^{-1}, indicating that benzene is chemisorbed with the loss of its aromatic character [48]. If benzene is adsorbed on a clean surface of highly disperse iron and palladium, then the absorption band of chemisorbed benzene is not observed.

Alkenes (ethylene and but-1-ene) [41] are adsorbed on nickel and platinum to form chemisorbed compounds of the type M–CH$_2$–CH$_2$–M and CH$_3$–CH$_2$–CH–M–CH$_2$–M and (in part) of M–CH=CHM, M$_2$CH–CHM$_2$ and MCH=CRM (where M is the metal atom, R is alkyl).

IR spectroscopic studies on the interaction of alcohols (methanol, ethanol, 1- and 2-propanol, 1- and 2-butanol, *tert*-butanol), oxyethylated alcohols, acetone, methyl ethyl ketone, acetaldehyde, formaldehyde, ethers (dimethyl and methyl vinyl), tetrahydrofuran and ethylene oxide on the surfaces of cobalt, iron, nickel and silver have shown that, simultaneously with physical adsorption, these compounds form chemisorbed layers on the metal surface [41].

Of particular interest are the interactions of nitrogen-containing compounds, in which nitrogen acts as an electron donor towards the clean metal surface. Studies conducted [41,49] on the adsorption *in vacuo* of amines (diethylamine, isopropyla-mine, monoethanolamine, *n*-butylamine) on sputtered films of aluminium, silver, magnesium, copper and other metals have shown that four to five monolayers of chemisorbed molecules of the amines appear on the surface of certain metals (magnesium, aluminium). Thus, it is possible to consider that the adsorption of these substances leads to a new phase on the metal surface.

The presence of chemisorbed layers of amines causes inhibition of metal oxidation in air and in water vapour due to a net decrease in the free energy of the surface and to the difficulty in dissociating water or oxygen molecules on it [41,49].

Chemisorption on the metal surface is also typical of nitriles, another group of nitrogen-containing compounds [41,50]. Investigations of nitrile adsorption on palladium, platinum, rhodium, ruthenium and nickel have shown major changes in the structure of these compounds. Thus, the adsorption of capronitrile on metals results in reduction of the C≡N bond to C=NH at the expense of the alkyl hydrogen atom and the absorption band at 2230 cm^{-1} of the C≡N bond in benzonitrile either shifts to 2200 (palladium) and 2220 cm^{-1} (platinum, rhodium) or disappears. The aromatic nature of benzonitrile is preserved during chemisorption on metals. It has been concluded [50] that chemisorption of benzonitrile on metal surfaces proceeds in two directions:

(i) formation of donor–acceptor and π-donor bonds of the type M←N≡C–Ar with palladium, platinum and rhodium (thus explaining the low-frequency shift of C≡N during chemisorption), and

(ii) formation of a covalent bond between the C≡N group and the metal surface resulting in a decrease in bond order

$$N \equiv C - Ar$$

$$M \quad M \quad M \quad M$$

The second possibility increases in importance in the series: Pd<Pt<Rh<Ru<Ni.

Of prime interest is the interaction of monomers with a clean metal surface which, to some extent, may model the interaction of polymers with the metal surface. Adsorption of styrene on a clean aluminium surface is accompanied by polymer formation. However, the bond strength between the adsorbed layers of styrene and the surface is weak and styrene does not inhibit the oxidation of aluminium [15]. However, during the adsorption of styrene on silver [52] no chemisorption is observed. Conversely, during the adsorption of acrylic acid, chemisorption occurs with simultaneous polymerization on the surfaces of both silver [52] and of other metals (aluminium, copper and nickel) [41,51,52]. Acrylic acid forms stable chemisorbed polymer layers on these metals. Chemisorption and polymerization of acrylic acid also take place on the oxidized surfaces of metals [41,51,52]. The polymerization of unsaturated monomers on the clean surface is most probably either initiated by surface compounds or is due to polarization of the double bond. Electron transfer from the metal to the monomer molecule in these cases seems less probable.

Thus, during the production of highly disperse metals in the presence of protective materials, chemisorption of the latter on the metal surface usually takes place. Generally, hydroxyl, hydride and other groups are always present on the surface of highly disperse metals. Depending on the chemical properties of the surface groups and compounds formed, they may play the role of initiators of the degradation of the polymer or, by interacting chemically with a second polymer molecule, produce network structures, thus stabilizing the polymer. Other types of influence of the surface groups on the thermal stability of polymers are also possible.

It should be noted that complex chemical processes take place on heating (to 470–500 K) polymers filled by metals with clean surfaces. These processes partially change the chemical structure of the polymers in forming chemical bonds with the solid surface [42,53]. This leads, as a rule, to an increase in the thermal and thermal–oxidative stability of the polymers.

Polymer modification of the disperse metal surface may provide one method of producing metal fillers possessing various specific properties, including the ability to increase the thermal stability of filled polymers [41, 54].

2.1.2 Salts

Calcium carbonate and, less frequently, other salts insoluble in water, such as $BaSO_4$, CaF_2, $MgCO_3$, ZnS, MoS_2, etc., have been employed as polymer fillers more than other salts [55].

Calcium carbonate has found wide application as a polymer filler owing to a useful combination of properties, including stability over a wide temperature range. (It decomposes to form CaO and CO_2 only at 1100–1200 K.)

Four well-known methods are employed to obtain commercial grades of disperse calcium carbonate:

(1) pulverizing of natural calcium carbonate (chalk) by dry and wet methods with subsequent purification and fractionation;
(2) precipitation of $CaCO_3$ as a by-product from sodium hydroxide production;
(3) precipitation of $CaCO_3$ as a by-product from sodium carbonate production;
(4) precipitation of $CaCO_3$ from lime water [55].

One should note that natural calcium carbonate (chalk) is the starting material for all methods of filler production. Depending on the methods of production and treatment, $CaCO_3$-based filler contains 94–98% (mass) of the basic compound.

Under the action of mechanical grinding of calcium carbonate and fluoride and also of barium sulphate, anion and cation vacancies (F-, F'- and V-centres) form on the fracture surface and intensive electron emission is observed [41,56]. In the EPR spectrum of ground $BaSO_4$ at 77 K there is a narrow singlet 159–239 A m^{-1} in width and with a g-factor equal to that of the free electron. On heating ground $BaSO_4$ to room temperature, the narrow singlet disappears and a wide absorption band of several thousands of A m^{-1} appears. On recooling, the narrow signal reappears. These spectral changes indicate that spin-lattice interaction is the main factor determining the linewidth of the resonance in $BaSO_4$, and the origin of the free electrons is related to electron release on grinding. The process of mechanically grinding salts like $CaCO_3$, CaF_2, and $BaSO_4$ is used for the mechanochemical polymerization and grafting of polymers, the degree of grafting being proportional to the electron emission intensity on grinding [127,145]. This method may be used for modification (lyophilization) of the surface of fillers on being ground in a monomer or polymer environment.

The polarity and high reactivity of calcium carbonate make possible chemical modification of its surface by organic and polymeric acids [55,57]. As with mechano-chemical modification, this achieves a decrease of the hydrophilicity of the calcium carbonate surface, thus improving its distribution in the polymer environment. Its ability to neutralize acids present in polymers as additives or formed during their degradation has a stabilizing effect on polymer composites.

2.1.3 Metal oxides

Among metal oxides Al_2O_3, MgO, ZnO, TiO_2, Fe_2O_3, Fe_3O_4, PbO, Pb_3O_4, ZrO_2 and BeO are those most often used as fillers of polymers [55]. The great diversity of metal oxides as regards chemical composition, crystal structure and methods of production results in a wide range of surface chemical properties, e.g. the nature of the centres and their activity in various reactions. The physical and chemical, as well as the thermal properties of the surface of oxides are determined to a considerable extent by the concentration and acidity of the OH groups present. The properties and concentration of surface OH groups depend on numerous factors, especially on the composition and crystal structure of the oxides and the methods of their production and activation.

There are many papers, reviews [58,59] and monographs [60] dealing with the chemistry of metal oxide surfaces. Here they will be tackled only to an extent sufficient to clarify the influence of disperse oxides on the thermal and thermal–oxidative degradation of polymers filled with them.

The acidity (the concentration and nature of centres) of the surface of oxides is one of their most important properties. The methods available for determination of the concentration and nature of the acidic sites [41,58,60] are rather imperfect and, depending on the methods employed, the results obtained differ in a number of cases. The sequence of oxides is established by the customary methods for determining the acidity of acidic materials (titration of aqueous and non-aqueous solutions by bases, adsorption and desorption of gaseous bases, and spectroscopic studies of the interaction of adsorbed molecules with the acidic site of the surface). The proton-donor ability (or Brönsted acidity [61]) of oxides decreases in the series $TiO_2 > SiO_2 > Al_2O_3 > ZnO \gg MgO$, while their electron-accepting ability (or Lewis acidity [62]) decreases as follows: $Al_2O_3 > TiO_2 > ZnO > MgO > Co_2O_3 > CuO$.

The rule that the acidity of metal (M) oxides is higher the greater the bond energy M–O, gives the following acidity sequence: $SiO_2 > TiO_2 > Al_2O_3 > PbO > ZnO > MgO > CdO$.

Other means of estimating the acidity of solid metal oxides are available. Since acidic oxides have an essentially covalent bond while basic oxides are ionic, to approach the problem it is useful to establish the effective charge on the oxygen atom. A series of oxides [64] arranged according to the decrease in the charge on the oxygen atom, or to the difference in electronegativities, can be given, i.e. $MgO < Al_2O_3 < CdO < ZnO < SiO_2 < Fe_2O_3 < TiO_2$. There have also been efforts to estimate the acidity of metal ions in oxides based on the ionization constants of the complexes in aqueous media [155]. According to these results the acidity increases in the series: $Mg^{2+} < Zn^{2+} < Cd^{2+} < Cu^{2+} < Pb^{2+} < Al^{3+} < Fe^{3+}$.

Clearly, the orders in these various series are somewhat different for the reasons given above.

Aluminium oxides

The aluminium oxide most frequently used as a disperse filler of epoxide and polyester resins is obtained either synthetically or from natural ore (bauxite, corundum, etc.) [55]. The surface chemistry of aluminium oxide, in particular the structure of its hydroxylic coating, has been studied intensively [41,58–62]. If we consider the hydroxylic coating of Al_2O_3 as a set of structural OH groups and strongly bound water molecules (which is not removed even at 800–900 K), then the concentration of OH groups on the surface may reach 12–13 groups nm^{-2} [58–62].

Based on these and other data, the following scheme for the OH coating of the Al_2O_3 surface is suggested [60,65,66]. In the case of a uniform distribution, the OH groups are approximately a distance of 1.3 nm from each other and the IR bands at 3800–3700 nm^{-1} correspond to these. The bands in the region 3600–3500 cm^{-1} are attributed to O–H bond vibrations in H_2O, which is coordinatively bound to the aluminium atoms and removed from the surface at temperatures above 800 K. The wide absorption band maximal at 3520–3470 cm^{-1} is attributed to the vibrations of water molecules hydrogen bonded to the Al_2O_3 surface. This water is removed on heating to 523–573 K. Water which is removed from the surface at temperatures up to 423 K is attributed to clusters, the presence of which are indicated by the low-frequency absorption at 3400–3300 cm^{-1} [65,66].

Al_2O_3 at high dehydration temperatures (973–1223 K) exhibits five individual absorption bands in its IR spectrum in the region 3800–3700 cm^{-1}, which are attributed to isolated OH groups being in contact with different numbers of oxygen atoms and having different acidities.

The adsorption of different molecules by a solid surface subject to thermovacuum treatment at different temperatures are usually examined by IR spectroscopy, which determines the nature of the surface acid sites [60,67]. These studies have established that the aluminium oxide surface is more active in its chemical interaction with electron-donor adsorbate molecules than a silicon dioxide surface. Since the properties of the surface OH groups of these oxides towards adsorbates differ only slightly [68], the observed difference in chemical activity may be referred to the existence on the Al_2O_3 surface of other types of active site, e.g. Lewis acid sites, such as coordinatively unsaturated aluminium atoms.

The numerous studies on the adsorption of organic bases and ammonia by the Al_2O_3 surface made it possible to identify at least four types of interaction:

(1) physical adsorption, with the formation of hydrogen bonds;
(2) coordinative interaction with Lewis acid sites;
(3) surface reactions with acid sites;
(4) surface reactions with Brönsted acid sites [41,60,68].

The ratio of protic and aprotic centres on the surface of Al_2O_3 depends on the temperature of its thermovacuum treatment: at temperatures above 700 K there are mainly Lewis acid sites on the surface [41,61,62,65,66].

Detailed IR investigations on the adsorptive interaction of hexachloroacetone with Al_2O_3 surfaces of different degrees of dehyhdration and dehydroxylation enabled determination of the nature of the Lewis acid sites and their distribution in terms of acidity. Three types of acid sites have been shown to exist on the surface of Al_2O_3 which has been vacuum-treated at room temperature. The thermovacuum treatment of Al_3O_3 at 423 K leads to the disappearance of the two most acidic sites and to the appearance of three new more strongly acid sites, and after thermal vacuum treatment at 523 K only two of the most strongly acid Lewis sites remain. These results indicate the presence on Al_2O_3 of several types of Lewis site of different acidity, with low degrees of stability of adsorption complexes at the more weakly acid sites. Based on data for adsorption of CO_2 on an Al_2O_3 surface, it has been proposed that a further type of centre exists which differs from those mentioned above,.i.e. a stressed bridge structure of type Al–O–Al or $Al^+–O^{2-}–Al^+$ which arises during dehydroxylation of the Al_2O_3 surface.

Strong adsorption and chemisorption, especially at high temperatures, of polymer molecules containing oxygen atoms (ethers, esters, polysiloxanes, epoxide resins) and nitrogen (polyamides, polyurethanes, polyimides, polybenzimidazoles, etc.) lead to structurization of the filled systems which should increase their thermal stability. However, the presence of acid sites of different natures and strengths as well as of water adsorbed at the Al_2O_3 surface should promote thermal degradation processes with simultaneous hydrolysis and acidolysis of polymer molecules, in particular of polyamides, polyimides, polysiloxanes, etc.

Magnesium and zinc oxides

The magnesium oxide used as a stiffener of polyester resins and a filler of thermo-plastic polymers is generally obtained by the calcination of carbonates or magnesium hydroxide as well as during the joint calcination treatment of magnesium chloride with lime [55]. Polymer composites containing magnesium oxides are characterized by higher heat transfer, rigidity, hardness and resistance to creepage.

IR spectroscopic studies of the hydroxylic coating of magnesium oxide subject to thermal–vacuum treatment at different temperatures have established the existence of several types of OH groups characterized by absorption bands at about 3750, 3710 and $3550 \, cm^{-1}$ [41,69]. That at $3710 \, cm^{-1}$ disappears after thermal–vacuum treat-ment of the oxide at temperatures above 470 K. After heating MgO at 870 K only the band at $3750 \, cm^{-1}$ remains, disappearing only during thermal treatment above 1200 K [70]. This high-frequency absorption band is attributed to free surface OH groups while the other bands are assigned to various types of OH groups coupled with different numbers of Mg atoms. The absence of any marked shift in the absorption bands during adsorption of different types of material on the magnesium oxide surface is explained by the general character of the OH groups. No Brönsted and Lewis acid sites are found on a pure MgO surface.

From these data one might expect that dehydrated magnesium oxide will exhibit low chemical activity during the thermal and thermal–oxidative degradation of filled polymers lacking oxygen-containing groups. In the latter instance, the formation of salt-like surface compounds is possible, which should possess higher thermal stability.

Zinc oxide is used to fill polyalkenes, unsaturated polyesters, polysiloxane rubbers, etc. The introduction of zinc oxide into rubbers containing functional groups facilitates their vulcanization. Polymers filled with zinc oxide possess superior hardness, thermal stability and conductivity [55]. This filler is obtained by the oxidation of zinc powder, and the calcination of a number of zinc-containing minerals with coal followed by oxidation of the metal with air [55].

Three types of OH groups are found on a pure zinc oxide surface, two of which refer to isolated OH groups coupled to different numbers of zinc atoms, while the third type refers to groups mutually coupled via a hydrogen bond [41,71].

The insignificant shift of the IR absorption bands associated with the surface OH groups of zinc oxide during the adsorption of benzene is evidence for their low acidity.

Zinc oxide increases the thermal and thermal–oxidative stability of filled rubbers, unsaturated polyesters and other polymers which are readily structurized on the incorporation of this filler.

Titanium dioxide

Three crystalline modifications of titanium dioxide are known — anatase, rutile, and brookite. The first two are most widely employed as white pigments in the varnish and paint industries. The titanium dioxide-based varnish and paint coatings have higher rigidity and stabilities towards heat and the atmospheric environment. The natural mineral ilmenite is used to obtain the anatase modification of titanium dioxide, and chlorination of natural rutile followed by oxidation of the chlorides produced is used to obtain the rutile modification [55]

In the crystal lattice of titanium dioxide each oxygen atom is bonded to three titanium atoms. In this case the titanium atoms to which OH groups are coupled with may be present at two fixed distances: 0.300 and 0.373 nm (anatase) and 0.295 and 0.365 nm (rutile).

Data on the hydroxylic coating of anatase (which have been obtained by many authors [41,72]) clearly define three OH group IR absorption bands at 3715, 3670 and 3650 cm^{-1}. The first band refers to isolated OH groups, while the other two bands refer to OH groups which are coupled to two titanium atoms situated at different distances in the TiO_2 lattice.

Absorption bands at 3685, 3655 and 3410 cm^{-1} are evident in the IR spectrum of rutile [41,72]. The first bond refers to the vibrations of isolated OH groups, while those at 3655 and 3410 cm^{-1} refer to OH groups of the rutile surface which are coupled via a hydrogen bond. The band at 3410 cm^{-1} is typical only of rutile, which is interpreted in terms of the different mutual arrangements of the OH groups on the rutile and anatase surfaces. The view has been put that OH groups coupled with five- and four-coordinate titanium atoms are associated with the absorption bands at 3655 and 3410 cm^{-1} respectively, and may be located on the rutile face (110). The presence on the TiO_2 surface of water molecules coordinatively bonded to titanium atoms has been revealed by IR spectroscopy.

Investigations of the adsorptive interaction of different molecules (benzene, acetone, diethyl ether) with the titanium dioxide surface made it possible to establish that the OH groups of anatase possess a higher acidity than those of rutile, an effect related to the difference in the crystal structures of the modifications. The anatase and rutile surfaces are also characterized by differences in the concentration of other surface-active sites, i.e. basic OH groups [73] and electron-donor [74] and Lewis sites [75]. It has been established that approximately half of the OH groups on anatase are acidic, while the rest are basic [73].

According to [75] the Lewis acid sites (coordinatively unsaturated Ti^{3+} and Ti^{4+} ions) play a key role on the rutile surface, while according to other authors [76] the rutile surface is solely a Lewis acid, not showing Brönsted acidity.

Electron-rich centres, such as O^{2-} ions are found on the anatase surface. Their number is twice the sum of the Brönsted and Lewis surface sites. Centres of this type are also found on the rutile surface.

One may suppose that the titanium dioxide surface is able to engage in strong adsorption and, probably, chemical interaction with polymers having nitrogen and oxygen atoms in their chains or side-groups as well as with polymers possessing acidic functional groups and unsaturated bonds. The strong physical and chemical interactions of polymer molecules with the titanium dioxide surface undoubtedly have a substantial influence on their thermal and thermal–oxidative degradation. At higher temperatures water molecules coordinatively bound to the titanium dioxide surface may participate in hydrolysis and acidolysis of polymers.

Oxides of iron, nickel, chromium and of other transition metals

The surface chemistry of oxides of iron, nickel and other transition metals has been studied only to a limited extent [41,77,78]. According to [79] the absorption band with a maximum at $3410 \, cm^{-1}$ refers to the vibrations of OH groups of iron oxide mutually coupled via a hydrogen bond. It has been established [78] that the concentration of OH groups on the surface of nickel oxide (NiO) is sharply reduced during thermal treatment at temperatures above 523 K. Data concerning the surfaces of cobalt and copper oxides are few and, in some cases, highly contradictory.

Studies on the adsorption of ammonia, polyacrylamide, butylene and stearic acid on an iron(III) oxide surface have established that nitrogen-containing compounds coordinate with atoms of the Fe_2O_3 surface, while alcohols hydrogen-bond to the surface OH groups, and acids form chemisorbed salt-like compounds [41,77].

There are four types of OH group on the surface of chromium(III) oxide (α-Cr_2O_3), featuring IR bands at 2720, 2670, 2565 and $2460 \, cm^{-1}$ according to [80]. The latter bands disappear during the thermal–vacuum treatment of the oxide up to 473 K and the high-frequency bands decay above 720 K. The 2720 and $2670 \, cm^{-1}$ bands refer to isolated or weakly bound surface OH groups which are surrounded by different numbers of oxygen atoms. The presence on the chromium oxide surface of coordinatively unsaturated chromium atoms with coordination numbers 5 and 4 [41,80] has been established by adsorption studies.

Fe_2O_3 and Fe_3O_4 are used for the filling of polymeric materials. They are produced from hematite, a natural mineral, and are by-products of a number of productions (Fe_2O_3) or from magnetite ore (Fe_3O_4) [55]. Iron oxides when used as fillers and pigments increase the thermal stability of polyalkene-based composites [142] as well as of copolymers of vinyl chloride and vinyl acetate.

2.1.4   Silicas, glass and layered silicates

Silicas

Of all the disperse inorganic fillers of polymers, this group is the most numerous and widely applied in practice. Silicon dioxide, having over 20 different modifications, forms the basis of most silica and silicate fillers. The surface chemistry of silicon dioxide has been extensively studied [58–62]. It has been established that the mean concentration of OH groups on the silica surface is 7.0–9.5 $\mu mol \, m^{-2}$ or 4.2–5.7 groups nm^{-2} [60]. The concentration of OH groups on a quartz surface is almost the same.

Dehydroxylation is the simplest method for activating the surface of silica. The numerous data available in the literature [60] enable the conclusion to be drawn that molecularly adsorbed water is almost completely removed from the developed silicon surface after prolonged pumping-off at temperatures up to 473 K. On thermal–vacuum treatment at temperatures above 550 K, the silica surface becomes partially dehydroxylated. The removal of OH groups coupled by hydrogen bonds from the silica surface occurs in the temperature range 570–1000 K, and above 1000 K only free OH groups are retained. The maximal (but incomplete) dehydroxylation of the silica surface is reached only after prolonged thermal–vacuum treatment at temperatures of 1300–1400 K, resulting in the formation of the stressed-bridge siloxane structure on the surface [60].

Spectral studies of silicas (silica gel, aerosil, etc.) have shown [58–60] that they are characterized by the presence in the IR spectra of a narrow intense absorption band at about 3750 cm^{-1} which is related to isolated, non-interacting OH groups, with a mean separation of more than 0.3 nm [60]. This band is also observed in the spectrum of silica after thermal–vacuum treatment at 870–970 K.

Absorption bands at about 3680, 3500 and 3400–3300 cm^{-1} are revealed in the spectrum of silica in the lower-frequency range. That at about 3680 cm^{-1} refers to OH groups mutually coupled by a hydrogen bond, being mainly in the bulk of the silicon dioxide particles [60]. That at about 3550 cm^{-1} refers to the absorption of surface OH groups coupled by a strong hydrogen bond; the range 3400–3000 cm^{-1} refers to the stretching vibrations of physically adsorbed water, while the band at 1630–1640 cm^{-1} corresponds to the region of deformation vibrations.

It has been established by study of the adsorptive interaction of the hydroxylated surface of silicas with molecules of diverse chemical nature that the OH groups are acidic [41,60].

A number of physical methods (IR spectroscopy involving total internal reflection, diffusion reflection, absorption in the overtone region of the IR spectrum, UV, NMR, and EPR spectroscopy) have been suggested to determine the quantity and arrangement of OH groups on the surface of silica, their interaction with water and other compounds, and their acidity [41,60].

At present different methods (pyrogenic, mechanochemical, chemical) for the production of disperse silica fillers have been developed in some detail [41, 55]. There are also natural microcrystalline and amorphous deposits of silicas which are also used as fillers after purification, grinding and drying [55].

Now we shall consider briefly the basic methods for producing disperse silica fillers, the influence of these methods on their surface chemistry and procedures available for surface modification.

The pyrolytic method for silica production consists of the hydrolysis of silicon tetrachloride in the plume of the oxygen–hydrogen flame [55]:

$$2H_2 + O_2 \rightarrow 2H_2O \;\Big] \!\!\rightarrow 2H_2 + O_2 + SiCl_4 \rightarrow SiO_2 + 4HCl$$
$$SiCl_4 + 2H_2O \rightarrow SiO_2 + 4HCl$$

By varying the concentrations of SiCl$_4$ vapour and inert gas in the mixture, the flame temperature and the rest-time of the newly formed SiO$_2$ in the combustion chamber, one may regulate directly the dimensions of the particles, and their specific surface area, surface chemistry and powder macrostructure. Pyrogenic silicon dioxide (aerosil) is a powder consisting of spherical colloidal particles 3–10 nm in diameter and having a high specific surface area, i.e. $50\,000$–$400\,000$ m^2 kg^{-1}.

Aerosil is amorphous, and the silicon atoms on its surface are usually coupled with OH groups: on average, three groups of Si–OH groups are present on each square nanometre of surface [60]. The existence of OH groups on the aerosil surface

(i) promotes its hydration, with the formation of hydrogen bonds with adsorbed molecules, and
(ii) opens ample opportunities for its chemical modification, in particular by treatment with silanes and siloxanes having reactive functional groups and by graft polymerization and polycondensation [41,81].

The main merits of aerosil are its stiffening and thixotropic effects in liquids, the prevention of segregation of composites, good dispersibility in most polymers, prevention of film adhesion, etc. [41,55,81]. Aerosil is applied in both modified and unmodified forms as a stiffening admixture to elastomers, epoxide compositions and thermoplasts [55].

The chemical method for obtaining silicas depends on chemical reactions (e.g., sodium silicate with mineral acids) in an aqueous medium, owing to which sufficiently highly disperse particles (up to 0.002 μm) are formed — the so-called silica gel. The specific surface area of the precipitated silica gel is $175\,000$–$800\,000$ m^2 kg^{-1}. In their properties and surface chemistry, silica gels are in many cases similar to pyrogenic silicon dioxide. However, it should be noted that in the case of aerosil there is occluded HCl in its particles, its extracts always having a low pH (about 2–3), whereas in silica gels there exist admixtures of alkali and alkaline-earth metals which may block the surface OH groups. Depending on their conditions of production silica gels show either a neutral or weakly alkaline (or acid) reaction. Silica gel and precipitated silicon dioxide are widely employed for the filling of thermo- and reactoplasts as well as of elastomers.

The mechanochemical method for production of silica fillers depends on the grinding of natural raw material (quartz, quartzitic sandstone), at first in coarse grinders and then in mills of different types [41,55]. After coarse grinding the powder is often allowed to stand in settlers to remove pollutants. The powder obtained is either sifted or subjected to air flotation. The filler particles are 2–10 μm in diameter and their specific surface area is 500–2000 m^2 kg^{-1} [41,55]. The ground quartz surface includes OH groups and sorbed water (0.05% (mass)). Being modified, the surface OH groups may undergo chemical reactions.

During the mechanical grinding of quartz, active sites appear on freshly formed surfaces, which, in their turn, may also be used to chemically modify the filler, in particular by graft polymerization of monomers [41,81].

Direct studies (by EPR) of ground quartz revealed the concentration of active sites on its surface to be 2×10^{20} spin kg^{-1} (specific surface area 0.7 m^2 kg^{-1}) [82]. The EPR spectral linewidth for quartz ground at 77 K is about 640 A m^{-1}.

Hyperfine structure is not observed in this spectrum and the g-factor corresponds approximately to that of the free electron. The concentration of paramagnetic centres, and the width and shape of the EPR signal do not vary during long-term storage at room temperature; the EPR spectrum of disperse quartz appears, probably, as a result of scission of Si–O bonds and the existence of surface atoms with free valences. Its nature differs considerably from the spectra of irradiated quartz and ground barium sulphate. It is hardly probable that its characteristics refer to electrons captured by structural defects, since in this case the broad peaks should be observed at room temperature. In addition, on dispersing quartz and silica gel, electron emission [41], which is able to initiate the polymerization of monomers contacting with solid surfaces at their moment of formation, may occur as for metals and certain oxides.

It has been found [83] that the rate of oxidation of CO to CO_2 during vibrogrinding of quartz is one order of magnitude greater than that found immediately after cessation of the grinding, and remains constant for a long time in spite of the growth of the specific surface area and concentration of paramagnetic centres. Consequently, the initiation of this reaction is directly associated with the destruction of the solid and the appearance of short-lived (10^{-4} s) chemically active states which ultimately either decay or become stable.

One should note that the rate of appearance of paramagnetic centres is two orders of magnitude lower than that of the oxidation reaction of CO and the quantity of bonds cleaved during the formation of a new surface unit, and so cannot be considered as centres leading to this reaction.

The paramagnetic centres fixed after grinding are thermally stable, chemically inert and are either by-products or secondary products which reflect the properties of the stabilized solid surface.

It has been established [41,82] that the vibrogrinding of quartz in air is accompanied by the formation of radicals of the type $\equiv$Si· or of Si–O–O· peroxy groups with a spin concentration of 5×10^9 g^{-1} SiO_2. The grinding of quartz at room temperature in a flow of oxygen and in the presence of 0.2% commercial carbon causes cold combustion of the commercial carbon with the formation of CO and CO_2, which is also observed on grinding the mixture in an inert atmosphere. However, the process in the latter case is slower and the spin concentration remains quite high. The idea has been advanced that in the interaction of carbon with O_2 there is elimination of the activation barrier due either to the vibroimpacts or to the fact that this is a catalytic reaction and transfer of O_2 is realized by the active sites formed.

Thus, the active sites formed on the surface of silica fillers during grinding are of varied types and possess different stabilities over time. These sites have a high activity as regards adsorption and interaction with different compounds, including monomers and polymers.

The joint dispersion of silicas with polymers facilitates dispersion of the filler particles with the simultaneous mechanochemical modification of its newly generated surface by the grafted polymers [53]. The grafting of polymers is achieved at the expense of the interaction between the active sites of the filler surface, which arise during dispersion, and the polymer macroradicals formed during mechanochemical rupture of the polymer chains. It should be noted that the latter process is massively accelerated in the presence of fillers [53]. Thus, the process of mechanical grinding of silicas and quartz in the presence of polymer admixtures (up to about 10%) is an effective and energetically advantageous method of accelerating the dispersion process with the simultaneous chemical modification of the filler surface.

Among the natural silica disperse fillers, the microcrystalline tripolite (average particle dimensions of 15–30 μm and a specific surface area of 700–1500 $m^2\,kg^{-1}$ [55]) and amorphous diatomite (particle dimensions up to 50 μm, specific surface area 700–3500 $m^2\,kg^{-1}$ [55]) have found wide application. The natural raw material is subjected to grinding, fractionation, drying or calcination. Tripolite and diatomite contain Si–OH groups on their surface [84] which are able to react. These fillers are employed in sealing compounds, glues, rubber-based stocks, etc.

Many papers, reviews and monographs are devoted to the chemical modification of the surface of disperse silicas by substances of a different class [41,54,55,58–62,81]. These publications consider the reactivity of groups and other active sites of the surface, the mechanism and topochemistry of surface reactions as well as the surface properties of modified fillers, including the thermal stability of organic groups and molecules on the surface of silicas. Silicon halides and organosubstituted halides of silicon, and other organic compounds containing groups which are able to interact with the silica surface, are widely employed as modifiers. In a number of cases modifiers grafted to the silica surface contain functional groups (OH, NH_2, COOH, CO, etc.) as well as unsaturated bonds which are able to interact with polymers or monomers into which the filler is introduced. The interaction (from weakly physical to chemical) of surface groups of silicas, and functional groups of the grafted modifiers, with polymers influences substantially the thermal and thermal–oxidative stability of the filled polymers. Additionally, silicas contain adsorbed water bound to the surface centres which may take place in chemical reactions proceeding at the polymer–filler interface at the temperatures of degradation of the filled polymer composites.

Glass

Glass for polymer filling is deployed as powders, solid or hollow microspheres and glass fibres (short and continuous) [55]. As the glass surface is hydrophilic, it is moistened weakly by hydrophobic polymers. The concentration of OH groups on glass in the limited hydroxylated state is 7–9.5 $\mu mol\,m^{-2}$ (4.2–5.7 groups nm^{-2}) [41,81] and is similar to their concentration on the surface of amorphous silica (aerosil, silica gel). In contrast to pure silicas, glass normally contains considerable quantities of admixtures such as oxides of aluminium, boron, phosphorus, sodium, potassium, calcium, magnesium, lead, etc., which provide a substantial influence on the formation and nature of the active sites on its surface.

During the thermal treatment of glasses above 800–900 K, the concentration of impurity atoms on their surface increases, in particular those of boron and aluminium [85] which possess electron-accepting properties towards the adsorption of pyridine, aniline, p-dimethylaminobenzoate, etc. The introduction into glass of impurity atoms able to form coordinatively unsaturated centres enhances the interaction of polymers with the glass surface and its catalytic activity in reactions proceeding at the interface, including those of the thermal and thermal–oxidative degradation of the filled polymers.

The high chemical activity of OH groups on the glass surface is widely used for its chemical modifications by different compounds (organochlorosilanes, chlorosilanes, amines, etc.) as well as by metal halides ($TiCl_4$, $SnCl_4$, VCl_3, $AlCl_3$, etc.) which are catalysts of many chemical reactions on the surface [41,81]. The presence of modifiers on the glass surface also influences the degradation processes of filled polymers at higher temperatures. However, systematic studies of those processes simulating polymers filled with modified silicas are unavailable in the literature.

Aluminosilicates and layered silicates (clay minerals)

Currently, of the different disperse fillers (metals, salts, oxides, silicas, silicates, aluminosilicates, glass, natural and synthetic minerals, graphite, commercial carbon, etc.) which are employed for the production of polymer composites, natural minerals, especially clay (layer) silicates, are given special attention. The interest in these minerals lies in the fact that, owing to their widespread and considerable reserves, their accessibility and low cost, they are promising fillers for the production of polymer composites. Furthermore, clay minerals possess good adsorption, ion-exchange and catalytic properties.

The sheer range of practical uses of disperse clay minerals in the production of filled polymers poses a number of problems concerning the investigation of the nature of the surface active sites and the role of these sites in processes proceeding at the interface and also the degradation of polymers at high temperatures. Exploitation of the utility of clay minerals in activation and modification (including ion-exchange) of their surface chemical properties enables the formulation of fillers exhibiting stabilizing properties.

Kaolinite and montmorillonite, which are typical examples of clay minerals, are those most widely used (and also as fillers of polymers). Vermiculite and palygorskite are less frequently employed as fillers. The structure of these minerals is based on silicon–oxygen tetrahedra [86] with vertices connected via oxygen in the apices and in the same plane. The silicon atoms are localized in the centre of the tetrahedra, whose apices are directed to an octahedral network of hydroxyl groups which has aluminium atoms in its centre. The lattice dimensions are limited by both the octrahedral aluminium layer and the tetrahedral silicon layer in which the hydroxyl groups of the octahedron are replaced by oxygen atoms.

Kaolinite does not swell in water and other polar liquids owing to the bond strength between the layers, which arises from the interaction between the outer OH groups of one layer and the oxygen atoms of the other. The distance between the layers (packets) of the kaolinite structure is 0.715–0.720 nm [86] and for poorly crystalline kaolinites it is, to some extent, greater, which is caused by the presence of insignificant quantity of water between the packets.

In the montmorillonite packet, two tetrahedral networks of silicon–oxygen are connected via the central octahedral layer of aluminium–oxygen, owing to which the upper and lower surfaces of the complex layer contain oxygen atoms. Since montmorillonite packets are joined via adjacent layers of oxygen, the bond between them is weaker than that between the OH groups and oxygen of the kaolinite packets. In this connection the montmorillonite structure is characterized by the fact that molecules of water and other polar substances as well as of polymers and monomers may penetrate between the structural layers, thereby stimulating expansion of the lattice towards the c-axis [87]. Thus, the value of the c-parameter is not constant and varies from 0.96 nm, when there are no sorbed polar molecules between the structural layers, up to the complete uncoupling of certain layers. Air-dried montmorillonite, containing in its exchange positions the Na^+ ion, features one layer of water molecules between the silicate layers and in this case the interplane distance towards the c-axis is about 1.25 nm.

In studying the activity of layer silicates in their interaction with different substances including polymers, the ion-exchange sites of their surface are of special importance.

The exchangeability of the natural layer silicates has two causes:

(i) non-stoichiometric isomorphous substitution inside the structure, and
(ii) the cleavage of chemical bonds [88].

The non-stoichiometric isomorphous replacement of the quadruply charged silicon by the triply charged aluminium in the tetrahedral networks, and the triply charged aluminium by ions of lower charge, e.g. magnesium, in the octahedral networks, leads to the appearance of an uncompensated charge in the structural unit. The resulting negative charge of the lattice is usually compensated for by the extra structural exchange cations, which are mainly arranged on the basal planes of the clay mineral crystals.

In montmorillonites the capacity for cation exchange (E_{ex} = 900–1500 mmol kg^{-1}) is mainly a result of isomorphous substitution inside the lattice and to a lesser extent (about 15–20%) of chemical bond breakage.

In kaolinites the exchangeability is mainly caused by protons of external OH groups which compensate unequalized charges originating at the edge sites of the mineral crystal owing to bond cleavage in the tetrahedral and octahedral networks [86,88]. The distorted bonds appear on the vertical planes which are parallel to the c-axis of the mineral lattice rather than on the basal cleaved surfaces. Consequently, in kaolinites the exchanged cations are mainly concentrated at the lateral faces and edges of the crystal.

The exchangeability of clay minerals is their most significant property in determining the chemical and physicochemical character of the mineral particle surface. Minerals in salt (Li^+, Na^+, K^+, NH_4^+, Mg^{2+}, Ca^{2+}, Ba^{2+}, Ni^{2+}, Co^{2+}, Cu^{2+}) and acid (H^+ and Al^{3+}) ion-exchange forms are those studied most completely [86,88].

The presence of water strongly bound to the exchanging ions is necessary to form the protonic acid sites on the surface of the salt forms of clay minerals. The proton acidity of salt forms of minerals is induced by the protolytic dissociation of water molecules, which are strongly polarized in the fields of exchanging cations. The acidity of the disperse mineral surface depends to a considerable extent on the polarizing ability of the exchanging cations, which may be expressed as the ratio of the cationic charge to the cation radius (Ze/r). Exceptionally high polarizing ability is displayed by aluminium ions, and, owing to their strong polarization of adsorbed water molecules, mobile protons associated with a high acidity of the mineral surface appear in the structure of the Al form of disperse minerals. Indeed the acidity of water molecules coordinated by Al^{3+} cations exceeds that of 71% sulphuric acid (H_0=5–6) [89].

The exchange of doubly and triply charged dehydrated cations, especially of transition metals which are able to abstract electrons from electron-donor adsorbate molecules, may be considered as Lewis-type electron-accepting acid sites (L^+ sites) [88].

The non-exchanged acid sites are significant in the genesis of the acidity of natural layer silicates through coordinatively unsaturated atoms of metals, mainly of aluminium, sited at defect regions of the crystal lattice and protonated structural OH groups [86,88,89].

The numbers of Lewis and Brönsted acid sites are interrelated and, to a considerable extent, depend on the degree of surface hydration which, depending on the nature of the exchanged ions and other factors (for instance, on the content of surface OH groups), may make up from 1 to 15 mol kg^{-1} of the mineral [88,90]. The Lewis acid sites will predominate on a completely dehydrated mineral surface, their conversion into Brönsted sites occurring on adsorption even of tiny quantities of water.

The hydroxyl groups of the aluminosilicate layers influence the adsorption and catalytic properties of clay minerals; however, their degree of participation in these processes is largely determined by their location in the crystal structure of the minerals.

IR spectroscopic studies of kaolinite have shown that the low-frequency bands at about 3625 cm^{-1} refer to stretching vibrations of structural OH groups localized in the plane common to the tetrahedral and octahedral networks. Three high-frequency bands at 3700, 3675 and 3665 cm^{-1} characterize the stretching vibrations of intrasurface OH groups, these being on the surface of kaolinite packets [86].

The hydroxyl groups localized inside the packets do not participate in processes occurring on the mineral surface. The OH groups localized on the crystal faces and edges (genuine surface OH groups) make up only 5% of the total concentration of OH groups [86]. They take the most active part in the adsorption and catalytic processes taking place in filled polymers.

Absorption bands at 3745, 3695, 3665 and 3635 cm^{-1}, which are also in the stretching vibration region of OH groups are observed in the IR spectra of montmorillonite [41,86]. That at 3745 cm^{-1} is attributed to vibrations of 'free' OH groups localized on the surface of montmorillonite, while those at 3695–3664 and 3635 cm^{-1} depend on OH groups which are associated with different elements of its octahedral layer (structural and surface OH groups).

In the IR spectra of montmorillonite taken from mineral specimens at low temperatures, there are bands in the regions of 3635, 3605–3600 and 3585–3570 cm^{-1} which are assigned to stretching vibrations of the OH groups of the mineral coupled with octahedral cations of Al^{3+}, Al^{3+} and Mg^{2+}, and Fe^{3+} and Mg^{2+} [41,86]. At higher temperatures the OH groups of montmorillonite, like those of kaolinite, may participate in deuterium exchange. However, their contribution to the chemical processes occurring on the external surface should not be considered substantial, since most OH groups are localized inside the packets.

The number and topochemistry of the surface OH groups are determined by the crystal structure of the clay minerals, and their chemical properties mainly depend on which structural cation (or cations) they refer to.

The properties of OH groups coupled with Al^{3+} or Mg^{2+} cations of the octahedral layer of minerals, to a first approximation, are equivalent to those of OH groups on the surface of hydrated Al_2O_3 and MgO. In acid, neutral and even weakly alkaline media, OH groups coupled with Al^{3+} and Mg^{2+} cations on the lateral faces of mineral crystals participate only in anion-exchange reactions. Only at pH values above the isoelectric point (which for α-Al_2O_3 is 9.2 and for MgO is 12.5 [86,88]) do OH-group protons coupled with the surface cations of dioctahedral layers participate in cation exchange.

One may consider the properties of hydroxyl groups localized on the lateral faces of crystals and bound to silicon atoms to be similar to those of the surface OH groups of silica, the isoelectric point of which is at pH 1.7. In acid media at pH 2–5, a definite number of protonic centres already appear on the silica surface, while in neutral and alkaline media silica is characterized by its maximal capacity for cation exchange.

Thus, OH groups localized at the lateral faces and edges of mineral crystals and bound to silicon atoms, along with isomorphous substitution in the lattice, are also sources of ion-exchange capacity of minerals. The emergence of a negative charge on the silicon–oxygen networks due to the isomorphous substitution of Si^{4+} by Al^{3+} enhances the acid properties of silanol groups, and exchange of their protons for other cations is facilitated as compared with silica.

The concentration of OH groups of different types depends on the degree of perfection of the crystal structure of minerals. For the well-crystallized Glukhovian kaolinite the concentration of acidic OH-groups is 20 mmol kg^{-1}, while for basic $Al(OH)_3$ the figure is 12 mmol kg^{-1} and for imperfect kaolinite (from the Glukhovian deposit) the values are 75 and 65 mmol kg^{-1}, respectively [86,88]. In addition, there is also a small number of groups of the type

$$Al \Big\langle {\overset{\textstyle OH}{\underset{\textstyle (OH)^{1\!/\!2}}{}}}$$

on the facial surface of kaolinite crystals.

Data on the thermosorption of pyridine and on the electronic spectra of chemisorbed p-dimethylaminoazobenzene [88–91] have shown the existence of a small number ($0.06 \text{ mmol kg}^{-1}$) of strongly acidic sites, not fixed by non-aqueous titration, on the surface of the K- and Na-forms of kaolinite. Their appearance is due to the presence of coordinatively unsaturated ions of Al^{3+} on lateral faces of kaolinite particles, the concentration of which is $ca\ 5\times10^7 \text{ centres m}^{-2}$. On removal of adsorbed water molecules and surface dehydroxylation, aluminium (Fe, Mg) converts from the 6- into the 4-coordinated form and becomes a strong Lewis acid site. The quantity of such sites on the surface corresponds, obviously, to the concentration of basic OH groups. Along with the protons of silanol groups and exchanged ions, these sites influence the adsorption and chemical properties of the mineral surface.

EPR studies of kaolinite from different deposits have shown [92] that, unlike other minerals, there exists an intensive narrow band typical of an unpaired electron in its spectrum. The view has been advanced that oxygen species of the type O_2^{3-}, which may be present on the cleavage planes, are involved in the kaolinite structure. It was possible to calculate the concentration of such paramagnetic centres and to establish a correlation between their number and the imperfection of the mineral crystal structure.

2.1.5 Commercial carbon and graphite

These fillers have long been used for thermoplasts and rubber mixtures. The nature of the bonding and the mechanism of interaction of polymer molecules with the surface of commercial carbon have been studied to some extent. However, publications on the surface chemistry of commercial carbon and graphite are few [41,93–96].

The grinding of graphite at low temperatures in a dry atmosphere induces pyrophoricity. This is due to the chemisorption of oxygen which occurs vigorously at the active sites of the freshly cleaved surfaces of graphite crystals [41].

The concentration of adsorption-active centres on a fresh graphite surface formed during grinding at 393 K, as estimated by oxygen adsorption, reaches about 10^{14} centres cm^{-2} [41,47]. However, this value characterizes the mean concentration of centres over the whole surface, whereas only the prism faces are reactive. The ratio of the surface of the prism face to the total surface of graphite particles, which has been evaluated qualitatively from adsorption data, proved to be $1 : 6$. Recalculation of the active site concentration per surface area of prism faces gives a value of approximately 10^{15} centres cm^{-2}, which is similar to the concentration of carbon atoms on these faces. The natural conclusion was to consider the broken carbon bonds on the prism faces of graphite particles to be the active sites. However, according to data obtained from magnetochemical investigations of NO chemisorption, the total possible concentration of paramagnetic centres on a virgin graphite surface does not exceed 5% of the concentration of adsorption centres [41]. EPR studies [41, 97] of graphite ground at 293 K have confirmed that specimens of different dispersity produce a weak resonance adsorption. The absence of appreciable concentrations of free radicals on the graphite surface despite its high chemisorption activity leads to the view that most peripheral atoms are in a state different from the normal trigonal state of the carbon atom in the graphite lattice. Two states of the peripheral atoms are possible [41,97]:

A — Deformation of the lattice with approach of atoms 5 and 6 to atoms 2 and 3 may cause hybridization close to sp, which, in the limit, will comprise an acetylenic bond;

B — angle atoms (for instance $C-1$) pass from the sp^2 into the s^2p^2 state.

The considerable mechanical deformation implicit in the process of grinding, makes the achievement of state A quite possible, the spins being paired. On cleavage of the prism face a definite number of atoms will be angular, and state B is reached, in which case the state of the free atom (s^2p^2) should be triplet (^3P). The paramagnetism of the triplet state should be revealed by magnetic susceptibility measurements; however, as shown above, such measurements failed to detect significant concentrations of paramagnetic centres.

Some authors [41,97] believe that the angular atoms (type 1) are present in the singlet state (state B). On interaction of peripheral atoms in states A or B with adsorbed molecules, the reverse transition to the normal valence state occurs. Since a definite energy is consumed in the transitions of the peripheral atoms, the grinding of graphite at low temperatures should promote preservation of the primary state of the surface active sites. Powdered graphite ground at 77 K for 20 h produces an intense asymmetrical EPR signal with a linewidth $\Delta H = 45 \times 10^{-4}$ T and a g-factor of 2.0036. This signal, with unchanged linewidth, persists during a temperature increase to 293 K. The observed EPR signal is attributed to σ-electrons localized in sp^2 orbitals. The EPR signal of graphite after the supply of oxygen has $\Delta H = 20 \times 10^{-4}$ T and g = 2.0036, with an intensity similar to that of the unoxidized specimen. In this case the radical form is that of a chemisorbed oxygen-centred entity.

Presumably, the energy released during the destruction of graphite at low temperatures is insufficient for the transition of all the peripheral atoms to new electronic states although most of them realize this transition under these conditions. This is confirmed by the fact that an increase in the time of grinding from 20 to 40 h leads to an increase in the dispersity of the graphite without any growth in concentration of the spin centres, i.e. a proportion of the radical forms transforms either to state A or B. These data point once more to the different natures of the active sites formed on the graphite surface during grinding: on this surface carbon atoms exist in two different electronic states: atoms in the divalent singlet state and atoms which form highly strained quasi-acetylene bonds. In addition, there are also free radicals formed by the cleavage of π and σ bonds between carbon atoms.

Attempts have been made [98] to elucidate the nature of the interaction between freshly cleaved graphite and alkenes such as butene-1 and isoprene. The adsorption of alkenes is clearly established as being irreversible. In the initial stage, the differential heats of adsorption of these substances reach 92 and 100 kJ mol^{-1}, respectively, i.e. close to the heats of polymerization of alkenes. Evidently, the opening of the double bond of the monomer molecule and formation of a strong σ bond with a peripheral carbon atom (in the singlet state) of the prism faces of graphite lattice, take place in the initial stage of adsorption. In this case one radical C centre remains in the adsorbed molecule. In fact, EPR studies on a graphite specimen after adsorption of but-1-ene show an absorption band with the g-factor of its free electron. The concentration of spin centres is equal to 3×10^{17} spins m^{-2}, i.e. close to the value of irreversible adsorption.

Oxygen adsorption at a graphite surface irreversibly saturated with adsorbed but-1-ene or isoprene produces values of 1.0 and 0.8 μmol m^{-2} respectively of irreversibly bound oxygen. This provides evidence that adsorption of unsaturated monomers on a fresh surface leads to incomplete coating of the existing active sites and to the binding of oxygen by free radicals of the adsorbed alkenes to form peroxide groups.

Lactone, carbonyl, carboxyl, phenol, quinone and other functional groups are known to exist on the surface of disperse graphite and commercial carbon on standing in air. Groups containing nitrogen and sulphur atoms are also apparent on the surface of commercial carbon [41,93–96]. The quantity, nature and relationships of the different functional groups on the surfaces of graphite and commercial carbon vary depending on the methods of production and conditions of thermal treatment.

With the aim of improving the surface properties of carbon fillers, they are often subjected to chemical modification. In particular, some workers [99,100] have succeeded in obtaining commercial carbon, graphite and diamond powders which contain on their surface only one type of functional group (Cl, OH, NH_2, COOH) attached to virtually all the carbon atoms situated at the surface of the carbon filler particles. In a number of cases these functional groups may enter into chemical reactions, including the curing of epoxide and phenol–formaldehyde resins filled with them [101,102]. The formation of chemical bonds between the polymers and the surface of carbon fillers increases the thickness of the three-dimensional network and the thermal stability of the polymers [102,103].

In certain cases the surface of commercial carbon and graphite is modified by the grafting of organic compounds including peroxides and unsaturated compounds. This also enables chemical bonding between the modified filler surface and the polymer, especially if the latter contains unsaturated groups.

The presence of active functional groups on the surfaces of commercial carbon and graphite also has a substantial influence on the degradation of filled polymers [100–103]. Depending on the nature of these groups the fillers may either accelerate or inhibit the thermal or thermal–oxidative degradation of polymers.

2.2 CLASSIFICATION AND MAIN PRINCIPLES FOR CHOOSING FILLERS WHICH PROVIDE THERMAL AND THERMAL–OXIDATIVE STABILITY OF POLYMERS

Disperse inorganic fillers are characterized by a complex of physical and chemical properties which do not necessarily depend on the conditions and aims of their application. In addition, disperse fillers may be characterized (resulting from these properties) by their particular influence on the properties of filled polymer compositions, including their thermal and thermal–oxidative stability.

2.2.1 Physical properties of disperse fillers
We shall consider briefly the following basic characteristics of disperse fillers: shape, size of particles and size distribution, specific surface area, pattern of particle packing, optical, thermal–physical, mechanophysical and electrical properties.

Shape, size of particles and size distribution
The choice of filler is often determined by the size of its particles and their polydispersity, i.e. by their size distribution. Most inorganic fillers are minerals mined from appropriate rocks and ores with the necessary recovery treatment followed by crushing and fine grinding. In this case the filler particles usually acquire

an irregular shape and are characterized by their size distribution or polydispersity. A number of fillers obtained by chemical methods (sedimentation from solution, pyrogenic types, etc.) have particles of reasonably regular shape and of high dispersity. These include precipitated silicates, glass spheres, aerosil, calcium carbonate, clay minerals and diatomite.

The fillers are divided into the following classes according to their approximation to an ideal geometrical shape: spherical (glass spheres, microspheres, metals, metal oxides, commercial carbon, aerosil), cubic (calcium, feldspar), block-like or prismatic (calcium, feldspar, quartz, barium oxide), lamellar or stratiform (kaolinite, montmorillonite, mica, talc, graphite, aluminium hydroxide), and needle-like, elongated or fibrous (palygorskite, asbestos, calcium silicate, glass fibre). It should be noted that most disperse fillers consist of somewhat large aggregates of differently shaped particles which, on being introduced into polymers, do not always disaggregate into individual particles.

The following parameters are used to characterize quantitatively the shape and size of filler particles: the ratio of the largest diameter of the particles to the least and also the 'equivalent sphere diameter', i.e. the diameter of that sphere the volume of which is equal to that of the particle [55].

Microscopy, sieve analysis and sedimentation methods are employed to determine the polydispersity of filler particles [104]. The microscopic method for evaluating the shape, sizes and polydispersity of filler particles is the most precise, but is highly labour-intensive and time-consuming.

Sieve analysis is widely employed to determine the size and rough estimation of the size distribution of filler particles. Large particles are studied by dry sieve analysis, while small ones (less than 100–150 μm) by wet analysis. Sieve analysis is most widely used for studying particles of diameter over 50 μm. The accuracy in estimation of sizes and size distribution depends on the method of producing the sieves and their mesh size. Sieves produced by the interweaving of fine wire are, as a rule, employed for the analysis of large particles (100 μm and more), since interwoven sieves cannot provide high accuracy in fixing the sizes of small particles passing through the meshes as a result of wire vibration, distortion of the mesh shape and size, wire wear, etc. Plane microsieves produced by electromoulding have mesh sizes from 120 down to 10 μm and give more accurate values of particle sizes.

Sedimentation methods based on Stokes' law are used for particles of less than 40 μm diameter, since for larger particles they introduce considerable errors, especially if water is used as a flotation liquid.

The size distribution of filler particles is an important characteristic: it provides the correct relationship between the polydispersity of the filler and its specific surface area and packing density, since the average particle size does not give a complete picture of the filler dispersity and considerable deviations from the mean value are possible. Variations in the pattern of the size distribution have a crucial effect on the rheological and abrasive properties, abrasive resistance, and pattern of particle packing as well as on the optical and mechanical properties, and chemical stability of filled compositions. Consequently, the filler dispersity should be fully characterized. The semilogarithmic or logarithmic curves of the mean numerical or mean mass size distribution of particles are usually employed to characterize the filler dispersity. The size distribution of particles in logarithmic coordinates is a straight line; deviation from the straight line characterizes the prehistory and peculiarities in the properties of the disperse filler.

Specific surface area

Specific surface area is one of the most important parameters of disperse fillers, since the efficiency of fillers in most cases is determined by their specific surface area. This characteristic plays a key role in cases when the filler surface is either subject to chemical modification or is able to interact actively with polymers.

The method of low-temperature adsorption of nitrogen based on the BET equation is the most precise and standard way of determining the specific surface area of fillers [105]. Other methods are also employed (adsorption of dyes from solutions [105] and blowing of gas through a powder [104]). It may also be estimated using Geit diagrams and the diameter of particles equivalent to the spherical diameter [55].

The specific surface area of fillers varies over wide ranges: from fractions of square metres per gram (barium sulphate, quartz, etc.) to hundreds of square metres per gram (commercial carbon, aerosil, sedimented silica, etc.). This wide range of specific surface areas should be taken into account when conducting comparative studies of the influence of fillers on the physicochemical, chemical and mechanical properties of polymer composites.

Pattern of particle packing

The method of oil adsorption is used to determine the packing density of all disperse fillers containing particles of the same size [55]. The procedure developed by Fournace [55] is employed to determine the optimal set of fractions which provide minimal or maximal particle packing. According to the particle size intervals determined by sieve analysis, the size interval from 1 up to $\sqrt{2}$ is taken as a unit interval. When determining the unoccupied bulk of a filler for particles having such a size interval, the shape factor is either excluded or compensated for during calculation. This method enables proper choice of the appropriate particle sizes for specific applications of a filler.

The set of fractions of different particle sizes is used to obtain the minimal unoccupied bulk which is filled with the polymer binder. In this case the larger particles make up the total filler bulk, while the smaller ones occupy spaces between the large particles without increasing the total filler bulk. A high degree of filling is reached using a broad distribution of particle sizes.

Particles of the same size possessing a high specific surface area and requiring a large quantity of polymer binder for wetting should be used to obtain the minimal packing density. The same effect is produced by particles with a high shape factor (fibres, needle-like particles, etc.).

Optical properties

The coloration and staining of fillers are usually determined by direct observational methods. The staining of fillers as dry powders is quantitatively estimated from the value of the reflection of monochromatic light from the plane surface of the moulded pellets. If the environment is air and standard inorganic fillers have a refractive index of approximately 1.5, then the reflection index, which characterizes the fraction of light reflected from the specimen, is 0.0438. In the polymer environment, the refractive index of which is approximately 1.5, the reflection index of filler particles does not exceed 0.00001, i.e. the filler particles dispersed in the polymer essentially do not reflect light.

Other optical properties of fillers are related to the X-ray, UV, IR and microwave spectral regions.

X-ray radiation is employed in the structural analysis of crystal fillers, since its wavelength (0.1–10 nm) is comparable with interatomic distances. The X-ray examination of fillers is of particular interest when, during chemical modification or on contact with monomers, oligomers and polymers, the lattice parameters vary, as in the case of certain clay minerals such as montmorillonite and vermiculite, which possess expansible crystal lattices [86]. The penetration of modifiers, polymers or other polar substances into the interlayer crystal space of these fillers may be determined radiographically from the change in interlayer distance [106]. These effects are of special significance when studying the topochemical characteristics of the interaction of a polymer with the filler surface.

The X-ray study of fillers also plays an important role in determining their phase and structural conversions during the thermal degradation of filled polymers. It is known that certain fillers (metals, metal oxides) may participate in oxidation or reduction reactions under the influence of the polymer decomposition products; thus they interact with decomposition products to form carbides, silicides, silicates, nitrides, etc. [107]. In addition, certain fillers for special applications readily decompose in the polymer phase, e.g. metal formates decompose to yield highly disperse metals and oxides possessing a chemically active surface [108].

Thermal–physical properties

Since filled polymers are processed and sometimes used at elevated temperatures, the thermal–physical properties of disperse fillers (thermal conductivity, specific thermal capacity) are of great importance.

The values of the thermal conductivity coefficients for inorganic fillers fall within the range of $(4.2–33.3) \times 10^{-3} \, W \, m^{-1} \, K^{-1}$. For graphite this value is $0.42 \times 10^{-3} \, W \, m^{-1} \, K^{-1}$. The thermal conductivity of polymers is usually one order of magnitude lower than that of many mineral fillers, which is caused by energy dissipation due to the free rotation of groups in polymers. The higher thermal conductivity of fillers compared with polymers is a result of energy dissipation which increases the thermal stability of polymers with weakly chemically-active fillers.

The specific thermal capacity of most inorganic fillers approximates to $0.8 \, J \, g^{-1} \, K^{-1}$, while that of polymers lies in the range $1.26–2.1 \, J \, g^{-1} \, K^{-1}$.

Most fillers expand differently in various directions owing to the heterogeneity of their composition or crystal structure. The linear expansion coefficient for inorganic fillers lies within $(1–8) \times 10^{-6} \, K^{-1}$. The application of elevated temperatures to filled polymers results in considerable stresses due to the substantial difference in the thermal expansion coefficients for the polymers and their fillers.

Physical and mechanical properties

The hardness of disperse fillers is an important physical and mechanical property, which is normally determined on Mohs' scale and widely used in comparison of the hardness of minerals and their abrasive capacity. Talc and vermiculite are the softest fillers; kaolin, mica and asbestos are harder; while calcite, barite, glass, feldspar, titanium and silicon dioxides are much harder; corundums, aluminium oxide and diamond are the hardest minerals.

Electrical properties

Essential differences in the electrical properties of disperse fillers are exhibited only in the complete absence of moisture adsorbed on their surfaces. Fillers having OH groups, water and other adsorbed compounds on their surface normally possess a higher surface conductivity.

In general, fillers with ionic and covalent bonds possess lower conductivity, while metal fillers possess a high conductivity. The introduction of fillers may either improve or worsen the electrical properties of filled polymers. Thus, special attention should be focused on the choice and method of introduction of the filler into polymers which are used in products designated for electrical and technical purposes.

2.2.2 Chemical properties of disperse fillers and their influence on properties of filled polymer composites

The chemical composition is clearly one of the principal characteristics of disperse fillers which determines their surface chemical reactivity, being a surface property. However, prediction of the surface chemical reactions of fillers in a polymer environment based solely on their chemical composition is impossible, since the chemical composition of the filler does not determine the pattern of distribution of other elements in the crystal lattice or the active sites on the surface of the filler particles. The chemical properties of the filler surface, rather than the filler in bulk, normally determine all the processes at the polymer–filler interface.

In aqueous and other polar media, the chemical properties of the filler surface are related to the acid–base behaviour of the active sites, surface conductivity, emergence of charge on the particle, electrophoretic mobility of the particles, ξ-potential, and the medium pH. In weakly polar and anhydrous media the chemical activity of the filler surface is exhibited via adsorption and chemisorption, which determine, to a considerable extent, the chemical properties of polymers at the boundary layers. The chemical properties of the filler surface influence a number of their physicochemical properties, e.g. their ability to aggregate or flocculate and their dispersity in polymer media. The chemical and thermal properties of the surfaces of certain classes of disperse fillers have been considered in detail above without analysis of their influence on the chemical and thermal properties of the filled polymer systems. Below we shall consider current ideas on filler activity in polymer media.

Fillers exert a rather versatile and complex action on polymers reflected in changes in the physical, mechanical, structural, kinetic, thermodynamic and chemical properties of filled polymers. [109] develops a broad analysis covering the structural, kinetic and thermodynamic activity of fillers. It treats the main influences of the filler on the complex of physicochemical and physicomechanical properties of polyomers as well as on their structure at different levels of organization. One should note that the surface chemistry of fillers plays an important role in determining the nature of the polymer–filler interaction, and, consequently, on the influence of the filler on these parameters.

[109] considers the structural activity of the filler as regards its ability to affect the polymer structure, leading to changes in the characteristics of supramolecular structurization (size, shape and type of size distribution) at one or several levels of the supramolecular organization or simply in the packing density (the change in ratio between the disordered and ordered parts of the polymer). The filler may influence all these structural characteristics simultaneously. Again, the structural activity of the filler takes a definite direction by mainly affecting the supramolecular structure or relative packing density of the polymer.

Generally, the main physical characteristics of a filler (shape, particle size, roughness, etc.) and its concentration influence the structural activity. However, the influences of the physicochemical and chemical characteristics of the filler surface should not be excluded, since they become manifest via the sorption interaction, wettability of the filler by the polymer, etc. Having such an influence at different levels of the structural organization of polymers, the fillers can substantially affect other properties of the polymers which are sensitive to structure. One may expect that introduction of a filler which increases the ordering and crystallinity of a polymer will improve its thermal stability.

It is known [109] that fillers exert a considerable effect on the mobility of different kinetic units (segments, groups, chain) of a polymer and on its relaxation time. Undoubtedly, such effects have an influence on the structural, physicochemical and mechanical characteristics of the filled polymer. The kinetic activity of a polymer is related to its ability to affect the mobility of kinetic units of different sizes and the spectrum of polymer relaxation times [109]. The filler may be kinetically active towards the whole set of kinetic polymer units, to some of them, or to one definite kinetic unit. Thus, it is possible to consider that, as for structural activity, the fillers may also possess selective kinetic activity. The extent and manifestation of kinetic activity depend on the nature of this interaction and the surface chemistry, the nature of the polymer, its ability to interact with the filler, and the nature of this interaction as well as on the ability of the polymer to transfer the results of this interaction into the bulk of the polymer. The kinetic activity of the filler also depends on the conditions of formation of the filled polymer system. The kinetic activity of a filler at the formation stage of the filled system is expressed in the production of structures differing in shape, size and packing density from those in the unfilled polymer. Thus, kinetic factors have a substantial influence on the structure and properties of the filled polymer.

In the filled polymer system produced, the kinetic activity of the filler becomes apparent via the filler-induced structural variations in the polymer, which alter the reaction of the polymer environmental factors and also to the duration of their action. This causes changes in stability over time and in resistance to the action of different factors on the structure and properties of the filled polymer compared with the unfilled.

It has been shown [109] that a number of thermodynamic parameters of polymers (density, entropy, enthalpy) are changed on filling. The production of a polymer in the presence of a filler may promote its transition to an either more or less equilibrium state than the analogous unfilled polymer. Thus, the thermodynamic activity of a filler lies in its ability to influence the equilibrium state and thermodynamic parameters of the polymer [109]. Quantitative changes in these parameters in the filled system depend on the chemical nature of the filler surface, the nature of the polymer, the mode of polymer–filler interaction and the conditions of formation of the filled systems.

The structural, kinetic and thermodynamic activities of fillers are interrelated, although they play different roles. The structural and thermodynamic activities of fillers are implemented during formation of the filled system and are controlled by kinetic factors (under definite preset environmental conditions).

The structural, kinetic and thermodynamic activities of fillers are related to, or depend largely on the chemical activity of fillers (the chemical activity means the ability of fillers to interact chemically with polymers during formation of the filled system). The chemical activity of fillers depends in the first place on their surface chemistry, i.e. on the presence of surface-active sites capable of interacting with a polymer [41].

It is known [41,85,86,88] that active sites (OH groups, coordinatively unsaturated metal atoms, V- and F-centres, free radicals, etc.) capable of chemical interaction with a polymer are, in practice, present on the surface of any filler. The chemical activity of fillers also depends on the nature of the polymer medium contacting the filler, i.e. on the presence in the polymer of groups capable of direct interaction with active sites on the filler surface. It should be noted that active groups in the polymer chains may arise from the catalytic influence of chemically active fillers. For example, the presence of certain fillers results in the formation under definite conditions of carboxyl, carbonyl, peroxide and hydroperoxide groups in polyalkenes [110] which are chemically inert towards surfaces. These groups appear, in the first place, at the polymer–filler surface interface, and may then interact chemically with the active sites of the filler.

The chemical activity of a filler depends to a considerable extent on the conditions of formation of the filled system. Thus, the filled systems produced by polymerization (or polycondensation) of monomers or oligomers in the presence of disperse fillers [41,81] differ, as a rule, in the greater contribution of the chemical interaction to the whole range of polymer–filler interactions, compared with filled systems produced by standard mixing in solutions or alloys of the polymer. In addition, the temperature of filler–polymer mixing substantially influences the chemical activity of fillers. The possibility of chemical interaction of a polymer with a filler increases with temperature, irrespective of the method of formation of the filled system. One should note that increasing temperature (up to 500–600 K) sharply enhances the hydrolytic activity of those fillers containing on their surface water which is bonded in various ways. Under these conditions those polymers sensitive to hydrolysis undergo different chemical changes. At higher temperatures (600–800 K) polymer hydrolysis may proceed in filled systems containing a disperse filler with surface OH groups. The hydrolysis occurs under the influence of water released during dehydroxylation of the filler surface; the removal of adsorbed water and dehydroxylation of the surface lead to a change (generally an increase) in its chemical activity relative to polymers in contact with it.

It should be noted that polymers and the products of their degradation at elevated temperatures result, in a number of cases, in variations in the chemical properties of the filler surface (grafting of macromolecular fragments, etc.), or even in alterations in the chemical composition of the filler (oxidation of metals to oxides, reduction of oxides, production of carbides, nitrides, silicides, silicates, etc.) [107].

At the interface these chemical processes influence all the physical and chemical properties of polymers, including their thermal and thermal–oxidative stability. It follows from the above that the surface chemistry of the filler is one of the main factors affecting not only the chemical but also the structural, kinetic and thermodynamic activity of the fillers. The analysis of the structural, kinetic, thermodynamic and chemical activity of disperse fillers has shown that this influence cannot always be characterized unambiguously, even for rather simple polymer–filler systems. This ambiguity is associated with the physical and chemical characteristics of the filler and its multifarious effects on the properties and structure of a polymer at different levels as well as the effects of the properties of the polymer itself on its processes of interaction with a filler.

Such parameters as the thermal and chemical properties of the filler and its surface, the presence of adsorbed water, modifying additives, and admixtures of other compounds are those most important in choosing fillers to provide thermal and thermal–oxidative stability of filled polymers. According to their activity (structural, kinetic, thermodynamic and chemical) all fillers may be roughly divided into three basic groups:

(i) chemically inactive fillers
(ii) chemically active fillers *increasing* the thermal and thermal–oxidative stability of polymers
(iii) chemically active fillers *decreasing* the thermal and thermal–oxidative stability of polymers.

The introduction of inactive fillers into the polymer normally increases its thermal stability, owing to two main factors: the decrease in thermal mobility of the polymer chains (the influence of the kinetic activity of a filler) and the higher thermal conductivity of the mineral particles. The thermal–oxidative stability of the filled polymer may also increase, provided that no adsorbed oxygen is present on the filler surface. In real polymer systems produced under ordinary atmospheric conditions, there is adsorbed oxygen and moisture which, on being desorbed, decrease the thermal–oxidative and thermal stability of the polymer, initially at the boundary layer.

At elevated temperatures, the introduction into polymers of disperse metals not interacting with the macromolecules may induce chemical interaction, with the formation of surface compounds which have either increased or decreased thermal stability compared with unfilled polymers. However, the thermal stability of filled polymers is normally greater owing to the decrease in kinetic mobility of the polymer chains chemically bonded to the surface. The thermal stability of polymers filled with disperse metals is normally greater than that of unfilled ones, owing both to the higher rate of oxidation of metals than of a polymer and to the elimination of peroxide and hydroperoxide radicals located at the solid metal surface [16].

An increase in the thermal stability of polymers with active fillers may occur during the formation of thermally stable chemical bonds between the polymer and the filler surface; the thermal stability of these bonds should be the same or greater than the bond strength of the macromolecule. The formation of cross-linking bonds and of a three-dimensional network of the polymer in the nodes of which there are filler particles should normally increase the thermal stability of a polymer; this also increases when a chemically active filler promotes the decomposition of thermally unstable groups present in the initial polymer to form more thermally stable bonds either within the polymer itself or with the filler surface.

The thermal–oxidative stability of polymers increases on filling with a chemically active filler, provided that the chemical bonds and groups formed during the polymer–filler interaction are more stable to oxidation than the initial polymer. Furthermore, the chemically active filler should not be an oxidant or contain adsorbed oxygen. Thus, manganese dioxide or its combinations in fillers promote the oxidative degradation of filled polymers. The presence of adsorbed water on the surface of chemically active fillers does not promote an increase in the thermal and thermal–oxidative stability of filled polymers. Chemically active fillers which either depolymerize polymers or inhibit the solidification of oligomers (for instance, copper oxide) [55] cause a decrease in the thermal and thermal–oxidative stability of the filled polymers.

However, in most cases the introduction of fillers increases the thermal and thermal–oxidative stability of filled polymers in proportion to the filler content. This results from the decrease in kinetic mobility of macromolecules caused by adsorptive interaction or by the formation of chemical bonds with the filler surface. An increase in the thermal and thermal–oxidative stability of filled polymers may also result from the decomposition of unstable groups in the polymer under the catalytic influence of a filler or from binding by the filler of dissolved oxygen. Stabilization may also be related to breaking of the kinetic chain of radical decomposition at the surface of the chemically active filler. Again the thermal stability may increase by dissipation of heat energy by the filler, which has greater thermal conductivity and thermal capacity than the polymer.

A decrease in the thermal and thermal–oxidative stability of filled polymers depends on the following.

  (i) the presence of water and oxygen adsorbed on the filler surface,
 (ii) the formation of relatively weak filler–polymer bonds,
(iii) the formation of polymer–filler reaction products which promote the thermal or thermal–oxidative degradation of polymers, and
(iv) the presence of admixtures acting as oxidizers of polymers or catalysts for the chain scission of polymer molecules.

Their conditions of preparation also play a key role in the thermal and thermal–

oxidative stability of filled polymers. Thus, introduction into a polymer of fillers containing no adsorbed water and oxygen or other admixtures favouring polymer degradation increases the thermal stability of filled polymers. Preliminary modification of the filler surface aimed at its hydrophobization or blockage of the active surface groups of admixtures which would otherwise decrease the polymer stability, improves the stability of the system. The targeted modification of the filler surface with the aim of creating on it groups capable of forming strong chemical bonds with macromolecules or acting as polymer stabilizers towards thermal and thermal–oxidative processes also markedly increases the stability of filled polymers.

3

Methods for studying the thermal and thermal–oxidative degradation of filled polymers

The degradation of filled polymers is characterized by a number of features which are atypical of normal (unfilled) polymers. These features are normally associated with the prehistory of production of the filled polymer. In particular, the methods available for the introduction of fillers may influence not only the physical and chemical properties of the polymers, but also their molecular characteristics. Thus, the mixing of melts or solutions of polymers with disperse fillers causes in a number of cases noticeable shifts in their molecular mass distribution. This is mainly associated with mechanocracking of filled polymers, which is enhanced in the presence of fillers [110]. The fragments of macromolecules produced interact either with each other or with the filler surface to form a grafted layer. These mechanochemical processes leading to variations in the molecular characteristics of polymers also affect their thermal and thermal–oxidative stability, normally decreasing it [111]. In addition, the conditions of introduction of fillers into polymers (temperature, concentration, intensity of mixing, environment, presence of adsorbed moisture, oxygen, etc.) also have a substantial effect on the polymer decomposition process. The filling plays a key role in the decomposition processes of polymers when they are synthesized in the presence of fillers, since the latter affect the whole complex of properties and structure of the polymers produced [81,112].

Below we shall consider the methods for introducing fillers and certain features of the methods available for studying the degradation of filled polymers.

3.1 METHODS FOR INTRODUCING FILLERS AND THEIR EFFECT ON DEGRADATION OF POLYMERS

There are several different methods for introducing disperse fillers into polymers, such as the mixing of a filler with a polymer melt at temperatures above their melting (softening) temperature, the mixing of a filler with solutions of polymers with subsequent removal of solvent during intensive agitation and the synthesis of polymers with the involvement of a filler based either on monomers in the gaseous or liquid states or on liquid oligomers. In the latter case mixing of the reaction system is also required.

Besides these principal methods, the mechanochemical technique is also employed for preparing compositions. The polymer, in a disperse state, is mixed with a filler and is then subjected to intensive dispersion (dry grinding). In this case both additional polymer-activated grinding of the filler and partial mechanocracking of the polymer take place, causing substantial variation in the filled polymer's molecular characteristics [53,110,111] and lyophilization of the filler surface. Subsequently, such a composition is subjected to processing into products at elevated temperatures and high pressures.

It should be noted that there are few publications on the influence of the methods for introducing fillers into polymers on the processes of their degradation. An unambiguous conclusion, however, may be drawn that the procedures for producing filled polymers, along with the chemistry of the disperse filler surface, are the most significant factors affecting the thermal and thermal–oxidative stability of polymers.

Thus, when introducing fillers, in particular magnesium chloride, into butyl rubber and polyisobutylene, the thermal degradation of these polymers is activated at the expense of water bound to the filler surface [113]. Under these conditions the combination of initiation processes of decomposition both by random scission and involving terminal groups is a distinctive feature of polymer degradation. The hydrolytic activation of the thermal degradation of PMMA and of its copolymer with methacrylic acid was observed during contact of these polymers with a steel surface [114].

Bound water makes a significant contribution to activation of the thermal degradation of polymers when the filler surface is highly developed and hydrophilic (silicas, clay minerals, etc.) and the polymers bear groups sensitive to hydrolysis (polyamides, polyesters, etc.). Water tightly bound to the filler surface possesses acidic properties due to its polarization in the field of coordinatively unsaturated atoms of metals or exchanged cations [86,88]. This leads both to the acceleration of hydrolysis of the macromolecules and to their acidolysis, especially at elevated temperatures. Consequently, the removal of water from the surface of the filler before its introduction into a polymer or, at least, control of the water content on the filler surface are significant in improving the thermal characteristics of filled polymers.

There are different ways of decreasing the water content on the filler surface. The process of drying or vacuum drying at temperatures not below 400–500 K is the simplest, but an energetically costly, technique. The introduction of a filler into a solution of a polymer in a number of cases (especially if the solvent is readily mixed with water) enables removal of water from the system together with the solvent [115]. However, such a method of dehydration of the filler surface is not very effective, as it is extremely labour-intensive.

The most effective method for removing water from the filler surface is to render it hydrophobic with grafted compounds, including polymers [41,81]. Chemical interaction of the modifying agent carrying the hydrophobic moiety with the hydrophilic groups (usually hydroxyl) of the filler surface leads to its hydrophobization and increases its affinity for the polymer. The latter process promotes a better distribution of the filler in the polymer bulk, which may critically improve its physical and mechanical properties. The hydrophobizing agent should possess a thermal stability at least matching that of the polymer.

Hydrophobization of the filler surface by compounds which possess structuring [116] or thermostabilizing [117] properties or which are antioxidants [118] considerably enhances the thermal and thermal–oxidative stability of polymers. Preliminary chemical modification of the filler surface by materials possessing definite functional properties makes it possible to create fillers for special purposes (for instance, those increasing the overall thermal–oxidative, thermo-, and photo-stability, etc.) [41,54,81].

In order to increase the thermal–oxidative stability of filled polymers it is important to remove adsorbed oxygen from the filler surface. This may be achieved by mixing the filler with either the polymer melt or its solution in a fluid or gaseous medium. It is established [119,120] that, even in the atmosphere, a long polymer–filler contact at an enhanced temperature, causing the thermal–adhesive interaction of the components, lowers the content of atmospheric oxygen on the interfacial surface and, consequently, decreases the contribution of thermal oxidation to degradation of the filled polymer. It should be noted that chemical modification of the filler surface with organic substances also normally decreases the quantity of absorbed oxygen and thus promotes thermal–oxidative stabilization of the filled polymer.

The method of production of fillers (disperse metals and oxides) directly in the polymer medium by the thermal decomposition of various types of compound (formates, metal carbonyls, organometallic compounds, etc.), previously introduced into solutions or melts of the polymers, is widely employed [42,121]. Metal-filled polymers [42,53,108,121] usually have a greater thermal and thermal–oxidative stability, which is associated with the following factors:

(i) the formation of new chemical bonding (including a three-dimensional network) of the polymer with the solid surface, which results in chain scission and recombination of the macroradicals on the metal surface [224];

(ii) the formation of metal compounds with polymer fragments which may be stabilizers towards the thermal and thermal–oxidative degradation of the polymer [123];

(iii) the formation of a fresh chemically active surface on the metal particles which promotes scavenging of the oxygen in the polymer by virtue of the relatively high rate of metal oxidation [16,124].

The production of filled polymers by the polymerization of monomers in the presence of disperse fillers of varied chemical nature [41,81] leads to a definite increase in their thermal and thermal–oxidative stability. Thus, it has been established by means of thermographical analysis, volume measurement and g.l.c., as well as by variations in the molecular mass of polyethylene synthesized in the presence of perlite and other fillers, that the initial temperature of the thermal degradation of a polymer increases. Polyethylene produced by the same method in the presence of chalk, kaolin and perlite [125] has a greater thermal–oxidative stability than polymer mixed with the same fillers. The following factors enhance the thermal and thermal–oxidative stability of a polymer:

(i)   the presence of a grafted layer, the structural and molecular characteristics of which increase the thermal stability of the polymer and

(ii) the absence of oxygen and water at the polymer–filler interface.

3.2   SPECIAL EXPERIMENTAL FEATURES OF THE DEGRADATION OF FILLED POLYMERS

The experimental results of studies on the degradation of filled polymers are often contradictory. This may be caused not only by differences in the methods of production of the filled polymers but also by the apparatus and experimental procedures (measurements of temperature, pressure, changes in the mass of samples, analysis of low- and high-molecular-mass products of degradation, etc.). Consequently, the description of the apparatus and methods for studies of the degradation of polymers, especially of filled ones, employed in different laboratories is essential, since it may promote the elimination of contradictions and errors which have been observed in certain investigations.

The degradation of polymers proceeding at high temperatures *in vacuo* or in an inert gas atmosphere (helium, argon, etc.) is referred to as thermal degradation, while in ambient air or oxygen, the term is thermal–oxidative degradation. However, the thermal–oxidative degration of a polymer may proceed either in an inert atmosphere or *in vacuo*, if there are voids filled with air and formed in the filling process at the polymer–filler interface. Again, at high temperatures, oxygen and other oxidizing compounds may be generated by a filler, its surface functional groups or grafted (sorbed) compounds.

Depending on the mode of heating of a polymer, its degradation may proceed under different conditions; i.e. (i) isothermal, when the temperature of a test polymer is held constant over the whole period of the investigation and (ii) dynamic, if heating of the polymer occurs to give a temperature rise at a definite rate. A combination of both of these conditions is possible, i.e. heating of the polymer at a preset rate to a certain temperature followed by isothermal heating over a definite period at a particular stage of the polymer degradation, followed again by heating under dynamic conditions, etc. [126–128]. Recently short-term thermal action (or so-called 'thermal shock') has been used more often in studies of polymer degradation [129,130].

The processes of thermal and thermal–oxidative degradation of polymers, being a set of chemical reactions proceeding at high temperatures, are characterized like any other chemical process by a variety of changes which may be determined, e.g.

(i)   a change in mass associated either with the liberation of gases or with oxygen uptake during thermal–oxidative degradation,

(ii)   alteration in the chemical structure, molecular mass, composition or phase state,

(iii) a change in physical properties (e.g. electrical conductivity) and

(iv) the appearance of exo- and endothermal effects, etc.

All devices used for investigations of polymer degradation are based on such phenomena.

3.2.1   Methods based on variation in mass

In most cases, degradation is accompanied by the release of volatiles, leading to a decrease in mass of the test polymer. This phenomenon provides the basis of TGA. This method is based on the regular, repeated determination of mass loss by polymers during pyrolysis. The measurements may be conducted by either periodic or continuous weighing of the sample during decomposition at a constant (isothermal TGA) or regularly increasing (preset) rate temperature (dynamic TGA) [126–128; 131–133]. That temperature which initiates a decrease in polymer mass is often considered to be a characteristic of the thermal stability of a polymer [1,9].

The mass loss is determined by different devices based on a balance which is designed for operation under definite temperature conditions, operating either in the atmosphere or *in vacuo*. Currently the following standard instruments are most often employed for TGA under both isothermal and dynamic conditions: the Paulik derivatograph obtained from MOM (Hungary) [1,9,134], the B-60 thermobalance obtained from DAM (France) [127], the Eraud Electronic Thermobalance (USA) [1,9] and the Linseis Messgerate apparatus (Germany) [9,135]. The designs of particular instruments enable measurement of the change in polymer mass *in vacuo*, in a non-reactive environment or in air, either at a constant temperature or during a steady rise in temperature. Very often the differential curves of mass loss (DTGA) and the differential thermal analysis (DTA) curves detailing the exo- and endothermal effects of the polymer decomposition processes are recorded together with the curves of the temperature at which the mass loss by the polymer sample is studied. Such a complex thermal analysis of the polymer samples provides in some circumstances a reliable interpretation of the processes of polymer degradation [136,137].

In addition to these instruments, there are installations which have found wide application in TGA. They are designed for solving particular problems of polymer degradation and usually have definite advantages as regards certain parameters, since in using them it is possible to gain additional information on the degradation process.

The Jellinek quartz spring balance (Fig. 3.1) is an instrument in which measurement of the rate of polymer degradation is based on determination of the mass loss by samples on heating under isothermal conditions *in vacuo* [3]. This instrument enables determination of the degradation of small polymeric samples (up to 20 mg) with a residual pressure of 10^{-3}–10^{-4} Pa and with temperature maintenance accurate to 1 K. The variation in the sample mass is determined by observation of the position of the quartz rocker relative to the scale located in the telescopic eye-piece in front of the glass plate.

The spring microbalance with a tungsten spring [3] or electronic microbalance, shown as block-diagrams in Fig. 3.2, are also used to measure the degradation rate of polymers from their mass loss [3]. The temperature in such installations is maintained accurately to 0.2 K, while the vacuum is of the order of magnitude of 10^{-3} Pa. The electronic balance features automatic recording of the temperature and mass

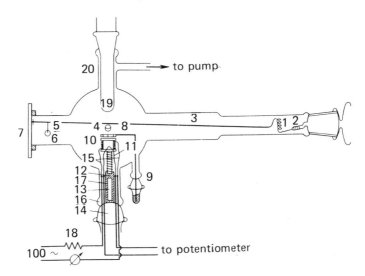

Fig. 3.1 — The Jellinek quartz spring balance [3]: 1, quartz spring; 2, quartz–pyrex junction of spring and plug; 3, quartz weighing beam; 4, quartz reactor; 5, holder; 6, 9, 14, microsections; 7, glassy plate; 8, silver mirror; 10, electric furnace; 11, 13, metal cores, 12, asbestos gasket; 15, thermocouple wires; 16, tungsten wire; 17, glassy tube; 18, rheostat; 19, cooler, 20, lead-in tube.

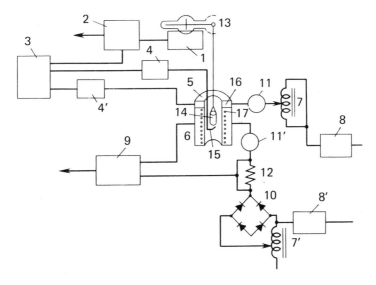

Fig. 3.2 — Block diagram of electronic microbalance [3]: 1, balance; 2, electronic part of balance; 3, three-point potentiometer; 4,4′ voltage dividers; 5, upper heater; 6, lower heater; 7,7′, alternating current autotransformers; 8,8′, voltage regulator; 9, electronic thermostat; 10, bridge rectifier; 11, ammeters; 12, resistor; 13, weighing beam; 14, melting pot with sample; 15, chrome–constantan thermocouple; 16, Chromel–constantan thermocouple of top heater; 17, platinum resistance thermometer.

loss [3]. When studying the thermal oxidative degradation of polymers in an atmospheric environment it is possible to use simpler installations (Fig. 3.3) [138].

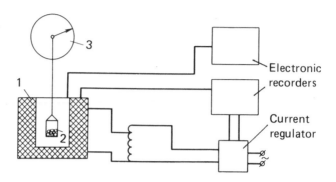

Fig. 3.3 — Diagram of installation for thermal–oxidative decomposition of filled polymers [139]: 1, thermal chamber; 2, melting pot with sample; 3, balance.

Devices incorporating thermal shock (a sharp reduction in the time to heat a sample to a preset temperature) are employed to study the short-term stability of polymers [129,130]. Under such conditions the reactor is firstly heated to the preset temperature and then the polymer is placed in the reaction zone. Contact between the pan containing the sample and the gaseous thermal carrier is the most commonly used method of heating. In this case heating of the pan occurs mainly owing to the beam flux from the reactor walls. To determine the mass loss, the sample should be weighed before and after heating to the preset temperature. Such an installation has been described in detail [139].

It should be noted that for installations involving thermal shock, the following two parameters are important: the warm-up time of the reactor–polymeric sample system, which is defined as the delay of the zero-time reference of the polymer mass loss under isothermal conditions, and the distance of the measured thermocouple from the sample. The shorter the delay time and the closer the thermocouple end to the sample (ideally the thermocouple is located directly at the sample itself), the more accurate and definitive are the results obtained.

Simultaneous measurements of the sample and furnace temperatures [140] indicate that the protocols mentioned above should be strictly followed for polymer degradation under thermal shock conditions and, evidently, for other modes of heating. Under isothermal conditions for testing different polymer samples such as PMMA, polyethylene, polypropylene, polystyrene, etc., the difference between the furnace and sample surface temperatures ranged from 15 to 515 K. These results demonstrate the need to measure the temperature of the polymer sample itself, in order to obtain meaningful results in their degradation tests. These conclusions are of great significance for studies of the degradation of filled polymers in which certain components differ substantially in their thermal conductivity.

It is possible to decrease the delay time in determining isothermal conditions without using the reactor at all and by locating the sample directly at the thermocouple junction. In this case the polymer sample sharply decreases in quantity, its mass not exceeding several milligrams, and the time to heat the sample to the constant temperature reduces to several seconds [140]. A reduction in the delay time may be achieved if metals (liquid and solid) [141] are employed as heat conductors, which enables acquisition of the required temperature in approximately 1 s, the heating rate being 300–500 K s^{-1}.

The highest rates of heating of polymer samples to the constant temperature (10^3–10^5 K s^{-1}) are obtained on conducting the current through a metal strip or wire onto which a fine layer of polymer has been initially applied (flash pyrolysis) [141]. The possibility of the polymer peeling from its base (the main disadvantage of this method) does not enable precise temperature measurement of the sample, and it is inappropriate for testing polymer composites. Moreover, differences in thickness of the polymer samples lead to substantial measurement errors in such experiments.

Also described are heating units in which the pyrolyzed sample is heated by means of a high-frequency electromagnetic field to the Curie temperature of the ferromagnetic material from which the heating element (to which the polymer has been applied) is constructed [19]. Depending on the pyrolysis conditions, the heating-up time in such units is usually about 0.1 to 1 s, but it may reach several hundreths of a second. Ferromagnetic heating units have the following advantages: a well-defined, consistent and reproducible pyrolysis temperature, rapid heating of the sample and the possibility of standardization of pyrolysis conditions when required. The inevitability of operation at precisely fixed temperatures and the consequent impossibility of working under dynamic and stepwise heating conditions are disadvantages of these units.

The most desirable method for studying polymer degradation is one [129] in which a regulator makes it possible to preset the requisite conditions for heating the sample, i.e. the temperature inside the sample drops as little as 3 to 5% between its surface and centre, rather than the temperature of the reactor, heat-carrier or sample surface. In one such method [129] for the correct measurement of temperature, the thermocouple was placed either between layers of the polymeric material or onto the side of a sample 0.1–0.2 mm thick, and then a layer of glass fabric 0.05–0.1 mm thick was glued to it. The thermocouple was joined to the automatic servo(motor) of the heating unit. In this case, according to the preset program, it was possible to conduct the degradation of polymeric materials under both isothermal and dynamic conditions. The method enabled the carrying out of tests at a heating rate of 50 K s^{-1}. A mechanotron (a 'YP-1' amplifier) is a sensitive element of such a thermobalance (Fig. 3.4). The results of the temperature and polymer-sample mass measurements are recorded automatically by an 'ZPP-09' instrument [129].

3.2.2   Methods based on the determination of volumes of adsorbed and released gases

Volumetric methods (or methods based on pressure measurements) for studying the degradation of polymers are of special interest since they may be used either independently, expecially for investigation of the thermal–oxidative degradation of polymers, or to supplement TGA. Methods based on measurements of the volume of released gases or their pressure (thermovolumetric analysis, TVA) may be used

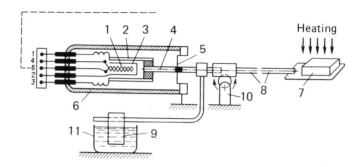

Fig. 3.4 — Schematic diagram of beam balance with electromechanical pickup of small displacements and forces (movable-electrode tube) [129]: 1, immovable cathode of movable electrode tube; 2,3, movable anode; 4, metal rod isolated from anode; 5, membrane of Kovar sheet; 6, glassy vessel; 7, sample; 8, lever of length 120 mm, 9, balance weight; 10, arrester; 11, damper.

only for the degradation of those polymers which produce considerable quantities of low-molecular-mass volatile products or for studies of thermal–oxidative degradation when the gaseous decomposition products are formed of necessity. In addition the determination of the volumes of adsorbed oxygen is also possible when investigating thermal–oxidative degradation.

Typical of the methods based on measurements of pressure is that developed by Grassie and Melville, described in [3]. The polymer degradation occurs in a glass molecular cube, the pressure of gases being released during degradation being determined by a Pirani gauge with a simple Wheatstone bridge. The calibration of the installation for pressure measurement is conducted by passing the condensed product of polymer degradation at a different rate via the needle valve and by collecting it in a liquid nitrogen trap. The product is then distilled into a calibrating capillary and its volume measured.

When studying the thermal degradation of polymers, Madorsky *et al.* [3] used various instrumental modifications enabling the condensation and volume measurements of liberated liquid and gaseous pyrolysis products. In one modification, the quartz reactor is located horizontally in order to give access to a heater, which is heated to a preset temperature and then moved into the appropriate position. For polymer pyrolysis at 1300–1500 K the quartz reactor is replaced by one of platinum. The heating element of the furnace comprises two sections: the inner is wrapped into the platinum wire, while the outer is located around the inner section and made of Ni–Cr wire. The massive platinum cylinder fitted to the heater muffle acts as a distributor for uniform heating of the platinum reactor. When the heater operates at temperatures of 1100–1300 K, the temperature in the reactor is maintained accurately to ±5.0 K.

3.2.3 Other methods for studying degradation of filled polymers
Physicochemical and physical methods including IR spectroscopy, EPR, mass spectroscopy, g.l.c., radiography, etc., have very wide potential application for the

quantitative and qualitative analysis of volatile products. An appropriate combination of methods based on change in the mass of test samples or released products with another of the methods indicated yields the most informative and accurate results in studies on thermal and thermal–oxidative degradation. The choice of a particular method depends on the nature of the problem, on the individual characteristics of the polymer degradation and on changes in the filler which are observed in its polymeric environment.

IR spectroscopy

IR spectroscopy is mainly employed for determining qualitative variations taking place in the chemical structure of a polymer during its degradation in the presence of a filler. In a number of cases IR spectroscopy establishes (from analysis of the decomposition products) the role of the filler in this chemical process. It has been shown [8,142–144] that during the thermal–oxidative degradation of polyethylene filled with disperse metals, metal carboxylates are produced in the bulk of the polymer; these compounds, formed in the initial stage of thermal degradation, inhibit the process.

At sufficiently high degrees of filling, polymer degradation can be studied by IR spectroscopy using multiply-disturbed total internal reflection (IRS-MDTIR).

Quantitative IR spectroscopy is utilized for calculating the degree of oxidation of polyethylene by the carbonyl index at about $1850–1650\ cm^{-1}$ [8]. Automated data processing has enabled information about the diffusion of the copper salts produced in the sample volume to be obtained. It has been established [144] from the COOH band at about $1590\ cm^{-1}$ that the concentration of COO^- ions increases with time in the oxidation of polyethylene, but at a distance of $1\ \mu m$ from the metal surface it becomes zero. The integral carbonyl absorption ($1720\ cm^{-1}$) incorporating the oxidized polyethylene groups indicates that on prolonged exposure the concentration of such groups is maximal near the polymer–metal interface. Thus contemporary forms of IR spectroscopy give not only data concerning the quantitative and qualitative changes in the filled polymer, taking place during thermal–oxidative degration but also the topochemical characteristics of the process.

Mass-spectrometric analysis

In recent years mass spectroscopy in combination with IR spectroscopy, TGA, chromatography and elementary analysis has been widely used to study the degradation of filled polymers [145–150]. The application of pyrolytic mass spectrometry not only enables the thermal stability of filled polymers to be estimated but also yields data on their structure, and relations between the components and the decomposition kinetics [145].

The MX 1303 mass spectrometers [145] and R-10-10-C chromatomass spectrometers (France) [150] have been used to study the degradation processes of filled polymers. One advantage of mass spectrometry lies in the possibility of using very small quantities of sample (1 mg) at a preset variation in temperature over a sufficiently wide range and at different heating rates. Mass-spectroscopic analysis makes it possible to identify a considerable number of the volatile products of degradation and to characterize their kinetics of formation [150]. Thus, when studying the thermal degradation of polyethylene-based polymer composites it was possible, using gas chromatography–mass spectroscopy to identify over 50 compounds, mainly C_{2-18} hydrocarbons. The number of products formed in the decomposition of polyethylene in the presence of oxygen increases to 70, and such oxygen-containing compounds as CO_2, formaldehyde, acetaldehyde, acetone, acrolein, aldehydes and the like appear among them [150]. One should note that the number and composition of the thermal-degradation products vary at different polymer–filler ratios, which is owing to the different degree of polymer cross-linking in the interface layer.

Mass spectroscopy is widely employed to identify the products and their formation kinetics in the degradation of filled reaction layers, e.g. phenol–formaldehyde resins [146,147], epoxide resins [145,148], and polyesters and acrylates [151].

Chromatographic methods

Since gaseous, liquid and low-volatile solid products may form during polymer degradation, for their analyses gas chromatographs [152–154], liquid chromatographs and chromatomass spectrometers should be employed [145,150]. The pyrolyses of filled polyalkenes [155], PTFE [156], PVC [157], polyamides [158], polyorganosiloxanes and others [159] have been studied by chromatographic methods.

3.2.4   Miscellaneous methods of studying the degradation of filled polymers

A variety of other methods have been applied to study the degradation of filled polymers. Thus differential scanning calorimetry (DSC) has been used [160] to investigate the kinetic parameters of the thermal-oxidative and thermal degradation of polymers.

In recent years the EPR method [14,161] has found wide application in studies of the decomposition processes in filled polymers of different types and of their influence on the formation of paramagnetic pyrolysis products [14,161]. Using this method it was possible to study the formation kinetics of paramagnetic centres in filled polymers at different temperatures and degrees of filling, as well as the influence of the nature of the filler on the formation of paramagnetic centres in the polymer.

Such experiments are carried out using EPR spectrometers supplied with devices for heating samples under isothermal or dynamic conditions both in inert and in oxidative atmospheres directly in the spectrometer cavity [14,161].

X-Radiographic methods have been used to investigate the involatile residues of the decomposition of filled polymers and the phase transformations of fillers occurring at high temperatures during polymer degradation [162,163]. Thus, X-ray photoelectron spectroscopy has been used to examine [162] the chemical changes at the surface of ZrO_2 filler particles during the decomposition of poly(vinyl acetate). The data obtained confirm participation of the filler in the high-temperature reactions, leading to changes in the stoichiometry of the ZrO_2 particles in its surface layer.

It has been shown [163] that oxidation of a metal with oxygen-containing degradation products at comparatively low pyrolysis temperatures (around 700 K) is observed during the decomposition of carbochain and heterochain polymers (including polyorganosiloxanes) filled with disperse metals. Partial reduction of oxidized metals or of initially introduced oxides, as well as the formation of crystalline products of interaction of the degrading polymers with fillers (carbides, nitrides, silicides, silicates, etc.), occur at higher decomposition temperatures.

3.2.5   Kinetic methods for studying the degradation of filled polymers

TGA, under both isothermal and dynamic conditions, is extensively used for studying the kinetics of decomposition reactions [164–168]. Certainly, determination of the kinetic parameters of polymer degradation reactions under isothermal conditions yields more precise and accurate results; however, this is a labour-intensive method, needing much time and many samples. In this connection dynamic thermogravimetry has been widely employed for the last 15–20 years for the analysis of polymers and of polymer composites [169,170]. Despite several substantial disadvantages (lack of reproducibility, difficulty of control of temperature and rate of heating, sensitivity to the presence of low-molecular-mass admixtures and to the thermal prehistory of the sample, overlapping of certain stages of the process [164], etc.) the method makes it possible not only to obtain the quantitative characteristics of the decomposition process (initial and final temperatures of the process, the degree of decomposition as a function of temperature, etc.) but also to describe this process with reasonable accuracy in the form of kinetic equations, the parameters of which are calculated from the experimental data. A number of publications describe precise methods for the determination of kinetic parameters by mathematically processing the TGA curves [166–168,170–173]. Such calculations are valid providing that the thermal and diffusion barriers are insignificant and that the Arrhenius equation holds. The first condition is satisfied when small samples of powdered material, having a sufficiently large area of contact with the heating medium, are used and if the removal of volatile products of the degradation is provided for.

The degradation of polymers by the dynamic TGA yields, in the simplest case, sigmoid kinetic curves. This behaviour means that, in the initial stage the sample mass slowly decreases; there then follows a sharp growth of the reaction rate over a narrow temperature range (the maximal decomposition rate); and, towards the end of the process, when only a small amount of residue remains, the mass loss again becomes extremely slow.

The shape of the TGA curve depends firstly on the kinetic parameters (the order of reaction n, the pre-exponential factor A and the activation energy E), which are of paramount significance for elucidating the mechanism of polymer degradation. In real polymer systems, including filled materials, the shape of the TGA curves can become more complex than those described above. If the polymer decomposition is a multistage process, and the reaction orders and activation energies of individual stages are close, then instead of a complex TGA curve one may obtain (at a sufficiently high rate of heating) a relatively simple curve which gives, however, averaged kinetic parameters for the degradation. In contrast, if the kinetic parameters of individual stages of the process differ considerably from each other, then the TGA curve consists of two or more sigmoidal regions.

The methods for calculating n, E and A used for simple TGA curves may also be applied to determine the same parameters for each stage of compound curves. However, if the values of E for each stage entering the total TGA curve differ only slightly (i.e. if certain reactions overlap), then the kinetic analysis of the TGA curves becomes difficult or even impossible. Dynamic TGA in most cases makes it possible only to determine the values of the total kinetic parameters of the multistage processes, which, taken separately, do not normally give evidence concerning the mechanism of each individual stage. Therefore the TGA method is best supplemented by DTA data [174,175] as well as by the results of the chromatographic, mass-spectrometric, IR, EPR and X-ray analyses [142–163].

The method of dynamic TGA used for the determination of the kinetic parameters of polymer degradation has the following advantages over the isothermal method:

(i) the temperature dependence of the rate of mass loss by the sample may be determined for different temperature ranges using the results of one experiment,

(ii) the continuous recording of the mass loss at different temperatures enables account to be taken of the individualities of the kinetic decomposition, and

(iii) since only one sample is required for dynamic TGA, then the introduction of inaccuracy from measurements on a large number of samples is excluded.

The last factor is of particular importance for filled polymers.

Determination of the values of the kinetic parameters for simple one-stage processes from the rate of mass change is described by the equation

$$-\frac{dW}{dt} = Ae^{-E/RT}W^n \,, \tag{3.1}$$

where W is the dimensionless mass of the sample subjected to degradation, t is the time, A is the pre-exponential factor, E is the activation energy of degradation, and n is the effective reaction order.

Different modifications of this equation are widely employed for the determination of the kinetic parameters of most unfilled polymers which decompose via a chain mechanism to form considerable quantities of monomer [164].

The kinetic analysis of more complex, multistage processes of polymer degradation is more difficult. One should remark that hitherto there have been few theoretical and experimental studies related to the kinetic analysis of the degradation of polymer composites. Procedures for the calculation of multistage processes of the thermal degradation of filled polymers have been developed most completely in two studies [168,170]. The characteristics of the peak maxima on the DTGA curves are used for preliminary estimation of the various stages of the overall process, and for rough determination of the effective kinetic parameters in [168]. By differentiating equation (3.1) with respect to time, assuming that at the maximum $(d^2W/dt^2)_m = 0$ and using the ratio

$$W_m = n^{1/(1-n)} ,$$ (3.2)

as suggested in [292], we can obtain an equation which relates the characteristics of the peak on the DTGA curves to the kinetic parameters of the process, viz.

$$-\left(\frac{dW}{dT}\right)_m T_m^2 = \left(\frac{E}{R}\right) n^{1/(1-n)} = C ,$$ (3.3)

where $(dW/dT)_m = (dW/dt)_m/(dT/dt)$ and C is a constant for the particular process.

Failure to adhere to equation (3.3) indicates that the mechanism of the process either does not satisfy condition (3.1) or that the process does not proceed in one stage.

If it transpires that we are dealing with a multistage process, then subsequent analysis is carried out by the sequential elimination of stages [177].

Supposing that certain stages, each violating equation (3.1), proceed independently of each other, then the total rate of mass change of the sample is described [168] by the equation

$$-\frac{dw}{dt} = -\sum_{i=1}^{m} \frac{dw_1}{dt} = \sum_{i=1}^{m} A'_i e^{-E/RT} w_i^{n_1} ,$$ (3.4)

where

$$A'_i = A_i w_0^{1-n}; \quad \sum_{l=1}^{m} w_{0l} = w_0 - w_n; \quad \sum_{l=1}^{m} w_l = w - w_{1l} ,$$

and that, after a definite time, all reactions with the exception of the latter have been completed, it is possible, using the corresponding sections of the TGA curves, to calculate the kinetic parameters of the mth stage by any of the known methods. Determining then from the integral form of equation (3.1),

$$l(w) = \frac{A'E}{BR} P(X) ,$$ (3.5)

where $l(w) = [(w_0 - w_k)^{1-n} - (w - w_k)^{1-n}]/1 - n)$ at $n \neq 1$, $l(w) = \ln[(w_0 - w_k)/(w - w_k)]$ at $n = 1$, $p(x) = \exp(-x)x^{-1} - \int_{x}^{\infty} \exp(-x)x^{-1} \, dx$, $x = (E/RT)$; $B = (dT/dt)$, it is possible to determine the initial mass of the substance which decomposes at this stage, and having solved the direct problem (having calculated the dependences $w_m(T)$ and $dw_m/dt(T)$), we exclude it from subsequent consideration. Having written equation (3.4) in the form

$$-\frac{d(w - w_m)}{dt} = \sum_{l=1}^{m-1} A_i' e^{-E_1/RT} w_i^{n_i} , \qquad (3.6)$$

we determine the parameters of the $(m - 1)$th stage, etc. In this way we obtain the mathematical description of the TGA curves corresponding to multistage processes using the mth sets of the kinetic parameters and the values of w_{0t} [168]. Coincidence of the total calculated TGA curves with the experimental ones is the criterion of correctness of the calculation.

The above method was used [168] to calculate the kinetic parameters of the thermal degradation of the composite based on epoxy resin and carbon fibrous filler; three independent stages of the thermal degradation of the composite were distinguished, and kinetic parameters (n, E and A) were determined for each of them.

The conditions for carrying out kinetic studies yielding reliable data on kinetics of the thermal degradation of polymers and polymer composites under programmed and high rates of heating are analysed by [170] based on general non-stationary equations of conservation of mass and energy. [170] has formulated a theoretical and experimental approach which enables, based on estimates of the characteristic times of the processes under consideration, the optimum geometrical sizes of the test samples and conditions for carrying out experiments using linear heating. The procedures for calculating the kinetic parameters are based on the characteristics of the thermal conversions of polymers in their initial stages, i.e. the temperature and time of initiation of the thermal degradation.

The problem of the influence of the inhibition of diffusion on the profile of the TGA curves is important when estimating the results of thermal analysis. Since, during the thermal degradation of polymeric materials, there occurs the formation of a melt or non-melted pore layer via which the gaseous products of degradation diffuse from the sample's centre to its surface, the effective coefficients of diffusion are determined for the polymer melt [170,178] as

$$D_{ef} = D_{exp}(- E_D/RT_s) , \qquad (3.7)$$

where T_s is the surface temperature and E_D is the activation energy for diffusion, which in a number of cases [178], may be associated with the activation energy of the thermal degradation process, i.e.

$$E_D = E - (1 - f)RT_s$$

(f is the number of degrees of freedom).

The diffusion coefficient for the polymer pore layer is determined according to [179] by the equation

$$D_{\text{ef}} = D\pi^2 , \tag{3.8}$$

where π is the porosity of the material.

The existence of the melt or pore layer decreases the effective diffusion coefficient by an order of magnitude and more, which leads to a critical diffusion inhibition of the decomposition processes and to a shift of the TGA curves to higher temperatures.

In order to conduct kinetic studies correctly, during the thermal analysis of polymers and composites the following conditions should be satisfied [170]:

$$t_1^T < t_2^T;\ t^f \leqslant t_1^d < t_2^d \ll t^{\text{ch}};\ t_1^d > t_1^T , \tag{3.9}$$

where t_1^T and t_2^T are the thermal lag times in the sample and between the medium and sample respectively, t^f is the characteristic filtration time for the pore body, t_1^d and t_2^d are the characteristic times of the diffusional lag in the sample and between the medium and sample respectively, and t^{ch} is the characteristic time of the chemical reaction.

According to inequalities (3.9), of the characteristics of the thermal effect, the initial decomposition temperature T_{id}, as determined from TGA and DTA curves, may be considered one of the most reliable. If these inequalities (3.9) are not satisfied, as a result of diffusion inhibition, then the TGA curves experience greater distortion than the DTGA curves. This has a crucial influence on the errors of the kinetic parameters in question. Additionally, the geometrical dimensions of the sample and the transfer coefficients should be constant in the course of kinetic study, otherwise the times which characterize any changes should be added to the determinable characteristic times [170].

To calculate the kinetic parameters of polymer degradation using a system of energy equations in a solid body of different symmetry and conserving the mass of gaseous reaction products [170], the following conditions should be fulfilled,

  (i) the linear dimensions of the test sample should not change during thermal analysis,
 (ii) the rate of gas filtration via the pore layer, or the flotation rate of gas bubbles in the polymer melt, are such that $t^f \leqslant t_1^d$,
(iii) the thermophysical characteristics of the sample are constant, and
(iv) the absence of any temperature gradient in the sample (the isothermal case), i.e. $\Delta T_1 \rightarrow 0$; $t_1^T < t_1^d \ll t^{\text{ch}}$.

Thus we obtain an equation for the thermal balance [296]

$$\rho_s C_{ps} \frac{dT_s}{dt} = \alpha \frac{S}{V}(T_e - T_s) - Qk_0 f(\eta) \exp\left(-\frac{E}{RT_s}\right)$$ (3.10)

and the kinetic equation

$$d\eta/dt = k_0 f(\eta) \exp(-E/RT_s)$$ (3.11)

with the initial conditions $t = 0$, $T = T_e$, $\eta = 0$, where η is the degree of chemical conversion of the sample, Q is the heat effect of the reaction and k_0 is a pre-exponential factor. In this case the temperature of the medium changes linearly according to the equation

$$T_e = T_{SH} + bt ,$$ (3.12)

where b is the rate of heating, T_{SH} is the initial temperature, and T_e is the medium temperature.

Numerous methods of calculating the kinetics of chemical reactions using thermal analytical data are based on equation (3.10) [180], although the equation is strictly valid only if the assumption relating to the absence of any sample gradient temperature is fulfilled.

Estimation of the characteristic times of the principal processes shows that the most reliable data may be obtained using the initial decomposition stages ($\eta \leqslant 0.3$) and the initial decomposition temperature T_{id} as the characteristic temperature [170]. To determine T_{id} and t_{id}, optical and laser diagnostics are used in combination with conductivity [182] and thermogravimetry [183]. The medium temperature T_e is considered to be constant and is measured by optical or thermocouple methods, and the heat-transfer coefficient α is determined from calorimetric measurements.

Thus, knowing T_{SH}, T_e and α, as well as the experimental dependences $T_{id}(\Delta T/\Delta t)$ and solving the equation linearized in the form

$$\ln A = \ln(3\lambda_s Q k_0)\left(\frac{E}{R}\frac{1}{T_{id}}\right)$$ (3.13)

(where λ_s is the thermal conductivity of the sample), we can determine the values of the kinetic parameters E, Q and k_0 by a linearizing method.

Statistical methods of experimental design are employed in analysis of the initial experimental data and the results enable reliable estimation of the experimental data used in design formulae and determinable kinetic parameters [170].

Several papers [168–170, 184–186] describe attempts to study experimentally the influence of disperse fillers on the kinetics of thermal–oxidative degradation of polymers. Results on thermal oxidation of polyethylene in contact with the surfaces of metals (steel, copper, aluminium, duralumin, titanium, nickel, lead) has shown [169,185] that the activation energy (with the exception of lead) decreases from 114.5 (for polyethylene itself) to 69.0 kJ mol^{-1} (copper). This effect is associated with the catalytic action of the oxidized metal surface, which both accelerates the initiation and development of the kinetic chain, thus increasing the reactivity of oxygen, and activates the decomposition of hydroperoxides, thus shortening the induction period and catalyzing degenerate branching [169].

At the same time it is noted [185] that values of the activation energy for the thermal oxidation decrease with increasing thickness of the polyethylene layer (or decreasing filler content), which may be associated with an increase in the contribution of the diffusion process to the total oxidation process (the activation energy of gaseous diffusion in the polyethylene melt is 42 kJ mol^{-1} [185]).

The inhibitory action of lead [169] and commercial carbon [186] on the thermal–oxidative degradation of polyethylene is associated with the formation of surface compounds of the polymer with the filler, as well as with the ability of commercial carbon to inhibit the oxidation of polyalkenes by phenolic antioxidants.

The thermal–oxidative degradation of polyalkenes as well as of vinyl polymers such as poly(vinyl alcohol) (PVA) [184] and PMMA [138] is sensitive to the chemical nature of the disperse filler. Thus, when studying the thermal oxidative kinetics of PVA filled with KI, $MgCl_2$ or $(NH_4)_2HPO_4$, it has been established [184] that KI is characterized as the most effective stabilizer. Evidently, the introduction of KI into PVA increases to the greatest extent the degree of dehydroxylation of the polymer in the initial stage of thermal oxidation.

Studies on the kinetics of thermal–oxidative degradation of filled PVA made it possible to establish that the kinetic parameters of the process, determined with the use of the Kolmogorov–Erofeev equation, vary over time even at the same decomposition temperature. This indicates the presence of different mechanisms for the thermal oxidation of PVA at different stages of the process. The activation energy of the thermal oxidation of filled PVA is 56.5 kJ mol^{-1} in the initial stage, becoming in the late stages 97.0 kJ mol^{-1}, the rate constant being a factor of 1.5 to 2 smaller. The reaction order calculated from the initial sections of the kinetic curves is comparatively low ($n < 0.5$), indicating a diffuse pattern of PVA oxidation in the initial stage [184]. The reaction order at the late stages of decomposition of filled PVA is close to 1. The introduction of fillers decreases initially the duration of the initial period of thermal oxidation of PVA.

The available experimental studies on the kinetics of the thermal and thermal–oxidative degradation of filled polymers confirm the picture of a complex and multistage character of these processes. This is largely associated with the presence of the polymer–filler interface and also with the chemical participation of the latter at different stages of polymer degradation. The presence of the filler in the bulk of the polymer influences the mechanism of the diffusion and heat processes occurring in polymers during their thermal and thermal–oxidative degradation which in turn affects the values of the determinable kinetic parameters of the process.

Analysis of the publications on the thermal and thermal–oxidative degradation of filled polymers indicates that differences in production methods are one of the reasons for the contradictory results of many publications. These are caused by the dependence of thermal effects not only on the technique for production of the system but also on the concentration, purity and nature of the filler introduced, the temperature conditions and method of study, as well as on a number of other factors.

The concentration of filler is found to affect the thermal degradation of the filled system. In particular [5,186], highly disperse commercial carbon ($S_{sp} =$ 150 000 $m^2 kg^{-1}$) at small concentrations inhibits the thermal–oxidative degradation of polyethylene, but at concentrations over 5% accelerates its thermal oxidation.

Little attention has been paid, as a rule, to the properties of the filler in the thermal–oxidative and thermal degradation of filled polymers. The initial primary characteristics of a filler (specific surface area, porosity, state of surface) are virtually uncontrolled and it is simply accepted that the filler undergoes no change during the thermal degradation. However, as a result of their chemical nature, fillers may be divided into the inactive, which are unchanged on heating to definite temperatures under conditions of decomposition of the polymer (glass, titanium dioxide, talc, etc.) and the active, which do change in this process, including highly disperse metals and certain metal oxides. In systems filled with active fillers, new compounds, e.g. of carboxylate salts in the polyethylene–copper system, may be formed during degradtion [123,142]. The possibility of the appearance during thermal treatment of surface or bulk phase oxides on the metal surface for polyethylene-based systems containing Cu, Ti, Ni, Pb in a 1:1 ratio (by volume) is shown in references [41,42,169,187]. Thus, proper study of the thermal degradation of filled polymers is impossible without a detailed investigation of the changes occurring in the filler at the interface; in addition, any comparison of the thermal stabilizing or thermal activating influence of fillers is invalid if the magnitude of their specific surface area is ignored.

One of the reasons for the often poor agreement between the literature data is that the influence of a filler on polymer degradation is frequently observed only over a particular temperature range, and this influence may change with temperature. Thus, it has been established that the oxidation of a polyethylene coating on iron and copper is initiated at temperatures below that of the oxidation of free polymer, but with increasing temperature the catalytic activity of the substrate decreases. The influence of the substrate on the degree of thermal oxidation of polyethylene film is negligible at temperatures at which the induction period of the thermal oxidation of coatings on the inactive substrate is zero [123,142,188]. Again, at the early stages of the thermal oxidation of polyethylene on a copper support there occurs catalysis of the thermal oxidation of polyethylene by the copper surface, followed by inhibition of the process, due to which the oxidation of the polymer is virtually independent of the duration of the thermal treatment.

The effect of the filler on the thermal degradation of a polymer (irrespective of the method of production of the system) is determined by the temperature conditions of oxidation, in particular by the sample heating rate. For example, at a heating rate of 0.1 Ks^{-1}, the oxidation of polyethylene filled with powders of Cu, Ti, Ni and Pb and the steel-3 alloy in a 1:1 ratio (by volume) starts at the same temperature (473 K) as for unfilled polyethylene. At a heating rate of about 0.03 Ks^{-1}, the initiation temperature of polyethylene oxidation in the presence of steel decreased by 29 K, while for the other fillers the decrease was 14 K; moreover the peak of the oxidation effect shifted towards lower temperatures, i.e. for steel by 25 K and for the other metals by 5–10 K. A decrease in the heating rate reveals more precisely the initial zone of the activated oxidation of a polymer [169].

Comparative studies on the degradation of filled polymers under isothermal and dynamic conditions are also unavailable in the literature. Besides, the results of such studies would be distorted if the reaction conditions in the kinetic region were not satisfied and if the degradation products were not removed from the reaction zone.

Experiments on the effect of fillers on polymer degradation are conducted by various methods, but their results are not always comparable. These methods include IR spectroscopy of polymer films after contact with the substrate, IR spectroscopy of the volatile products of degradation and of the solid residue, EPR of systems undergoing thermal treatment and mass-spectroscopic and chromatographic analysis of the degradation products. The degradation of filled polymers is also examined by virtue of the quantity of liberated gaseous products, the adsorption of oxygen and by samples in special static installations, as well as by the mass change of the sample in air as determined by the torsion balance and also *in vacuo* by the quartz spring balance. In addition, DTA and TGA are widely used in most experiments.

In our opinion, methods enabling the control of the individual properties of each component are to be preferred to those referring to the total response of the entire system. The preferred methods include therefore IR spectroscopy of polymers, chromatographic, mass-spectroscopic and chemical analysis of the solid residue and the volatile products of degradation, and X-ray diffraction analysis of the fillers and the products of their chemical interaction with polymers conducted at different stages of heat treatment of the system.

Only by taking into account the variety of factors and processes as a whole (the polymer degradation proper, the formation of three-dimensional chemical structures, the chemical interaction between a polymer or the products of its degradation and the filler, the surface chemistry of the filler and its variation during degradation, and the formation of involatile products from interaction of the polymer with the filler and their effect on the polymer degradation) which occur during the thermal–oxidative and thermal degradation of filled polymers, can a reliable interpretation of the experimental data be made, together with the successful application of the kinetic methods which have been employed recently to account for the effect on polymer stabilization of disperse fillers.

The heterogeneity of filled systems, and the related differences in chemical activity, thermal conductivity, thermal expansion coefficients and individual characteristics of diffusion processes proceeding in respective components, substantially impede study of mechanisms of the thermal and thermal oxidative degradation of filled polymers. However, the development of new experimental approaches should enable many of these recalcitrant problems to be overcome now that the basic problems have been set out.

4

Thermal and thermal–oxidative degradation of filled polymers

Consideration of the characteristic properties of the thermal and thermal–oxidative degradation of polymers related to their chemical structure as well as the analysis of the physicochemical (including thermal) properties of disperse inorganic fillers, especially taking account of their surface chemistry, forms the basis for an approach to analysis of the generalities in the degradation of filled polymers. The available data are analysed with allowance for the chemical participation of fillers in high-temperature chemical processes proceeding at the polymer–solid surface interface. Such an approach enables both systematization and comprehension of many scattered experimental data on the degradation of filled polymers.

4.1 DEGRADATION OF FILLED CARBON-CHAIN AND CARBON-CYCLOCHAIN POLYMERS

The carbon-chain and carbon-cyclochain polymers are those principally employed for practical purposes. They have found wide application as polymer composites, including structural materials. The behaviour of these materials under operating conditions, especially at high temperatures, is of seminal interest. Under such conditions, the filler plays a significant role in the thermal and thermal–oxidative stability of carbon-chain and carbon-cyclochain polymers.

4.1.1 Polyalkenes

A considerable number of works on the thermal and thermal–oxidative degradation of filled carbon-chain polymers are devoted to polyethylene–disperse filler systems [112,117–120,124,125,143,144,155,169,185,186], whereas publications on the degradation of other filled polymers, including polyalkenes, are few. The interest in the thermal behaviour of filled polyethylene (PE) is explained both by the wide use of this polymer in its filled form and by the comparatively simple mechanism for its degradation processes.

Polyethylene

Introduction of a filler into PE whose carbon–carbon bonds possess the same strength and, consequently, an equal probability for their cleavage on heating [3,4] (except for bonds located at the chain ends and at branching points) leads to the appearance of macromolecular sites differing in their properties from polymer chains in the bulk. Evidently, such a variation in these characteristics will alter the thermal behaviour of the polymer. Thus, a decrease in chain mobility in the adsorption and boundary layers [187] should increase the thermal stability of the polymer, since the majority of breaks of the carbon–carbon bonds are caused by tensions induced in the chains by thermal excitation. The grafting of macromolecules onto the filler surface and the formation of spatial chemical structures in the filled polymer should promote an increase in its thermal stability.

However, the introduction of a filler may also play a negative role in the thermal stability of polyolefins, since its catalytic and chemical actions may cause the formation of defects in the polymer chain such as peroxide, hydroperoxide, carbonyl and other groups [188].

It should be noted that the thermal degradation of filled PE has been studied to a limited extent [117,124,155,189–191]. Thus, it is shown in [124] that the introduction of small quantities (up to 1% (mass)) of highly disperse iron into high-density PE leads to a slight positive shift towards the initiation temperature of its thermal degradation (from 697 to 711 K).

The formation of highly disperse iron, copper and lead during thermal decomposition of the corresponding metal formates [42] in a low-density PE medium (metal content being 2–40% (mass)) leads to the formation of spatial polymer structures involving metal particles [191]. Such metal–polymer systems possess greater thermal stability than simple PE. However, there are definite peculiarities in the thermal degradation of the metal–polymer system. Variation in the copper concentration in the polymer over a wide range has practically no influence on the rate of its thermal degradation. Lead inhibits this process only at temperatures above 830 K, to an extent dependent on its concentration. As regards the low-temperature region of PE degradation, iron accelerates the process, but at higher temperatures (more than 700 K) there is a decrease in the decomposition rate. The authors [191] consider that an increase in the thermal stability of these systems is associated not only with a change in the polymer structure (via the formation of metal–polymer bonds and structurization of the polymer) but also with the readier dispersal of heat localized on the macromolecule.

Additions (up to 10%) (mass)) of metal salts ($FeCl_3 \cdot 6H_2O$, $CuCl_2 \cdot 2H_2O$, $CoCl_2 \cdot 6H_2O$) and oxides (ZnO, MgO, Al_2O_3, SiO_2) [189] to low-density PE exert no substantial effect on the thermal stability of this polymer. Again, it has been found that CuO and Cu_2O accelerate the thermal degradation of PE via their participation in redox reactions with hydroperoxides formed in the polymer [189].

However, as indicated in [191] the formation of CuO from decomposition of copper(II) tartrate in PE [117] increases the thermal stability of the system even at comparatively low concentrations (2%) of the filler. These results confirm the essential role of chemical bonding of the macromolecules to the filler surface in defining the thermal stability of the system.

It is shown in [190] that aluminium and iron oxides (Fe_2O_3) affect the thermal degradation of PE only slightly at temperatures up to 623 K, but above 700 K they accelerate the thermal degradation of the polymer. Introduction of the oxides does not change the kinetic order of the degradation reaction, but reduces the activation energy from 217.4 (PE) to 171.4 kJ mol^{-1} (PE + Fe_2O_3).

The role of the chemical properties of the surface and of the method for formulating the filled polymer in influencing its thermal degradation is rather well understood when considering the decomposition characteristics of PE filled with aluminosilicates. As is well-known [155], aluminosilicates are effective catalysts for the decomposition of polyalkenes with the formation of large quantities of gaseous and liquid products (alkanes, alkenes, aromatic compounds). However, the polymerization of ethylene in the presence of various aluminosilicates (kaolin, perlite, etc.) with the formation of filled PE yields a thermostable composite the thermal stability of which increases with the degree of filling. This is evidently associated with both the stabilizing action of the filler which functions as a radical trap [192] and with the more ordered structure of PE formed during its synthesis [112].

Modification of the surface of aluminosilicate fillers (talc, kaolin) by the products of the thermal transformation of polyacrylonitrile (PAN), which have a noticeable thermal stabilizing effect, results in a substantial improvement in the thermal stability of filled PE [117]. Thus, if high-density PE at 650 K *in vacuo* loses 40% of its mass over 3 h, then the same polymer containing unmodified kaolin (10% (mass)) loses 23% over the same period, while material containing thermalized PAN loses only 8% of its mass.

Kinetic studies on the thermal degradation of PE containing thermalized PAN-modified fillers has shown [117] that its degradation occurs with a noticeable induction period which decreases with an increase in the thermolysis temperature. Evidently, the presence of induction periods in the thermal degradation of PE filled with the modified fillers supports the view that thermalized PAN structurizes PE. After the induction period, the composition rate of filled PE remains relatively low due to the capacity of thermalized PAN to break kinetic chains [117].

The influences both of the chemical nature of the filler and of the methodology for production of the samples on the processes of thermal–oxidative degradation are demonstrated in many publications [119,120,125,169,185,193–198]. Thus, certain authors [119,120,193–195] have established that introduction into PE of disperse iron, talc and quartz sand in quantities of from 5 up to 15% (vol.) by means of joint dispersion or hot rolling depresses the temperature at which oxidative degradation begins. This tendency is enhanced as the filler concentration is increased up to 20% (vol.). This phenomenon is most marked with samples containing disperse iron, being less pronounced for fillers such as talc, quartz sand and glass powder. The decrease in the thermal–oxidative stability of filled PE is explained by increases in both the contact area and the oxygen concentration in the system. The introduction into PE of different quantities (0.5, 2.0, 10, 20, 30%(vol.)) of disperse quartz sand, talc and glass microspheres reveals [196] that glass spheres do not influence the temperature at which thermal–oxidative degradation of the polymer begins, whereas quartz sand lowers and talc increases it. The difference in action of these fillers is related to the chemical activity of their surface, i.e. to the specifics of their catalytic influence on the thermal–oxidative degradation of PE.

The catalytic influence of disperse metals (Cu, Ti, Ni, Pb, duralumin and steel) on the thermal–oxidative degradation of PE is also established in [169]. Table 4.1 shows the catalytic influence of the above-mentioned metals, except for Pb, on the thermal oxidation of PE, evident from the decrease in the induction period and activation energy of degradation, the increase in oxygen uptake and the fall in temperature at which oxidation of PE begins. A proposal has been made that the catalytic degradation of PE occurs at the metal oxide coating rather than on the pure surface of the metal. The oxidized surface of the metal (according to [169]) accelerates the initiation and propagation of kinetic chains by increasing the reaction capacity of oxygen and also activates decomposition of the hydroperoxides formed, thus shortening the induction period and catalysing the degeneracy of branching. Unfortunately, comparative studies on the effect of these metal oxides on the individual processes in the thermal–oxidative degradation of PE are not presented in this work.

It has been indicated in some studies [119,120,197,198] that trends in the thermal–oxidative degradation of PE at disperse metal and oxide surfaces depend not only on the nature of the substrate but also on the prehistory of the composite. It is found that as the area of contact between PE and the filler increases (e.g. by multiple fusion and pressing of the composite) catalytic thermal oxidation of PE at first is enhanced but then decreases. This effect is explained by the simultaneous action of two factors, i.e. (i) by an increase in the catalytic action of the substrate (metal) due to its direct surface contact with the macromolecules and (ii) by a decrease in the quantity of atmospheric oxygen at the interface. One might suppose that the level of the thermal–oxidative degradation of filled PE decreases with the thermal mobility of the macromolecules interacting with the filler surface. This effect is manifested most clearly if the interaction is chemical in nature.

The principle of 'non-chain' inhibition has been suggested to explain the stabilizing action of a number of metals at particular stages in the thermal oxidation of filled PE [16,124]. The basis of this principle is the binding of molecular oxygen diffusing into the polymer by active acceptors, such as disperse metals. If the acceptor efficiency Z is high, and the kinetic criterion of 'non-chain' inhibition is fulfilled, i.e. $v_z \gg v_k$ (where v_z represents the reaction rate of 'non-chain' inhibition) and, v_k is that of any other oxidative degradation reaction), then only the reaction

$$nZ + \tfrac{1}{2}mO_2 \xrightarrow{\ k_z\ } Z_nO_m \qquad (4.1)$$

proceeds.

Other reactions (4.2–4.4)

$$RH + O_2 \longrightarrow R\cdot + HO_2\cdot \qquad (4.2)$$

$$2RH + O_2 \longrightarrow 2R\cdot + H_2O_2 \qquad (4.3)$$

$$R\cdot + O_2 \longrightarrow RO_2\cdot \qquad (4.4)$$

Table 4.1 — Parameters for the thermal–oxidative degradation of filled low-density PE [169]

Characteristics	Unfilled PE	PE filled with disperse metals (50% (mass))					
		Steel-3	Cu	Duralumin	Ti	Ni	Pb
Induction period at 423 K (s)	1500	600	600	900	900	900	2100
Quantity of consumed oxygen, (mg g^{-1} of PE) at							
423 K	1.3	5.7	5.1	3.4	4.0	3.4	1.1
453 K	4.6	13.0	15.0	14.0	9.1	7.4	4.6
473 K	21.0	29.0	31.0	39.0	29.0	25.0	2.0
Activation energy for the thermal–oxidative degradation of PE (kJ mol^{-1})	114.5	71.1	69.0	76.9	75.2	76.9	114.5

associated with polymer oxidation are virtually absent, since oxygen is absent from the bulk of the polymer. At this stage of the process the formation of hydroperoxides via reaction (4.5)

$$RO_2\cdot + RH \longrightarrow ROOOH + R\cdot \tag{4.5}$$

does not occur and the acceptor Z (a disperse metal) does not exercise its catalytic function in their decomposition:

$$ROOH \overset{z}{\longrightarrow} RO\cdot + HO\cdot \tag{4.6}$$

It has been shown [124] that the efficiency of the thermal–oxidative stabilization of high-density PE by disperse iron obtained by the thermal method [42] is higher than formulations containing the antioxidant Irganox 1010 (Table 4.2).

However, there are cases when disperse metals produce inert oxides via equation (4.1) only to a limited extent [16]. In addition, there are cases when the high activity of the metal in 'non-chain' inhibition is connected with its efficient catalytic decomposition (4.6) of the hydroperoxides [124]. The oxides formed from the metal, or the products of its interaction with compounds produced during the thermal oxidation of PE, may be active in the thermal–oxidative degradation of PE. It is most likely that conflicts in the literature concerning the thermal–oxidative degradation of PE either filled with metals or in contact with them are best understood in terms of the preceding discussion.

Table 4.2 — Thermal-oxidative stability of PE filled with highly disperse iron [124]

Composition	Temperature at which a given weight loss occurs (K)		
	2%	10%	50%
Initial PE	483	578	675
PE + 0.015% Irganox 1010	543	633	713
PE + 0.05% Fe	523	613	713
PE + 0.10% Fe	553	633	723
PE + 0.25% Fe	563	653	713
PE + 0.50% Fe	573	653	713
PE + 1.00% Fe	583	683	743

Publications concerning the nature of the compounds formed during decomposition and their role in subsequent thermal–oxidative processes are important in understanding the mechanism of the thermal–oxidative degradation of metal-filled PE [142–144,188,199–214]. Thus, references [188,200,201,213] show that the salts of fatty acids formed during PE thermal oxidation at the surface of metal plates exert a key influence on subsequent thermal oxidation of the system. It has been established that thermal treatment of PE films on copper produces a green colour associated with an IR band in the range 1550–1700 cm^{-1} (Fig. 4.1) typical of carboxylate ion. Some increase of absorption in this spectral region was also observed for PE coatings on steel. Similar compounds are not found for PE films on aluminium, the surface of which is shown not to be catalytically active as regards thermal oxidation of PE [202–204].

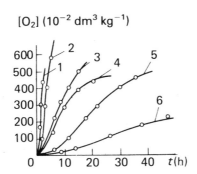

$[O_2]$ $(10^{-2}\ dm^3\ kg^{-1})$

Fig. 4.1 — Kinetics of oxygen consumption by PE containing 10^{-7}–10^{-3} mol/mol PE of cobalt stearate (1), cobalt chloride (2), cobalt oxide Co_3O_4 (3), cobalt sulphate $CoSO_4$ (4), metallic cobalt (5), PE without filler (6) [199].

Systematic studies of the chemical reactions and products formed at different stages of the thermal oxidation of PE filled with various metals, as well as the role of these products in the degradation of the polymer, have demonstrated that contact thermal–oxidation of PE is accompanied by diffusion of the following metals into the polymer: Cu [144,188,199–202,205,213], Pb [207,213], Zn [202,213], and Fe [206,208,209,213] in the form of compounds with the products of the thermal–oxidative degradation of PE (mainly with low-molecular-mass compounds containing COOH groups). Transport of these metal compounds into the bulk of PE occurs only if the metal activates the polymer oxidation and there is oxygen in the system. The metal complexes formed migrate into the bulk of the polymer to a depth of 1.0–1.5 μm and more [144,205,210–213]. The region into which metal compounds diffuse is characterized by their concentration gradient throughout its thickness and the transfer of the metals into the bulk of the polymer as controlled by diffusional processes [206].

These compounds at low concentrations are known to accelerate the thermal oxidation of PE and at high levels they inhibit it [188,200–203]. This conclusion is confirmed by data on the thermal oxidation of PE into which salts of stearic acid are introduced in varying quantities [199]. Inhibition of the thermal–oxidative degradation of PE at its later stages of conversion may be associated with the chemisorption of PE macromolecules onto the metal surface [191], with the accumulation of considerable quantities of the products of interaction of the metal with the functional groups of oxidized PE, as well as with the formation of spatial polymer structures under the catalytic influence of the metal. Thus with the emergence of chemical bonding between PE and the metal surface, there appears a new factor which inhibits the catalytic influence of disperse metals and promotes an increase in the thermal stability of the polymer [119,120,191,193–196]. As to weakly active fillers (talc, quartz, glassy powder) introduced in quantities from 0.5 to 20% (vol.) there is no substantial increase in the thermal–oxidative stability after thermal treatment of the system. This confirms the view that the physical interaction of PE macromolecules with the solid surface makes an insignificant contribution to the thermal stability of this system.

Data on the effect of salts, metal oxides, glass, aluminosilicates, natural layer silicates and commercial carbon on the thermal–oxidative degradation of PE are also available [117–120,186,191,196,197,199,203,204,214–222]. It has been shown that metal salts (cobalt, copper, zinc, cadmium, iron, tin and titanium chlorides, sulphates and stearates) exert a catalytic action on the thermal–oxidative degradation of PE, which is determined by the nature of the anion [199]. The introduction of these salts into PE at concentrations of 10^{-7}–10^{-3} mol/mol increases the rate of oxygen uptake by the polymer according to the series sulphate < chloride < stearate anions (Fig. 4.2). Disperse metals possess the weakest activity, and their oxides are comparable in their effect on the oxidation of PE with sulphates or chlorides (Fig. 4.1, curves 2 and 4). These differences in catalytic activity may be associated with differential solubility in PE. It also should be noted that the high catalytic activity of metal stearates introduced into PE in low concentrations confirms qualitatively the model concerning the mechanism of the thermal–oxidative degration of polymers filled with disperse metals [188] in the initial stages of the process when the concentrations of the carboxylate salts produced are rather insignificant.

Data on the effect of metal oxides on the thermal–oxidative degradation of PE are few and conflicting since the degradation of the samples has been studied by a

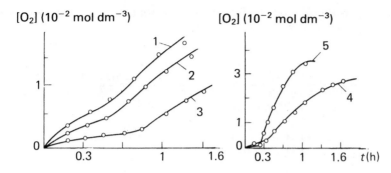

Fig. 4.2 — Kinetic curves of oxygen adsorption by PE containing 2%(1), 5%(2), 6%(3), 29%(4) and 38%(5) mass of commercial carbon; oxidation temperature 418 K [186].

variety of methods (DTA, TGA, oxygen uptake), with different contents of fillers differing substantially in their physical characteristics (specific surface area, crystalline modification, etc.). In particular, the data obtained by DTA and TGA (initial temperature of mass loss and temperature of maximal mass loss) indicate that aluminium and silicon oxides (including quartz) accelerate the thermal degradation of PE [196,197]. At the same time it has been shown [203,204] that, according to data on changes in the adhesion to aluminium of PE filled with Al_2O_3, it inhibits the oxidation rate.

According to [199] the oxides of Co (III), Fe (II, III), Zn, Ni(II), Cd, Co(II) and Ti(IV) introduced in tiny quantities (10^{-7}–10^{-3} mol/mol) into PE accelerate insignificantly oxygen uptake by the polymer during its oxidation at 393 K. According to their catalytic activity these oxides are arranged in the following series: $Co_2O_4 > FeO > CdO > CuO > NiO > Fe_2O_3 > TiO_2$. Based on the data on the rate of oxygen uptake and mass loss of PE filled with 10–30% TiO_2 (rutile and anatase), it has been concluded [216,217] that titanium oxides possess a stabilizing effect, i.e. the thermal oxidation rate of the polymer is essentially reduced.

The natural layer silicates (talc, kaolin) on introduction into PE at levels of 10–30% (mass) increase the initial temperature of oxidative decomposition [318], and noticeably increase the induction period for the thermal oxidation of PE (Table 4.3) [117,215,216] at comparatively low temperatures (423–453 K). At higher degradation temperatures (653–663 K) of filled PE this effect is considerably lower, while the mass loss of polymer filled with 20% kaolin is higher than that of unfilled PE [216].

It is noteworthy that chemical modification of the surface of aluminosilicate fillers, e.g. by thermalized PAN [213], leads to larger effects in the stabilization of PE as regards thermal–oxidative degradation as compared to the effect induced by unmodified fillers (see Table 4.3). The induction period of oxidation of PE filled with PAN modified talc or kaolin is two to three times as long. The stabilizing effect of the modified fillers is associated with the interaction of macroradials formed during the oxidative degradation of PE and also with the 'highly' conjugated structures of thermalized PAN.

Table 4.3 — Induction periods and decrease in oxygen pressure ($-\Delta P$) over 2 h during oxidation of filled samples of PE (initial oxygen pressure is 55.86 kPa [117])

Filler concentration	423 K		433 K		453 K	
	τ(h)	$-\Delta P$(kPa)	τ(h)	$-\Delta P$(kPa)	τ(h)	$-\Delta P$(kPa)
0	0.8	2.66	0.6	4.52	0.2	10.77
Kaolin						
10	1.33	1.86	1.06	3.29	0.28	9.57
20	1.23	1.86	0.76	3.99	0.28	7.45
30	1.16	1.46	0.58	5.05	0.28	6.12
10[a]	2.50	0	1.66	0.39	0.45	7.31
20[a]	2.50	0	1.83	1.59	0.50	4.65
30[a]	2.50	0	1.91	5.05	0.50	6.24
Talc						
10	1.16	1.33	0.75	2.53	0.20	10.24
20	1.23	1.33	0.75	3.99	0.20	10.77
30	1.33	0.93	0.75	3.32	0.20	9.04
10[a]	2.50	0	1.00	2.79	0.36	6.78
20[a]	2.50	0	1.25	3.19	0.41	6.38
30[a]	2.50	0	1.25	1.86	0.50	5.32

[a]Samples modified with thermalized PAN.

The introduction into PE of 10–30% (mass) of chrysolite asbestos considerably accelerates its thermal–oxidative degradation even at comparatively low temperatures (373 K) [218]. In the presence of inhibitors (santonox, oxaphenamide, etc.) the catalytic activity of the asbestos in the thermal oxidation of PE is lower. Some investigators [216] consider that the iron oxides (up to 5%) present in asbestos may be the activators of the oxidation processes of PE.

Investigations on the inhibitory power of commercial carbon in the thermal oxidation of polyalkenes are of great scientific and applied importance [5,223]. Explanations have been put forward that the inhibitory action is associated either with the presence of hydroxy (phenolic) groups at its surface which act like phenolic antioxidants [223,224] or with the fact that commercial carbon tends to decompose polymer hydroperoxides.

More detailed studies on the mechanisms of the inhibitory action of commercial carbon towards the thermal oxidation of low-density PE have shown [186,221,222] a complex dependence of the process on the degree of filling and the chemical nature of the filler surface. There are two zones on the oxygen uptake curves of PE containing up to 9% (mass) of PM-100 commercial carbon (Fig. 4.2). The first corresponds to inhibition by the carbon of the thermal oxidation of PE, which correlates with the degree of filling and the temperature, while the second refers to the considerable increase in rate of consumption of those surface centres inhibiting the oxidation of the polymer; the rate of oxidation at the second site corresponds to that of unfilled PE.

The introduction into PE of more than 9% (mass) of commercial carbon leads to a change in the kinetic curves of oxidation (see Fig. 4.2) [186]. In the initial region the thermal oxidation rate of PE decreases with increasing filler concentration. However *ca.* 0.3 h after the start of oxidation, the rate increases sharply, the more so the greater the concentration of carbon. These anomalous kinetics have been explained [186] in terms of the interaction of the macromolecules with the surface groups of commercial carbon to form chemical bonds which impede the thermal mobility of the chains at the decomposition temperature of PE. In addition, the thermal oxidation of the polymer is accompanied by degradation of the macromolecules, which leads to destruction of the spatial network. With an increase of the concentration of commercial carbon in PE, the process of polymer structurization predominates and, when a particular level of cross-linking has been reached, the rates of certain thermal–oxidative reactions begin to vary.

The thermal treatment of commercial carbon *in vacuo* at 1374 K before its introduction into PE leads to a change in the nature of its functional groups, thus the content of hydroquinone groups increases [186]. It has been found that the introduction of such heat-treated commercial carbon into PE decreases its power to inhibit oxidation and increases its tendency to cross-link.

Polypropylene and polyisobutylene
It has been established [113,225] that the thermal degradation of polypropylene (PP) and polyisobutylene (PIB) is activated by various inorganic compounds such as salts containing water of crystallization, metallic oxides, aluminosilicates and zeolites. Aluminosilicates and zeolites catalyse the decomposition of PP at a high rate to form monomer almost completely [220].

The anhydrous chlorides of lithium, magnesium, calcium and barium do not display catalytic properties towards the thermal degradation of PIB. However, their crystalline hydrates, especially the magnesium aquacomplexes ($MgCl_2 \cdot nH_2O$, where $n = 1, 2, 4$) are effective catalysers of the thermal degradation of PIB [113]: the yield of isobutylene in the gas phase is 95–99% (vol.) at all degrees of polymer degradation (see Table 4.4). The random scission of PIB macromolecules does not depend on their molecular mass, but does depend on the content of terminal C=C bonds. In particular, the total yield of products of the thermal degradation of 90%-hydrogenated PIB is a factor of 7 smaller. Thus, a combination of processes of initiation of decomposition by random scission and from terminal groups is a characteristic property of the thermal catalytic degradation of PIB in the presence of magnesium chloride hydrates.

The thermal–oxidative degradation of PP in the presence of disperse inorganic fillers has been extensively studied [227–229]. DTA and TGA methods have established [228] that disperse aluminium and silicon decrease, while zinc increases, the rate of thermal–oxidative degradation of PP. Metal oxides exert a negligible action, while aluminosilicates substantially increase the reaction rate.

It has been established [226,228] that copper and its oxides (CuO, Cu_2O, $CuO_{0.67}$) also act as effective catalysts in the thermal–oxidative degradation of PP. While the thermal oxidation of PP occurs both normally and autocatalytically in the absence of copper, on introduction of copper, it becomes catalytic and the autocatalytic contribution is either absent or negligibly small (Fig. 4.3). The catalytic oxidation of PP in the presence of copper and its oxides rapidly reaches a constant

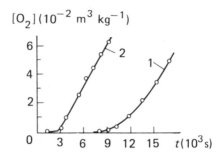

Fig. 4.3 — Kinetic curves of oxygen adsorption by PP without filler (1) and containing 1% (mass) of copper powder (2) at 403 K and atmospheric pressure [227].

rate without acceleration after a short induction period, which is little over one-third that in the absence of copper. The linear character of the dependence of the induction period on reciprocal temperature shows (Fig. 4.4) that the diffusion of oxygen via the polymer matrix plays no substantial role in the oxidation of PP at values close to the film thickness. The introduction of antioxidants into filled PP

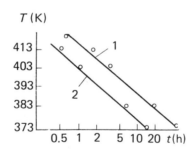

Fig. 4.4 — Effect of temperature on the induction period of thermal oxidation of PP without filler (1) and containing 1.4% (mass) of copper powder (2) [227].

somewhat reduces the catalytic acceleration of its thermal oxidation; however, in most cases the induction period is a factor of 10 to 100 shorter for stabilized and unfilled polymer.

It has been shown [226,227] that Cu_2O is a more efficient catalyst than copper metal or CuO. Investigation of the catalytic oxidation of model compounds (propylene, CO) has shown that p-type (Cu_2O) semiconductors are more active catalysts than n-type oxides, and the latter are more active than non-semiconductors (CuO). At the same time additional factors (e.g. differences in the specific surface area of powders of copper and its oxides) play a definite role; thus it has been found that copper stearate, while not a semiconductor, is a rather active catalyst of the thermal oxidation of PP [222].

The available data on the thermal and thermal–oxidative degradation of PP and PIB show that these polymers are even more sensitive to the surface chemistry of the fillers and their concentration in the system, and their methods of production than PE. This may be associated with the presence of tertiary and quaternary carbon atoms bearing small substituents (CH_3) in the macrochains of these polymers. This leads to a decrease of the strength of the C–C bonds and to abstraction of the hydrogen atom from the tertiary (PP) and quaternary (PIB) carbon atoms and, in the case of the thermal oxidation of these polymers, to the formation of hydroperoxide groups. The introduction of fillers into these polymers causes the appearance of uneven tensions along the chain due to the interaction of certain segments with the solid surface, which promotes thermal cleavage of weaker bonds (at tertiary or quaternary carbon atoms). Furthermore, the fillers exhibiting surface active sites, in participating in the catalytic decomposition of hydroperoxides or in redox reactions, promote decomposition of the weakest bonds in the thermal–oxidative degradation of these polymers.

4.1.2 Polydienes

Studies on the influence of disperse metals (Cu, Mn, Fe, Co, Ni, Zn, Pb, Al) and oxides (CuO, Cu_2O) on the thermal–oxidative degradation of natural rubber have established [230–232] that Cu, Cu_2O, CuO, Mn, Co are effective catalysts of its thermal oxidation, while Fe, Ni, Zn and Pb exert no action on this process. Copper is the most active catalyst of degradation, reducing the apparent activation energy of the process from 112.8 to 69.8 kJ mol^{-1}. As for PE and PP, copper and its oxides are believed to take part in the redox reactions of the thermal oxidation of natural rubber.

DTA, DTGA and TGA methods have been applied fairly fully [233] to investigations of the action of many high-purity oxides (Al_2O_3, TiO_2, V_2O_5, Cr_2O_3, MnO_2, Fe_2O_3, CoO, NiO, CuO, Cu_2O, ZnO, ZrO_2, MoO_3, SnO, SnO_2, Sb_2O_3, CeO_2, WO_3) on the oxidation of polybutadiene containing terminal hydroxyl groups, (hydroxylated poly(butadiene) or HPBD). The catalytic action of these oxides is shown not to be dependent on their semiconductor properties but to be associated with their activation of peroxide decomposition in the polymer, and to be proportional to their specific surface area (Fig. 4.5). However, no correlation between the catalytic activity and the influence of the specific surface area of the oxides on the thermal–oxidative activity of polybutadiene has been observed (e.g. for CoO, V_2O_5, Cr_2O_3, SnO, MoO_3, see Fig. 4.5). At the same time a satisfactory correlation *is* observed between T_2 (the second temperature of the maximal rate of mass loss) and the bandwidth of the oxide conductance (Fig. 4.6). There is no noticeable correlations between T_2 and the specific surface area of the oxides. It has been shown that the lower the value of U (the conduction band), the greater is the catalytic activity of the oxides, which is to be associated with their participation in redox reactions.

Studies on the influence of contact of polyisoprene with a metal surface (brass, fernico, steel, copper zinc, aluminium, etc.) on its thermal oxidation [359, 360] have shown that, during polyisoprene oxidation, as for PE and PP, the accumulation of

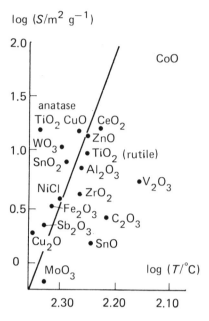

Fig. 4.5 — Logarithmic dependence of the temperature of the first maximum of mass loss (T_1) by polybutadiene containing different oxides on their specific surface area (S) [233].

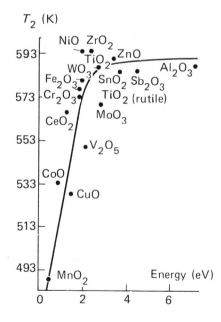

Fig. 4.6 — Dependence between the bandwidth of oxides and the temperature of the second maximum of mass loss by polybutadiene containing disperse metal oxides [358].

catalytically active compounds with the metals take place in its bulk. The reaction rates of the thermal oxidation, degradation and structurization of isoprene rubber on metals depend on the chemical nature of the metal support.

It has been shown in a few publications [230–238] that polybutadiene, natural rubber and polyisoprene display high sensitivity to the physical and chemical properties of disperse fillers which catalyse the thermal–oxidative degradation of elastomers.

4.1.3   Vinyl polymers

Polystyrene

Most studies on the degradation of filled polystyrene (PS) are aimed at its thermal–oxidative stability. As to the thermal degradation of filled PS, only the work performed by a Japanese group [239] is worthy of attention. These authors have shown the possibility of synthesis of the ethylene–styrene copolymer by the thermal degradation of PS in the presence of aluminosilicate. By selecting the conditions of PS decomposition, and the concentration and properties of the aluminosilicate, one may control the reaction of the C_6H_5 groups splitting from the PS, and effect the thermal synthesis of a new styrene–ethylene copolymer.

The results available on the thermal–oxidative degradation of filled PS have been performed by TGA, DTGA, DTA and IR spectroscopy [41,42,82,103,108,121,240].

Introduction of disperse metals into polymerizing styrene [41,42,81,108,121] markedly increases (by 30–50 K) the thermal–oxidative stability of PS as determined by its initial decomposition temperature and by the maximal rate of polymer degradation. Analogous results are obtained concerning the decomposition of PS synthesized in the presence of silica [41, 81] and various carbons (commercial carbon, graphite and diamond) [103].

The increase in thermal stability of PS synthesized in the presence of fillers is associated with non-chain inhibition (highly disperse metals with the fresh surfaces) [16] as well as with interaction of the macromolecules with the filler surface [41,42,81,103,108]. It has been found that chemical grafting of PS on the solid surface and the formation in some cases of a spatial network of the polymer occur during the polymerization of filled styrene. Additionally, the strong adsorptive interaction of the monomer and polymer with the filler surface decreases the possibility of formation of interlayers of air at the interface.

The functionalization of the surface of commercial carbon, graphite and diamond with CH_3, Cl_1, COOH or NH_2 groups [99,103,241] made it possible to elucidate the influence of the surface chemistry and the structure of carbon filler particles on the thermal–oxidative stability of PS and its copolymer with divinylbenzene synthesized in their presence. It has been found that the thermal stability of PS increases with the energy of adsorption and the degree of grafting of the polymer to the surface, which increases in the series of surface functional groups $CH_3 < Cl < COOH < NH_2$. The presence of functional groups of a given type on the filler surface enhances the thermal–oxidative stability of filled PS in the series: commercial carbon < diamond < graphite. This is due to the presence in graphite of π-conjugated structures to which the surface functional groups are bound. As a result their activity during interaction with initiators, monomers and the polymer produced becomes greater.

Polyacrylonitrile

The interaction of PAN with an inorganic filler surface (SiO_2) [242,243] completely changes the character of its thermal transformation. Thus on pyrolysing PAN at temperatures up to 573 K, it undergoes polymerization by the nitrile groups to produce conjugated chains [3], while PAN grafted on SiO_2 (aerosil) is not polymerized, and only the formation of imine groups occurs owing to the interaction of the nitrile groups with the silanol groups of the surface [242,243]. At temperatures above 573 K, the ketimine groups of PAN are converted under the influence of the OH-containing surface into enamine groups, which confirms the absence of cyclization of grafted PAN in contrast to the homopolymer. The transfer of imine hydrogen is evidently hindered, owing to the interaction of the carbon of the C=NH groups with the surface and to the formation of hydrogen bonds of imine and nitrile groups with the aerosil OH groups.

The activation energy of the thermal and thermal–oxidative degradation of grafted PAN is considerably lower than that of the homopolymer. This may be associated with the considerable difference in the chemical structure of the polymers, especially after thermal treatment at 573 K. Since at this temperature the CN groups of the grafted PAN are completely converted into amines, its mass-loss curves define the thermal degradation of the grafted amino-containing polymer [243] rather than of PAN itself. The grafted amine-containing polymer is characterized by a low activation energy for its degradation owing to the presence in it of a large number of ester bonds, $C-O-Si$ being the least stable thermally stable.

Poly(vinyl acetate) and its copolymers and poly(vinyl alcohol)

The filling of poly(vinyl acetate) (PVAc) accelerates its degradation with the formation of polyene structures and elimination of acetic acid. At the same time it is noted [162] that products of the thermal–oxidative degradation of PVAc interact with the filler surface (ZrO_2), the stoichiometry of the filler being decidedly changed in its surface layer.

Introduction of 20–40% $CaCO_3$, TiO_2, SiO_2, kaolin, talc or commercial carbon into the vinyl acetate–vinyl chloride copolymer considerably reduces its thermal–oxidative stability, which depends on the quantity of filler, its nature and its pattern of interaction with the polymer matrix [244]. Analogous mechanisms are observed for the thermal–oxidative degradation of the vinyl acetate–ethylene copolymer containing mineral fillers of different types [245].

Studies on the thermal–oxidative degradation of poly(vinyl alcohol) (PVA) with additions 5–10% (mass) of different metal salts, e.g. KI, $MgCl_2$, $(NH_4)_2HPO_4$, have shown [184,246] that such additions increase the stability of PVA through the formation of chelate compounds with the metal ions. In this case the cross-linking of PVA macromolecules is also possible via the multicharged metal ions, which is confirmed by the decrease in solubility of the polymer and the concentration of OH groups in it.

Poly(methyl methacrylate) and its copolymers

Studies on the thermal–oxidative stability of PMMA filled with disperse copper [247], cadmium, aluminium and zinc [121] have shown that disperse metals (except for aluminium) inhibit the initial stage of PMMA degradation (depolymerization) and the oxidation of decomposition products. The activation energy of the polymer degradation doubles and the thermal stability of the composite increases. One explanation is that this effect is associated with the metal particles acting as heat carriers [247]. However, such a view takes no account of the effect of the nature of the metals or their mode of introduction on the mechanism of thermal degradation of PMMA and cannot reasonably explain the observed differences in the influences of metallic fillers on the thermal–oxidative stability of the composite polymer systems.

Thus, according to reference [121], the thermal–oxidative stability of PMMA containing 2.5–12.5% (mass) cadmium produced by the thermal decomposition of bis(triethylgermyl)cadmium in a medium of monomer goes up by 40–50 K and the activation energy of the process from 88 (PMMA) to $210\,\mathrm{kJ\,mol^{-1}}$, although the molecular mass of the polymer alters, mainly owing to chain scission and depolymerization of the polymer [3].

Introduction into PMMA of disperse zinc or aluminium at the point of polymerization leads to a marked stabilization of the polymer filled only with zinc (Fig. 4.7), an effect related to [121] the non-chain inhibition [16] of the thermal–oxidative degradation due to breaking of the oxygen bond by unoxidized particles of zinc. Since aluminium particles are covered with a thick layer of oxide film, they exert practically no stabilizing influence on the thermal–oxidative degradation of the polymer.

$(\Delta p/p_0) \times 100\ (\%)$

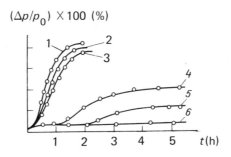

Fig. 4.7 — Thermal–oxidative degradation under isothermal conditions (523 K) of PMMA filled with aluminium (1–3) and zinc (4–6) (% (mass)) [121]: 1, 1.0; 2, 3.0; 3, 5.0; 4, 0.6; 5, 1.0; 6, 3.0.

The presence on the metal surface either of adsorbed water or of OH groups readily removed during the decomposition of PMMA catalyses the partial hydrolysis of the methyl methacrylate links with the release of methacrylic acid [114], which competes with PMMA for the metal surface. The activation energy of the degradation of the filled polymer degradation is accordingly reduced.

It has been found that the introduction of highly disperse iron into PMMA by joint dispersion decreases the thermal stability of the polymer, and the activation energy of the decomposition compared with filled PMMA which has not been subjected to mechanical activation [111]. However, this decrease is considerably less than that for the mechanical activation of the unfilled polymer. Thus, the introduction of iron into PMMA, even by the method of intensive vibrational dispersion combined with mechanical cracking of the polymer chains and dispersion of the metal, leads to thermal stabilization of the filled system.

The stabilizing action of copper on the thermal–oxidative stability of PMMA may be associated (i) with inhibition of the free-radical decomposition of PMMA, as is observed on filling with zinc chloride [248], and (ii) with interaction of the formed macroradicals with the metal surface, leading to inhibition of oxidation of the polymer at extensive levels of decomposition.

In the case of the thermal decomposition of PMMA adsorbed on the surface of dehydroxylated disperse oxides of magnesium, aluminium and silicon [249,250], the magnesium and aluminium oxides activate this process while silicon dioxide proved to be practically inert. This is associated with donor–acceptor interactions between the ester group of the polymer and the metal cations of magnesium and aluminium oxides which, on thermal treatment, are converted chemically (with the formation of carboxylate ions).

Studies on the thermal degradation of PMMA obtained by polymerization with the presence of small concentrations of up to 0.5% (mass) of TiO_2 have revealed [251] a dependence of the polymer decomposition rate at different temperatures on the filler content which features a maximum. The maximum in the mass loss lies in a narrow range of TiO_2 concentrations (about 0.12%) that, according to [251], is associated with the slight solubility of the filler in the monomer and the formation of a complex with the initiator (dicyclohexylperoxide carbonate). Such an interaction influences the molecular characteristics of the PMMA produced, especially the dependence of its molecular mass on the degree of filling, which correlates with the decomposition mechanism: the polymer decomposing at the greatest rate has the lowest molecular mass.

Introduction into PMMA of sufficiently high concentrations, i.e. up to 15% (mass), of mineral fillers (chalk, talc, kaolin) as well as of commercial carbon, along with stabilizers of thermal–oxidative degradation (dodecyl and lauryl mercaptan, dilauryl thiopropionate in levels up to 1%) causes no noticeable changes in the kinetic parameters of the process as compared with the unfilled stabilized polymer [138].

The copolymerization of methyl acrylate and butyl methacrylate with acrylic acid reveals the influence of the chemical interaction of the polymer carboxyl groups with the surface of the filler on the degradation processes. Thus, it has been shown in [252] that disperse barium, calcium and strontium oxides and their carbonates display different influences on the thermal behaviour of the butyl methacrylate–acrylic acid copolymer: the activation energy of the decomposition of the copolymer decreases in the presence of the oxides and increases for the alkaline-earth metal carbonates.

Changes in the mechanism of degradation of the copolymer containing barium, calcium and strontium oxides may be associated with the characteristics of the thermal behaviour of the carboxylates of these metals. The validity of this view is confirmed by data on the thermal degradation of a copolymer containing acrylic acid, whose functional groups are blocked by different ions: Zn^{2+}, Ni^{2+}, Co^{2+} and Cu^{2+} [253,254]. It has been found that, depending on the nature of the metal ion in the acrylate component, the thermal stability of the copolymer (according to the initial decomposition temperature) is reduced in the following series: zinc > cobalt > nickel > copper. The activation energy and pre-exponential factor correlate with the thermal stability of the copolymer and have the following values for each metal (depending on the chemical composition of the copolymer): Zn^{2+} 208–290 kJ mol^{-1}, 5.0×10^{13}–2.2×10^{19} s^{-1}; Co^{2+}, 197–306 kJ mol^{-1}, 8.0×10^{12}–7.7×10^{21} s^{-1}; Ni^{2+}, 165–275 kJ mol^{-1}, $10^{11} - 10^{20}$ s^{-1}; Cu^{2+}, 149–189 kJ mol^{-1}, 10^{9}–10^{12} s^{-1}. The reaction order of the thermal degradation reaction for most of the copolymers studied is close to 1. Based on these data, the conclusion may be drawn that, along with the chemical composition of the copolymer, it is the nature of the metal ion interacting with the carboxylate ion that determines the kinetic parameters of the thermal degradation of polymers containing functional groups and interacting with the surfaces of inorganic fillers.

4.1.4   Halogen-containing polymers

Poly(vinyl chloride)
Special attention has been paid [15,255,256] to the characteristic properties, including the thermal stability, of PVC. However, problems on the thermal and thermal–oxidative degradation of filled PVC have been studied to a lesser extent [157,257–261], although this material has found wide application.

The introduction of disperse copper into PVC [257] noticeably increases its thermal stability, perhaps owing to the partial binding by the metals of released HCl. In addition, interaction of the macroradicals produced with the metal surface is possible, inducing a three-dimensional structure of the polymer and an increase in its thermal stability.

In contrast to the metals, which act as acceptors of the HCl released during the dehydrochlorination of PVC, their chloride salts display a definite activating influence on the thermal degradation of the polymer [258]. It has been shown [258] that pyrolysis of PVC at 773 K in the presence of metal chlorides based on acidic oxides, accelerates the thermal degradation of PVC, while chlorides corresponding to basic oxides exert a negligible effect. Besides, the introduction of chlorides, as with metal oxides [259–261], alters the relationship between the aromatic and alkyl aromatic compounds liberated at the second stage of the thermal degradation of PVC. Comparison of the effects induced by metal chlorides and oxides on the thermal degradation of PVC indicates [258] that metal chlorides exert a greater effect on the thermal decomposition, resulting from the fact that many metal chlorides, especially transition metal chlorides, split to yield chlorine atoms during thermolysis. These atoms are able to interact with the polyene sites of the partially dehydrochlorinated macromolecules of PVC, promoting their cleavage.

Some publications [157, 257–261] show that certain metal oxides inhibit the release of aromatic compounds during the thermal degradation of PVC. This effect is of importance in formulating a general mechanism for the processes proceeding both in unfilled and filled PVC.

It has been shown [259] that the introduction into PVC of metal oxides (10–50% (mass)) of width differing type, (transition and non-transition, acid and basic) changes considerably the quantity and inter-relation of the aromatic products of decomposition, but their qualitative composition remains constant. In the presence of acidic oxides (TiO_2, MoO_3, Fe_2O_3) the quantity of aliphatic and aromatic hydrocarbons and their chlorinated derivatives liberated on pyrolysis increases, while most basic oxides (CaO, MgO, Ag_2O, etc.) induce a decrease in the quantity of aromatic hydrocarbons and their chloro-derivatives. Amphoteric oxides occupy an intermediate position between acidic and basic oxides. Alkali and alkaline-earth metal chlorides are able to retain strongly chlorine atoms during thermolysis while the chlorides of transition metals, copper, zirconium, cadmium and zinc lead to disproportionation and cleavage of chlorine. Therefore, the observed action of oxides on the degradation of PVC correlates well with the influence of the corresponding chlorides on the thermal stability of PVC [258,259]. Hence the conclusion can be drawn that metal chlorides formed during interaction of the liberated HCl with the metal oxides are responsible for the influence on the thermal degradation of PVC.

A study of the thermal decomposition of PVC (at 723–1173 K) in a mixture with various oxides conducted by the direct pyrolysis of the materials in a mass spectrometer and by pyrolysis on the electrical spiral in a gas chromatograph has shown that the thermolysis occurs in two stages [261]. Firstly, mainly unsubstituted aromatic hydrocarbons (benzene, naphthalene, anthracene) are liberated together with HCl, while in the second stage are formed alkylaromatic hydrocarbons (e.g. toluene). The liberation of unsubstituted aromatic compounds in the first stage of pyrolysis (about 523 K) makes it possible to suppose that polyene chains appearing on the dehydrochlorination of PVC undergo molecular rearrangement. The relatively large number of compounds formed indicate the existence of a series of different polyenes generated from the polymeric chain.

The formation of alkylaromatic compounds in the second stage of thermolysis (about 623 K) clearly indicates that, besides polyene chains, transversely cross-linked structures are produced during the dehydrochlorination of PVC. It is the decomposition of three-dimensional polyene structures at higher temperatures that leads to the formation of alkylaromatic compounds [261].

As regards PVC dehydrochlorination, zinc oxide is the most active of the metal oxides studied (ZnO, CuO, MoO_3, Al_2O_3, $3H_2O$, Sb_2O_3, SnO_2, Fe_2O_3 and $(BiO_2)CO_3$). All metal oxides except Sb_2O_3, $(BiO_2)CO_3$ and $Al_2O_3 \cdot 3H_2O$ (Table 4.4) sharply decrease the quantities of benzene and napthalene released in the first stage of the thermal degradation of PVC. The decrease in the quantity of toluene released in the second stage of decomposition occurs more slowly compared with benzene and naphthalene. As regards the thermal degradation of PVC filled with ZnO and SnO_2, the release of $ZnCl_2$ and $SnCl_4$ takes place simultaneously with that of benzene and HCl. According to [261] $ZnCl_2$ and $SnCl_4$ are responsible for the decrease in yield of aromatic compounds. During the degradation of PVC containing CuO, Fe_2O_3 and MoO_3, the corresponding metal chlorides are not detected and the mechanism for the decrease in the quantity of benzene released remains unclear.

The decrease in yield of aromatic compounds during pyrolysis of filled PVC is explained by the formation of cross-linking bonds in the polymer resulting from catalytic action of the metal oxides. This leads to a less-marked decrease in the yield of alkylaromatic compounds and to an increase in the formation of coke.

Table 4.4 — Relative quantities and maximal temperatures of release of aromatic hydrocarbons and metal chlorides during direct pyrolysis of filled PVC in a mass spectrometer [261]

Filler	$T_1{}^a$	$T_2{}^a$	Benzene		Toluene		Naphthalene		$M_xCl_y{}^c$
			T_{max}	A^b	T_{max}	A^b	T_{max}	A^b	T_{max}
Pure PVC	523	613	523	100	613	100	523	100	—
Sb_2O_3	513	623	513	78	623	44	513	50	503
$(BiO)_2CO_3$	513	613	513	96	613	53	513	60	478
ZnO	443	623	523	4	623	47	533	6	503–553
SnO_2	493	623	503	4	618	9	503	2	483–543
CuO	493	618	483	9	618	33	483	11	—
Fe_2O_3	503	623	503	33	623	50	503	36	—
MoO_3	513	618	523	9	618	30	523	6	—
$Al_2O_3.3H_2O$	513	613	513	72	613	68	523	72	—

[a] Maximal temperatures (K) for the first and second stages of PVC decomposition, respectively.
[b] Quantity of released material as a percentage of the quantity released during the degradation of unfilled PVC.
[c] $M_xCl_y = SbCl_3, ZnCl_2, SnCl_4$.

The increase in the thermal–oxidative stability of the system is associated with the appearance of additional bonds between the PVC molecules and the active surface of the fillers. The introduction into PVC of sand and kaolin, which have lower specific surface areas and a small number of active sites on their surface [86,88], reduces the thermal degradation temperature of the polymer by 15–30 K. This effect may be associated with the presence of air-filled voids at the interface and loose packing of the polymer chains weakly interacting with the surface, which promote diffusion of oxygen into the bulk of the polymer and acceleration of its thermal–oxidative degradation.

Polytetrafluoroethylene, poly(vinyl fluoride), poly(vinylidene fluoride)
There are few publications dedicated to the degradation of filled PTFE and other fluorosubstituted vinyl polymers [156,262,263]. The mass-spectrometric and gas-chromatographic analysis of the thermal degradation (733–873 K) products of PTFE filled with disperse metals (Al, Mg, Fe, Cu, Zn, Nb, Ta, the alloy $Al_3 Mg_2$) has shown [270] that they accelerate decomposition of the polymer to form readily volatile compounds (tetrafluoroethylene, octafluorocyclobutane) as well as decafluorocyclo-pentane, hexafluorocyclobutene, and dodecafluorocyclohexane. The ratios of the decomposition products depend on the nature of the filler (Table 4.5) [156].

Studies on the thermal degradation of poly(vinyl fluoride) and poly(vinylidene fluoride) filled with titanium dioxide heated at different temperatures (563–1073 K) made it possible to establish that the catalytic action of TiO_2 increases with its surface acidity, which depends on the temperature of its thermal pre-treatment [41]. With increasing acidity of the TiO_2 surface, the induction period for dehydrofluorination of both filled polymers decreases. It has been proposed [262] that the surface acid-sites of TiO_2 promote cleavage of the $C-F$ bond during the thermal degradation of poly(vinyl fluoride) and poly(vinylidene fluoride).

Table 4.5 — Composition of volatile products of decomposition (% (mass)) of PTFE filled with metals [156]

Decomposition products	Al	Mg	Al$_3$Mg$_2$	Fe	Cu	Zn	Nb	Ta
Tetrafluorethylene	55	38	12	23	78	—	—	5
Hexafluoropropylene	—	—	—	14	6	50	—	77
Octafluorobutene-1	—	—	32	—	—	—	—	—
Octafluoroisobutene	—	—	33	—	—	—	—	10
Octafluoropentene	—	—	—	—	—	6	—	8
Octafluorocyclobutene	45	62	—	58	14	5	62	—
Decafluorocyclopentane	—	—	22	3	2	13	37	—
Hexafluorocyclobutene	—	—	—	2	—	26	—	—
Dodecafluorocyclohexane	—	—	1	—	—	—	1	—

4.1.5   Carbon-cyclochain polymers

Studies on the thermal and thermal–oxidative degradation of filled phenol–formaldehyde resins (PFR) are aimed at elucidation of the role of additives of different types in the coking and graphitization processes when creating synthetic carbon materials [264–266]. In particular, it has been shown [266] that the effect of metals on coking depends on their dehydrating capacity. Such strongly dehydrating metals as nickel, copper, cobalt, even at extremely low concentrations, increase coke formation in the thermal decomposition of PFR. It has been found that disperse metals, as well as their salts and oxides, lower the temperature at which formation of the three-dimensional polymeric structure of semi-coke takes place [266].

A detailed study on the effects of different factors on the chemical transformations in filled PFR have provided a number of characteristics concerning the influence of fillers on the degradation of PFR [96,267]. Thus, when studying the thermal degradation of PFR filled with disperse iron prepared from iron carbonyl and electrolytic iron [267], it has been shown that on heating the system, two processes occur simultaneously: oxidation of the metal, which is accompanied by an increase in the mass of the sample, and degradation of the polymer with a decrease of mass. Analysis of these processes made it possible to establish two stages in the oxidative degradation of iron-filled PFR. In the first stage (473–673 K), inhibition of the rate of mass loss is observed at small concentrations of the metal, which is explained [267] by the structurization of PFR under the influence of the disperse metal at comparatively low temperatures and by restrictions on the mobility of the polymer chains associated with it.

The acceleration of the mass loss, especially by more extensively filled samples of PFR, is attributed to the catalytic influence of the iron oxides formed during pyrolysis of the polymer at higher temperatures. At this stage of the thermal–oxidative degradation the formation of a new phase occurs owing to the interaction between the metal and the solid polymer residue. The new compounds formed (carbides, carbonates, metal-containing coke, etc.) control the features of the final stages of degradation, which proceeds with minimal mass loss. Similar changes were observed in systems containing iron or ferrosilicon [up to 10% (mass)] during graphitization at high temperatures [258].

The thermal decomposition of PFR filled with $CaCO_3$, talc, commercial carbon [146] and carbon fibres [269] accelerates the degradation and carbonization of the resin. It has been found [146] that these fillers promote structurization of PFR even at temperatures below 370 K. In this case such low-molecular-mass volatile products as phenol, formaldehyde and water, as well as very minor quantities of aromatic compounds, are released. Subsequent degradation of filled, cross-linked PFR at temperatures above 620 K leads mainly to the release of phenol, cresol and xylenols, which are products of the radical reactions associated with $C-C$ bond scission. The partial release of CO at this stage is due to decarboxylation and carbonylation of the polymer. It has been remarked [146] that carbon fillers reduce the quantity of emitted volatiles, especially of phenol, obviously as a result of additional structuralization of the polymer during its interaction with the filler surface.

The introduction into PFR of commercial carbon, graphite or diamond powder bearing surface CH_3, Cl, COOH or NH_2 groups induces structurization of the polymer at comparatively low temperatures [101–103]. The density of the three-dimensional network at the same level of filling is found to be highest for carbon fillers bearing COOH and NH_2 groups. The highest density of the three-dimensional network of PFR is observed following filling with graphite containing NH_2 surface groups, which is explained by the high reactivity of NH_2 groups bound to the π-conjugated carbon atoms of graphite. The mass loss and degradation rate are shown to decrease with increasing degree of cross-linking of PFR resulting from fillers containing active surface groups [101–103].

4.2 DEGRADATION OF FILLED HETEROCHAIN AND HETEROCYCLOCHAIN POLYMERS

4.2.1 Polyethers

Polyformaldehyde

As is well-known [3] a key disadvantage of polyformaldehyde (PFA) lies in its low thermal stability, which decreases noticeably in the presence of additives, in particular acidic fillers [270,271]. Accordingly, the introduction of phosphoric or boric anhydrides (up to 2%) into PFA with terminal acetyl groups sharply lowers the temperature of thermal–oxidative degradation down to room temperature [270]. In this connection, it has been proposed that hydrated anhydrides form active complexes with PFA which, having decomposed, split the polymer chain at an ether bond. The multiple addition of anhydride to the polymer, with subsequent decay of the active complex, may lead to the formation of unstable glycols which decompose to release water. The water released is again bound to the anhydride and takes part in the cleavage of PFA.

An analogous effect is also observed during the filling of PFA with acidic and amphoteric metal oxides (Al_2O_3, Cr_2O_3, ZnO). Basic oxides (Fe_2O_3, Bi_2O_3) do not catalyse the thermal–oxidative degradation of PFA (Fig. 4.8). Obviously, the acidic and amphoteric oxides, being partially hydrated under experimental conditions, behave as acids and their mechanism of action is analogous to that of phosphoric and boric anhydrates [270]. However, unlike boric and phosphoric anhydrides, aluminium, chromium and zinc oxides do not cause dehydration of PFA at room temperature, their catalytic action being exhibited only at temperatures above 430 K.

The important role of water bound to metal oxides in the process of thermal–oxidative degradation of PFA, associated with its hydrolysis, is confirmed by studies on the decomposition of the polymer filled with aluminium, chromium and zinc oxides of different degrees of hydration. An increase in the water content leads to an increase in the decomposition rate of filled PFA [271].

The thermal–oxidative degradation of pentaplast (the polymer of 3,3-bis(chloromethyl)oxacyclobutane) is increased by disperse metal fillers in the series: aluminium < copper < zinc < iron. The accumulation of carbonyl groups in the polymer during thermal oxidation during thermal oxidation occurs in a similar manner for a series of metals (Fig. 4.9) [123]. In this connection it is reasonable to consider that the metal carboxylates formed are, as in the case of polyalkenes, catalysts of the thermal–oxidative degradation of pentaplast. It has been found that during the prolonged thermal–oxidative degradation of pentaplast filled with copper there occurs a transition from catalysis to inhibition of the process. Some authors [123] consider the metal carboxylates, which form in substantial quantities and diffuse to the polymer melt from the interface, to be the origin of such a transition.

Epoxide resins

It has been shown [145,149,272] that the introduction of highly disperse lead (up to 28% (mass)) into a mixture of the epoxide resin ZD-20 with polyaluminoethylsiloxane substantially decreases (from 20 to 6%) the mass loss when heating the system up to 620 K. It has been established by DTA, TGA and IR methods that lead catalyses hardening of the system to form a densely-cross-linked structure. In addition, lead may inhibit the thermal–oxidative degradation of the hardened resin. It has also been shown that the nature of the filler is also significant in the degradation of epoxide resins [149,272]. For instance, finely disperse iron (300 nm) is shown to accelerate the thermal degradation of epoxide resins, while aluminium influences this process only slightly. In this connection aluminated iron powders are used as fillers. Iron, manganese, aluminium and titanium oxides enhance the degradation of epoxy polymers based on a cycloaliphatic epoxide monomer and anhydride-hardened dianic oligomer. MnO_2 is found to have a stabilizing action which increases with its concentration.

Cellulose

The literature data [273–277] mainly refer to studies on the degradation of cellulose filled with metal oxides. Thus the introduction into cellulose of NaCl, NH_4Cl, $(NH_4)_2SO_4$ or $(NH_4)_2HPO_4$ [273, 274] enhances its thermal decomposition and changes the relationship between aliphatic and aromatic structures in the

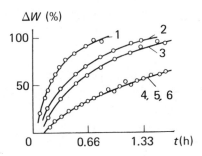

Fig. 4.8 — Kinetic curves of PFA at 463 K in the presence of 2% (mass) ZnO (1), Al_2O_3 (2), Cr_2O_3 (3), Fe_2O_3 (5), Bi_2O_3 (6); (unfilled PFA(4)) [271].

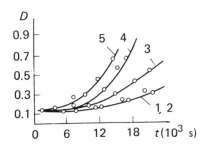

Fig. 4.9 — Kinetics of formation of COOH groups (optical density D at $1730 \, cm^{-1}$) on oxidation (513 K) of stabilized pentaplast coatings on glass (1), aluminium (2), copper (3), zinc (4) and iron (5) [123].

resulting coke. Analysis of the gas phase and degraded solid residues has shown that cellulose decomposes at C-6 to form an aldehyde group. The secondary reactions of this group with ammonium salts lead to nitrogen fixation by the polymer residue. The oxidation of the coke produced at temperatures *ca.* 900 K increases within it the concentration of ionogenic groups, as compared with coke produced from unfilled cellulose.

Systematic studies on the influence of chlorides and nitrates of various transition metals (iron, nickel, copper, etc.) on the thermal and thermal–oxidative degradation of cellulose hydrate have been carried out [275–281]. It has been noted such salts shift the dehydration process of cellulose hydrate towards the low-temperature range.

On introduction of nickel chloride into cellulose, partial separation of the thermal degradation process into two stages takes place, the change in pyrolysis rate at particular stages being proportional to the level of filling [275].

The thermal degradation of cellulose hydrate containing $NiCl_2$ [275,276] in the temperature range 363–500 K also involves its dehydration, which proceeds in the first place in the amorphous and less-ordered regions. The second stage of decomposition at 503–563 K depends on the thermal transformations of the ordered regions of cellulose hydrate.

Studies on the influence of $CuCl_2$ on the thermal decomposition of cellulose hydrate conducted by IR spectroscopy, DTA, DTGA, TGA, radiography and elemental analysis have shown [277] that $CuCl_2$ changes its direction and rate and the temperature ranges of the stages of decomposition. At temperatures below 600 K carbonization of filled cellulose hydrate is more significant compared with the unfilled hydrate. Simultaneously with dehydration and carbonization of cellulose hydrate filled with $CuCl_2$, the reduction of Cu^{2+} to metallic copper occurs in the system in two stages via the scheme: $Cu^{2+} \rightarrow Cu^+ \rightarrow Cu^0$.

The introduction of different iron salts into cellulose hydrate [278–281] has enabled elucidation of the influence of the anion on its process of thermal degradation. In particular, it has been shown that the presence of iron(III) nitrate (30%) in cellulose hydrate slightly decreases its rate of decomposition and shifts the maximum rate of mass loss by 35 K towards lower temperatures. Filling cellulose hydrate with iron chloride results in extensive dehydration which inhibits the depolymerization reaction and thus changes the direction and rate of the subsequent decomposition of the polymer [278,279].

It should be noted the solid residues resulting from pyrolysis of iron(III) chloride- and nitrate-impregnated cellulose hydrate differ considerably depending on the thermolysis temperature (Fig. 4.10) [281]. Above 600 K the yield of solid residue from iron(III) chloride-impregnated cellulose hydrate is considerably larger than that of cellulose hydrate containing iron(III) nitrate, which differs negligibly from that formed from the normal polymer. However, as seen from Fig. 4, 10(b), the iron content of samples impregnated with iron(III) nitrate is considerably higher than that in samples of cellulose hydrate impregnated with iron(III) chloride. Such a significant difference may be due to the high volatility of iron(III) chloride at elevated temperatures.

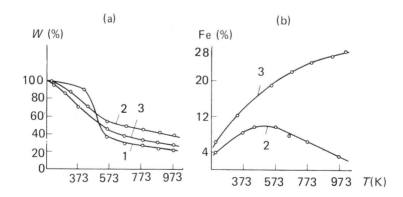

Fig. 4.10 — Dependence of the yield of solid residue (a) and iron content (b) of cellulose hydrate (1) containing $FeCl_3$ (2) and $Fe(NO_3)_3$ (3) on the thermolysis temperature [281].

4.2.2 Polyesters

The interface and chemical nature of the filler play a key role in the mechanism of the thermal degradation of polyesters, as is confirmed by data on the decomposition of PETP filled with iron oxide [282] and phosphorus-containing polyesters filled with glass fibre [151].

Introduction of a heterogeneous additive (2 and 20% (mass)) into PETP lowers the initiation temperature of its thermal degradation by 40 K. At 603–613 K the rates of mass loss of the undoped and γ-Fe_2O_3-filled PETP are low and degradation proceeds randomly. However, at 633 K the degradation mechanism of the filled polymer differs essentially from the undoped material. In this case, instead of random bond cleavage, degradation of PETP occurs at the end-groups. This causes a certain increase in the quantity of volatile degradation products as well as a decrease in the mass loss of the filled PETP. Evidently, at 633 K and higher temperatures, the chemical structure of the polymer varies substantially, leading to changes in its mechanism of degradation.

No variation in the composition of the gaseous, liquid and solid decomposition products are observed during the thermal–oxidative degradation of phosphorus-containing polyesters filled with glass fibre [105] compared with the unfilled, cross-linked polyester. This is probably explained by the fact that the reinforcing filler has a small specific surface area and that the contribution due to chemical interaction of the polymer with the glass-fibre surface to processes proceeding at the interface is negligible.

The influence of the nature of disperse fillers on the thermal and thermal–oxidative degradation mechanisms of polyesters is also confirmed by examination [283,284] of the thermal stability of polyacrylate F-2 filled with disperse copper and molybdenum disulphide (75% (mass)) or their mixtures (20 and 55% (mass), respectively. The stabilizing action of copper is accounted for in [283] by the possible formation of coordinative bonds, such as between the copper and an ester group, copper and a lactone ring or, more probably, by interaction of the free radicals formed with copper, with the appearance of species of $-R-CO-Cu-O-R'$ type, resulting in inhibition of the thermal decay of the polymer. As regards degradation of the filled system in air, copper may act as an oxidation inhibitor.

The heating of molybdenum disulphide in the filled systems induces chemical reactions which decrease the thermal stability of the filled system as compared with the normal polymer. Here SO_2 and other products released during heating play a key role. Certain results [151,282–284] confirm the conclusion that the thermal stability of the filled polymer systems is determined by the interaction of the fillers with functional groups of the polymer, the character of which depends on the chemical nature of the filler surface.

4.2.3 Sulphur-containing polymers

The thermally stable heterochain polymers featuring sulphur in the main chain are rather sensitive to the action of agents promoting the scission of the $C-S$ and $C-O-S$ bonds [16,18]. Introduction of fillers containing adsorbed water and oxygen as well as functional groups are expected to exert a substantial effect on the thermal stability of this class of polymer [285–287]. Thus, the studies of thermal and thermal–oxidative degradation of poly(diphenylene sulphone) (PPS) filled with carbon, metals (Ni, Al, Sn, Ag, Cu) and oxides (SiO_2, SnO_2, Al_2O_3, Cu_2O) carried out by the TGA method have established [286] that Ni, Al, SiO_2, SnO_2, Al_2O_3 and carbon exert practically no effect on the thermal stability of the polymer, while tin, copper and their oxides (Cu_2O, SnO), which are able to undergo oxidation, decrease the thermal stability of the filled polymer.

When fillers are introduced into PPS, its thermal–oxidative degradation occurs with release of the same compounds that are observed for filler-free PPS but to a considerably greater extent (Fig. 4.11) [287]. It has been proposed that the ability of fillers to absorb oxygen results in more extensive oxidation of the filled PPS. At high levels of incorporation and with developed surfaces, fillers can play a substantial role in the initiation of oxidation of the polymer at the interface.

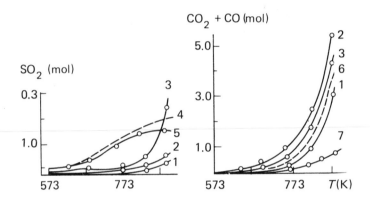

Fig. 4.11 — Curves of SO_2 and $CO_2 + CO$ liberation on the thermal oxidation of PPS over 1 h [287]: 1, PPS; 2, PPS + 60% (mass) graphite; 3,4, PPS + + 60% (mass) MoS_2; 6, PPS + 60% (mass) graphite (calculated curve); 7, graphite.

It should be noted that the influence of molybdenum disulphide on the thermal oxidation of PPS is more complicated than that of graphite. This is confirmed by comparison of the quantities of SO_2 released during the thermal oxidation of PPS, molybdenum disulphide and the polymer–MoS_2 composite at 570–870 K (oxygen pressure 32.5 kPa). Fig. 4.11 shows that extensive oxidation of MoS_2, with the formation of large amounts of SO_2, occurs at a temperature of 620 K. Two temperature ranges of release of SO_2 are observed for filled PPS. The total quantity of released SO_2 in the temperature range 570–820 K is less than would be expected from the contributions of PPS and MoS_2 to the process. This may be associated with the fact that PPS, on interacting with the molybdenum disulphide surface, protects it from oxidation. In addition, the interaction of PPS with the elemental sulphur formed during MoS_2 decomposition is possible, thereby preventing release of SO_2. The formation of complex compounds of molybdenum with organosulphur compounds is also possible.

The quantity of SO_2 released during the thermal–oxidative degradation of the composite at temperatures above 820 K is greater than that calculated from the individual components. This may be due to the decomposition of the structures formed in the initial stages of degradation with the chemical participation of the filler [287].

4.2.4   Nitrogen-containing polymers

Aliphatic and aromatic polyamides
Introduction into polyamides of fillers which may interact with the terminal functional groups of the polymer should show a substantial effect on the thermal stability of composites. Indeed [288–291], the filling of PCA with highly disperse metals, graphites, glass fibre, etc., increases its thermal and thermal–oxidative stability. In particular, the introduction into PCA of highly disperse lead produced by the thermal decomposition of lead formate in the polymeric medium [42] impedes the release of CO during the thermal degradation of filled PCA (Fig. 4.12) [290]. The CO_2 output is intiated by the filler, and this influence increases with the metal concentration in the polymer (Fig. 4.13). No water is found in the pyrolysis products.

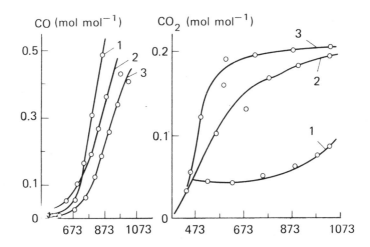

Fig. 4.12 — Effect of lead content in PCA and its decomposition temperature on liberation of CO and CO_2 [290]: 1, PCA; 2, PCA + 20% (mass) Pb; 3, PCA + 30% (mass) Pb.

A comparison of the data obtained by pyrolytic gas chromatography and TGA made it possible to postulate [290] that the initial process of the thermal degradation of PCA, which is accompanied by a negligible mass loss and the release of CO_2, is due to homolytic cleavage of the amide bonds and to decarboxylation. The main degradation of the polymer, which is accompanied by a considerable mass loss, is induced by secondary decomposition reactions leading to the formation of CO. The absence of water in the volatile products of thermal degradation of filled PCA may be associated with the fact that its terminal COOH groups form salt-like components with the metal surface. There is the possibility of formation of complex compounds between the amino groups and a metal [42] as well as of inclusion compounds [87]. The formation of such chemical compounds between PCA and lead increases the thermal stability of the polymer at higher decomposition temperatures.

Studies on the thermolysis of aromatic polyamide (poly-(m-phenylene isophthalamide)) have shown [292] that, beginning from a temperature of 393 K, H_2O and CO_2 are the basic volatile components, while from 620 K there is an additional component, HCN. Increasing the temperature to 670 K does not change the qualitative composition of the gaseous pyrolysate whose molar ratio is $1:1:0.6$ ($H_2O:HCN:CO_2$). The filling of aromatic polyamide with activated carbon fibre results in the earlier release of HCN, which begins even in the initial stages of the process, i.e. at 393 K. Moreover, the molar ratio of the water, HCN and CO_2 products of the thermal degradation of the composite is not constant. The introduction into aromatic polyamide of *inactivated* carbon fibre does not change the qualitative composition of the gaseous degradation products; however, as with activated carbon fibre filler, the ratio of components is shifted towards an increase in the share of H_2O and CO_2 [292]. One may suppose that the observed effects are related to the catalytic action of the fibre surface during the polymer degradation, which affects the release of HCN even at the initial stages of the process. However, the shift in ratio of the volatile decomposition products in favour of H_2O and CO_2 may occur owing to the participation of the water and oxygen adsorbed by the carbon fibre surface.

Polyurethanes

The introduction of fillers into PUs should have a substantial influence on their thermal stability, since the formation of coordinative bonds between the nitrogen-containing (urethane) polymer groups and the atoms of the metal surfaces becomes possible. This assumption is confirmed by [122,293–296] concerning studies of the thermal stability of filled PUs. Lead and its oxides are known to accelerate the thermal degradation of the polymer owing to the formation of unstable complexes with the urethane groups, in particular during the degradation of linear and network polydimethylsiloxane urethane synthesized from OH-containing oligoisoprene, dimethyl dichlorosilane and a mixture of 2,4- and 2,6-toluene diisocyanates in the presence of highly disperse lead and iron [1–15% (mass)] (Fig. 4.13) owing to their interaction with the urethane and isocyanate groups.

The formation of linear and network PUs in the presence of disperse fillers and on substrates [122,292–296] introduces additional factors which influence their thermal stability. In this case the functional groups (isocyanate, hydroxyl) of components along with the polymer urethane groups also interact with the solid surface, thereby changing the molecular mass, chemical structure, density of cross-linking and hydrogen bonding between macromolecules [41,81].

Structural variations in PUs arising during their synthesis on a solid surface undoubtedly affect the thermal stability of the polymers. However, the diversity of these various factors makes it impossible to determine with confidence the contribution of the filler to the degradation of polyurethanes. The influence of the solid

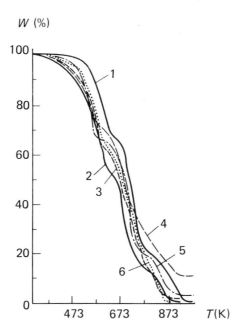

W (%)

Fig. 4.13 — Curves of mass loss by polyurethane obtained with a ratio of NCO:OH equal to 1.25 (1) and 4.0 (2) which contains 1.5 (5) and 8.5% (mass) (6) lead; the ratio of NCO:OH in samples 3–6 is 1.25 [294].

surface is ambiguous and depends both on its nature and on the chemical structure of the corresponding PU. The diversity of chemical structures produced also exerts an influence on the mechanism of thermal degradation: there are cases both of an increase in the decomposition rate and of net stabilization of the polymer in the presence of solid materials [122].

Polyimides and polybenzimidazoles

Few literature data on the degradation of filled PIs [297] and polybenzimidazoles [298] indicate that fillers activate the decomposition of labile bonds in these polymers. Thus, the mass loss of PI filled with graphite and boron nitride [50% (mass)] [297] at 573 K is 2.1% and for unfilled PI it is 0.8%. However, further exposure of the system at the same temperature promotes stabilization of the physical and mechanical properties of the system, which depend on secondary cyclization of the polymer. Temperature increase enhances the mass loss and decreases the physical and mechanical characteristics of the filled polymer, which may be induced by decomposition processes influencing the backbone of the polymer, in particular, its aromatic links.

It has been shown [298] that the nature of the filler substantial affects the thermal and thermal–oxidative degradation of polybenzimidazoles. Thus finely disperse (300-nm) iron accelerates the thermal degradation of PFR, epoxide resins and polybenzimidazole, while aluminium has only a slight effect. It has been suggested that the use of aluminized iron powders for filling polybenzimidazole makes it possible to preserve the mechano-physical and magnetic characteristic properties of the composite.

Based on the mass-spectroscopic analysis of volatile products of the degradation of filled polybenzimidazole, the following schemes for its thermal–oxidative decomposition under the catalytic influence of both iron and the iron oxides produced have been suggested [298]:

$$\text{(benzimidazole-C-phenyl-CO-O-phenyl)} \xrightarrow[\text{[O]}]{Fe_2O_3}$$

$$\longrightarrow \text{(benzimidazole-C-phenyl)}^{\cdot} + {}^{\cdot}\text{(phenyl)} + CO_2$$

$$\text{(benzimidazole-C-phenyl-CO-O-phenyl)} \xrightarrow[\text{[O]}]{Fe_2O_3}$$

$$\longrightarrow \text{(benzimidazole-C)} + {}^{\cdot}\text{(phenyl)}^{\cdot} + CO + {}^{\cdot}\text{(phenyl)}$$

4.2.5 Polyorganosiloxanes and polyelementoorganosiloxanes

Noting the high sensitivity of siloxane bonds to nucleophiles and electrophiles, one may assume that inorganic disperse fillers exert a greater effect on the degradation of polyorganosiloxanes than on organic polymers.

The first publications [299–301] dealing with the influence of metals (tin, antimony, copper, lead, aluminium, nickel, selenium, tellurium, zinc, iron, cadmium, silver, platinum, gold, etc.) on the degradation of PDMS applied as thin films on the metal substrate established that, in an inert atmosphere, none of the metals (except lead) participate in gelation and formation of a three-dimensional polymer structures. In an atmospheric environment, lead, tellurium and selenium accelerate the formation of a three-dimensional polymer structure and the degradation of PDMS. A proposal was made that the metals break the siloxane chain and, on reacting with the resulting fragments, form species containing metal atoms in the chain. These compounds are unstable and decompose with the subsequent gelation. However, Metkin and Pietrosky [302] have shown that copper and iron (and to a lesser extent, steel and duralumin) produce a stabilizing action on the thermal degradation of PDMS at 623 K. The mass loss of PDMS in contact with a copper surface for 18×10^3 s does not exceed 10%, while for iron the figure is 15%, whereas on a fluoroplast surface it is about 30%. The nature of the substrate has no substantial influence on variations in the molecular PDMS.

From these results the authors of [302] concluded that inhibition of the thermal degradation of PDMS on copper and iron surfaces is associated with a reaction which proceeds between the active polymer sites responsible for depolymerization (terminal OH groups) and the metal to form a stable complex taking no part in depolymerization. From these data [302] one may expect that the thermal stabilization of polyorganosiloxanes will be enhanced on doping with highly disperse iron and copper and, obviously, other metals. Indeed, it has been found [16,42,299,303–311] that doping with disperse metals, especially those formed in the polymeric medium during the thermal decomposition of certain metal compounds, can inhibit the thermal–oxidative and thermal degradation of polymers.

Stabilization of polymers with disperse metals is possible at the expense of both the chemical interaction of the polymer with metals and, owing to the substantial difference between oxidation rates of the metal and the polymer, of stabilization by oxygen diffusing through the bulk of the composite.

The statement that the stabilizing agent (in the case of a highly disperse metal) should produce stronger bonds with the polymer than those whose presence in the polymer induces its thermal instability [299] is valid from the thermodynamic standpoint. From the kinetic viewpoint, the thermal–oxidative degradation of a polymer may be prevented by the introduction of a stabilizer or filler which possesses, at higher temperatures, great reactivity towards oxygen, thus forming an inert product or compound able to stabilize the polymer by the thermodynamic mechanism.

In publications [16,299,303–311] the mechanism of non-chain inhibition of the thermal–oxidative degradation of thermally stable polymers, including polyorganosiloxanes, is theoretically substantiated and studied experimentally. The elementary process of the interaction of oxygen with the acceptor, called 'non-chain inhibition', means that, with stabilizer at a sufficient concentration, oxygen does not take part in reactions initiating the formation of hydroperoxide (see reactions (4.1)–(4.6)) but instead is completely adsorbed by the stabilizer.

This mechanism of stabilization is verified in studies of the high-temperature oxidation (570–770 K) of polyorganosiloxanes stabilized by the active oxygen scavengers (Fe, Cu, Co, NiO, FeO, etc.) generated during the thermal decomposition of metal oxalates in the polymer.

The data of [311] confirms the existence of a non-chain mechanism for the stabilization of polyorganosiloxanes in the presence of Fe, FeO and Cu. They show that

(i)   the quantity of metal (or oxide) obtained during the decomposition of the corresponding oxalate is in accord with that calculated from its decomposition reaction;

(ii) as oxygen diffuses into a sample, the entire metal (or oxide) is converted into the corresponding stable oxide and the quantity of oxygen adsorbed is close to that calculated from the stoichiometry (Table 4.6);

(iii) polyorganosiloxane, which is readily subject to thermal oxidation, and which decomposes at once in the absence of stabilizer, in the presence of metals begins

Table 4.6 — Oxygen uptake by highly disperse iron and copper generated in trimethylcyclopolysiloxane [311]

Metal	Reaction	Quantity of O_2 adsorbed by sample (cm^3)	
		Calculated	Experimental
Fe	$Fe + O_2 \longrightarrow Fe_2O_3(Fe_3O_4)$	1.00	1.02
		1.28	1.33
Cu	$Cu + O_2 \longrightarrow Cu_2O \longrightarrow CuO$	1.00	1.05
		1.30	1.32

to oxidize rapidly and to lose catastrophically its mechanical and physical properties after complete oxidation of the metal;

(iv) the stabilizing effect is determined by the ability of the metal or its lower oxide to form a stable oxide, as well as by the rate of oxygen uptake under the experimental conditions;

(v) the lifetime of the polymer, τ, calculated by the formula $\tau = [Z]l^2$ (where $[Z]$ is the acceptor concentration and l is the sample thickness) [307] satisfactorily agrees with the experimental data;

(iv) the kinetic parameters of the thermal oxidation of polyorganosiloxane–metal composites agree satisfactorily with those calculated.

The results obtained enable one to predict that the methods of non-chain inhibition of the thermal–oxidative degradation of thermally stable polymers, including polyorganosiloxanes, may be successfully used, along with procedures for chain inhibition, to create polymer composites containing disperse metals, oxides and sulphides as fillers.

Highly disperse metals generated in polyorganosiloxane composites are able to interact at a high rate not only with oxygen to form the corresponding stable oxides but also with groups of the type $Si(R)_2-O\cdot$ to form the grouping $-Si-O-M$. The formation of such a grouping would, undoubtedly, influence the subsequent thermal stability of the filled polyorganosiloxane: an increase in the bond energy of $M-O$ as compared to that of $Si-O$ would improve the thermal properties of polysiloxane and *vice versa*. For instance, the introduction into PDMS of Ti, B, P, Al and Fe during synthesis increases the thermal–oxidative stability of the polymer [312,313]. The thermal degradation of PDMS filled with disperse titanium and iron oxides [10–15% (mass)] is similar to that of PDMS bearing titanium and iron atoms in the chain. This points to the chemical interaction of the polymer macromolecules with metal oxides during the thermal degradation of polyorganosiloxane.

Consequently, even after oxidation of the highly disperse metals to oxides, they may still play a substantial role in the thermal degradation of polymers.

We have studied the thermal–oxidative degradation of polyorganosiloxane synthesized by the thermal polycondensation of diphenylsilane diol filled with

(10–35% (mass)), highly disperse iron, nickel, cobalt, copper, cadmium, lead and bismuth [314–323], which are generated in the monomer solution by electrolytic or thermal methods [42].

Iron, nickel, lead, cadmium and copper shift the initiation of polymer degradation towards lower temperatures and bismuth towards higher temperatures, whereas cobalt has no influence on the initiation temperature of the thermal–oxidative degradation of polyorganosiloxane. The observed difference is explained as follows. A considerable quantity (10–60%) of cyclic molecules — hexaphenylcyclotrisiloxane and octaphenylcyclotetrasiloxane is formed during the thermal polycondensation of the monomer, including the filled system [321]. In addition, during the polycondensation of diphenylsilane diol filled with disperse metals, low-molecular-mass products of their interaction, i.e. silanolates, are produced. The molecular mass of the polymer formed also varies substantially depending on the nature of the metal. Furthermore, there is a different relationship between the linear and branched polymer chains formed, depending on the nature of the metal introduced into the monomer. The set of molecular and structural characteristics of polymers synthesized in the presence of metals of different types determines their thermal properties.

According to TGA and IR data, the removal of cyclic siloxanes contained in the polymer system occurs on heating the filled polyorganosiloxane at the initial stage of thermal–oxidative degradation (600–700 K). Consequently, the mass losses at this stage are completely determined by the quantity of cyclosiloxanes formed during the polymer synthesis, i.e. by the nature of the metal introduced.

At the same time, degradation with the scission of $Si-C_6H_5$ bonds takes place at these temperatures in polymers filled with metals, which is confirmed by the appearance of benzene in the volatile degradation products. This results from the fact that disperse metals possessing a polarizing action interact by adsorption and chemisorption not only with the silanol groups of the polymer but also with the C_6H_5 groups. The adsorptive interaction of the polymeric C_6H_5 groups with the metal surface induces a redistribution of the electron density in the $Si-C_6H_5$ bonds and decreases their strength; evidence for this is provided by the degradation of the polymer filled with lead, iron and nickel, which occurs mainly by $Si-C_6H_5$ bond scission, from which benzene is isolated at comparatively low temperatures.

It should be noted that a relationship exists between the quantities of benzene and cycloorganosiloxanes released at the same disperse metal concentrations (20%) in polysiloxane, which gradually changes in the series $Pb > Fe \geqslant Ni \geqslant Cd > Bi > Cu > Co$, ranging from the elimination solely of benzene (lead) to the release solely of cycloorganosiloxanes (cobalt) [315,319–322]. This effect is accounted for by the different relative effects on the metals on $Si-O$ and $Si-C_6H_5$ bond cleavage, which is due to differences in the polarizing action of the metals [64].

Distinctions in the interaction of metals with diphenylsiloxane-based polyorganosiloxane also affect the rate and extent of mass loss by the polymer as well as the formation of three-dimensional networks. Disperse lead, iron and nickel, which promote the degradation of polyorganosiloxane, mainly by $Si-C_6H_5$ bond scission with subsequent formation of a three-dimensional structure, decrease the rate of mass loss, especially at temperatures above 673 K.

Disperse powders of iron, cadmium and lead have been introduced into the polyorganosiloxane with the purpose of excluding the influence of the adsorptive interaction of diphenylsilane diol with the metal surface on the chemical structure of the polymer and on the formation of free radicals. The activation energy of the thermal–oxidative degradation of the polymer filled in this way increases in the series from cadmium (138–150.5 kJ mol^{-1}) to lead (150.5–175.5 kJ mol^{-1}) and iron (159–209 kJ mol^{-1}). High values of the activation energy for the degradation of polyorganosiloxane indicate that disperse metal powders, introduced mechanically into the polymer, influence first of all restriction of the thermal mobility of the molecules and, secondly, promotes cross-linking during degradation.

EPR studies of the polyorganosiloxane synthesized by the thermal polycondensation of diphenylsilane diol filled with disperse bismuth, cadmium and lead have shown that, even before the initiation of thermal degradation, it contains paramagnetic centres (PMCs), the concentration of which is 10^{15}–10^{16} spins g^{-1} of the polymer (Figs 4.14, 4.15) [318,320,323]. The EPR spectrum of the polymer samples

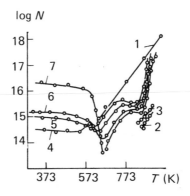

Fig. 4.14 — Temperature dependence on PMC concentration (as number of spins N g^{-1}) in polyorganosiloxane filled (% (mass)) with cadmium (1–3) and lead (4–6) [318]; 1, 5.0; 2, 9.6; 3, 17.5; 4, 2.8; 5, 4.5; 6, 35.0; 7, 0.

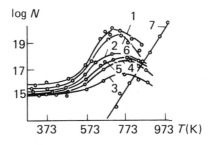

Fig. 4.15 — Temperature dependence of PMC concentration of disperse bismuth in filled polyorganosiloxane (% (mass)) [320]: 1, 0; 2, 0.3; 3, 0.97; 4, 3.0; 5, 7.5; 6, 9.3; 7, 21.5.

is a symmetrical singlet of line width $\Delta H = 477.6\text{--}636.8 \, Am^{-1}$. Hence, the highly disperse metals formed in the diphenylsilane diol medium promote polymer degradation at higher temperatures. One may surmise that the presence of PMCs in the filled polyorganosiloxane is one of the reasons for the lower activation energy of its thermal–oxidative degradation.

The validity of this supposition is confirmed by the appearance of PMCs at 670–870 K both in the unfilled polysiloxane and in samples containing up to 3.0% (mass) of bismuth, the mass loss from which begins at temperatures higher than those of other filled samples (see Figs 4.14 and 4.14). The dependence of the PMC concentration on temperature shows maxima, the positions of which correspond to the maximal rates of mass loss by filled polymer samples. The maximal PMC concentration in polyorganosiloxane samples filled with lead increases, but for cadmium decreases, with increasing the metal concentration. Increasing lead concentration not only increases the PMC concentration but also reduces the temperature at which their maximal concentration is reached in the polymer mass. The opposite dependence is observed for polyorganosiloxane containing cadmium (see Fig. 4.14) [318].

There are two turning points corresponding to two stages of degradation on the PMC concentration–temperature dependence curves for polyorganosiloxane filled with bismuth. On heating samples filled with bismuth, the PMC concentration reaches a minimum at 620–670 K, the position and value of which are directly dependent on the metal concentration. Subsequent elevation of the temperature to 773 K results in a gradual increase in the PMC concentration, which reaches a maximum, the value of which is inversely proportional to, while the corresponding temperature is directly proportional to, the bismuth concentration. A second minimum in the PMC concentrations is observed within the temperature range 770–870 K. According to the character of the dependence on the bismuth concentration, it corresponds to the first minimum, although is less clearly defined. At temperatures above 870 K there is a sharp increase in the PMC concentration. In the same temperature range (*ca.* 920 K) PMCs appear in the samples of polyorganosiloxane with low levels of filler (Fig. 4.22). In unfilled polymer, PMCs appear at 620–670 K and their concentration is always higher than that of the bismuth-filled polymer, but lower than that of polyorganosiloxane containing lead or cadmium (Fig. 4.14).

The complex character of the PMC-concentration dependences in metal-filled polyorganosiloxane can be explained by a variety of chemical processes which take place in the polymer on heating (fission of the Si—O and Si—C_6H_5 bonds, polymer structurization, recombination of PMCs at the metal surface, the production of cross-linked polyelementoorganosiloxane, etc. [314–323]). The processes promoting either the formation and accumulation of PMC (splitting of the Si—C_6H_5 and Si—O bonds) or their removal (cross-linking of segments of the polymer chains, PMC recombination at the metal surface, etc.) dominate, depending on the temperature.

One should note that, at extensive levels of degradation of metal-filled polyorganosiloxanes, the products of their chemical interaction are formed in the solid residue in the form of carbides, silicates, silicides, etc., which are determined by X-ray diffraction as separate phases.

The effect of disperse oxides of metals on the thermal–oxidative and thermal stability of polyorganosiloxanes is similar in many cases to that of metals, especially at high temperatures where both the oxidation of metals and the reduction of oxides are observed [315,324–326]. In contrast to metals, disperse oxides are characterized by the presence on their surface of Lewis- and Brönsted-active sites [58–62], which may exert a considerable action on the destruction of polyorganosiloxanes, especially in the low-temperature range (up to 673 K). This action may also play a key role in the degradation of polyorganosiloxanes, because water bound to the acid sites is present at the oxide surface [58–62]. The bound water is a carrier of protons of the surface acid sites and promotes not only degradation associated with hydrolysis but also the formation of three-dimensional polymeric structures and thermal ageing of the filled siloxane elastomers [326,327]. The silanol groups at the surface of silica, glass and quartz are established as being additional centres for the depolarization of polyorganosiloxane rubbers at the $Si-O$ bond and as inhibiting the oxidation of organic radicals of the macrochains. The depolymerization of siloxane rubbers is especially pronounced in the presence of water bound to the surface silanol groups of silica.

The influence of disperse metal oxides on the thermal and thermal–oxidative degradation of polyorganosiloxanes has been described in detail in a number of publications [325–333]. According to [334–337] not only the oxides and hydroxides of aluminium, iron and beryllium but also the oxides of titanium, silicon, cobalt, copper, nickel, manganese and chromium and sulphides of copper and iron [10–15% (mass)] affect stabilization of the system by preventing the destruction of siloxane macrochains. The stabilizing influence of oxides is explained by the formation of stable complexes. The authors of [338] concluded that the thermal stabilization of PDMS by iron and titanium oxides is due to their chemical interaction with the polymer chains to form, during the degradation process, a new thermally stable high-molecular-mass compound with metal atoms in the siloxane chain. Based on the agreement between experimental data on the mass loss, change in intrinsic viscosity, content of gel fraction and formation of volatile products during the degradation of PDMS samples filled with titanium and iron oxides and PDMS containing iron and titanium atoms in the siloxane chain, conclusions were drawn on the chemical interaction of the oxides with polyorganosiloxane and the incorporation of hetero-atoms into the chain.

The influence of SiO_2 (quartz, aerosil), NiO, Al_2O_3, MgO, CaO and BeO on the thermal oxidation of organic radicals and the destruction of the PDMS siloxane chain has been studied [335]. It has been established that, up to 573 K, SiO_2, NiO and Al_2O_3 slightly affect the polymer mass loss but at temperatures above 573 K noticeably accelerate its thermal oxidation. Magnesium, calcium and beryllium oxides, which possess pronounced basic properties, enhance the depolymerization of PDMS to form hexamethylcyclotrisiloxane. The disperse oxides MnO_2, Fe_2O_3 and Ni_2O_3 shift the initiation of the thermal–oxidative degradation of polymethylphenyl-siloxane towards higher temperatures [339], while Cr_2O_3, SnO_2, ZrO_2 and Co_2O_3 lead to a broadening of the temperature range of polymer degradation. The greatest polymer mass losses are observed on the introduction of V_2O_5 and Cr_2O_3, while the smallest are given by Ni_2O_3. The reasons for these variations have not been fully elucidated.

Thus, the influence of disperse oxides on the thermal and thermal–oxidative degradation of polyorganosiloxanes, according to many researchers, is associated with the same factors as for metals, with due allowance for the acid–base properties of the oxides [315,325].

The influence of the surface chemistry of disperse oxides is displayed rather clearly in studies of the thermal and thermal–oxidative degradation of polyorganosiloxanes containing C_6H_5 groups which are able to undergo π-interaction with the surface acid-sites of the oxides.

TGA of the polyorganosiloxane samples obtained in the presence of several metal oxides (Co_2O_3, MgO, ZnO, NiO, CuO, Bi_2O_3, PbO, CdO, SiO_2, TiO_2, Fe_2O_3 and Al_2O_3) during the thermal polycondensation of diphenylsilane diol has shown [325] that they may be divided, approximately, into several typical groups depending on the rate of mass loss, the temperature characterizing the maximal rate of mass loss, and their influence on the quantity of solid residue. Magnesium, zinc, nickel, cobalt and copper oxides exert practically no action on the rate of polymer mass loss (Fig. 4.16) irrespective of the level of filling. The temperatures of initiation of

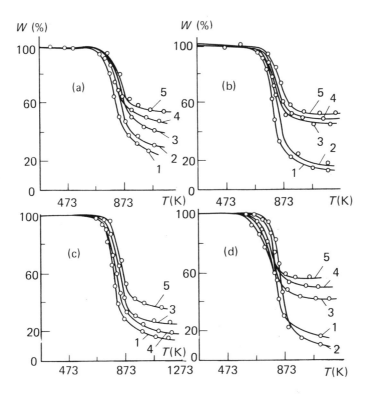

Fig. 4.16 — Curves of mass loss by polyorganosiloxane containing disperse oxides of zinc (a), magnesium (b), cobalt (c) and copper (d) (% (mass)) [325]: 1, 0; 2, 9.1; 3, 16.6; 4, 37.5; 5, 44.5.

degradation and of maximal rate of mass loss shift to low temperatures by about 20–50 K. The quantity of solid polymeric residue after complete cessation of the mass loss is lower than that for unfilled polysiloxane for samples containing NiO_2, Co_2O_3 and MgO and coincides for copper and zinc oxides. Cycloorganosiloxanes are the main volatiles of polyorganosiloxane degradation in the presence of these oxides. Minor quantities of benzene, i.e. less than during degradation of the unfilled polymer, are released only at temperatures above 820 K.

The shift by 50–100 K towards high temperatures of the maximal rate of polymer mass loss is peculiar to bismuth, cadmium and lead oxides (Fig. 4.17). The half-life

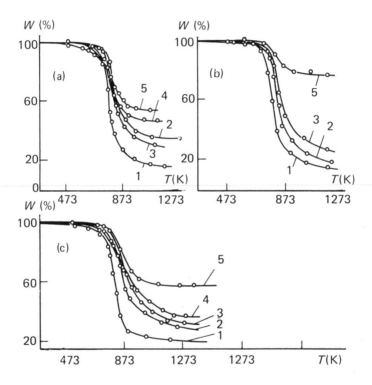

Fig. 4.17 — Curves of mass loss by polyorganosiloxane containing cadmium (a), bismuth (b) and lead (c) oxides (% (mass)) [325]: 1, 0; 2, 9.1; 3, 16.6; 4, 37.5; 5, 44.5.

temperatures (i.e. for a mass loss of 50%) are 850 K (Bi_2O_3), 870 K (CdO) and 920 K (PbO) respectively, and for the unfilled polymer 820 K. It should be noted that the initiation temperature for the decomposition of polyorganosiloxane containing these oxides shifts towards low temperatures in the same sequence, i.e. Bi_2O_3, CdO. However, owing to the decrease in the rate of degradation of the filled polymer, a significant lowering of the mass loss and a rise of the half-life temperature are observed in the sequence of oxides indicated. The quantity of solid residue of the degradation of polyorganosiloxane at concentrations of Bi_2O_3, CdO and PbO oxides of less than 10% increases from Bi_2O_3 to PbO and exceeds the value of the solid residue from unfilled polymer. The relative quantities of cycloorganosiloxanes and benzene which are released during degradation alter in favour of increased benzene in the same sequence. The yield of benzene also increases with the concentration of each oxide in polyorganosiloxane.

When studying the degradation of polyorganosiloxane samples containing SiO_2, Fe_2O_3, TiO_2 and Al_2O_3, the indicated tendency becomes enhanced: the initiation temperature of degradation is reduced with a simultaneous sharp decrease in the rate of mass loss, which leads to a shift of the maximal rate of mass loss and the half-life temperature of the polymer by 100–120 K towards higher temperatures (the latter excepting Al_2O_3) (Fig. 4.18). The quantity of solid residue obtained with these

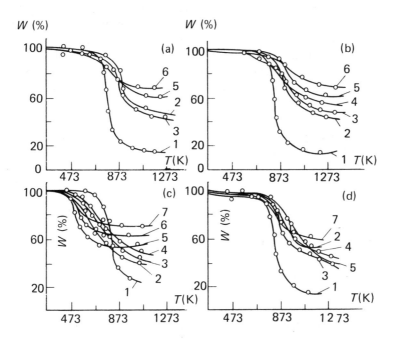

Fig. 4.18 — Curves of mass loss by polyorganosiloxane containing iron (a), titanium (b), aluminium (c) and silicon (d) oxides [325]. Concentration of iron and titanium oxides (% (mass)): 1, 0.2; 2, 9.1; 3, 16.6; 4, 28.5; 5, 37.5, 6, 50.0; concentration of aluminium and silicon oxides (% (mass)): 1, 0; 2, 2.0; 3, 4.0; 4, 9.1; 5, 16.6; 6, 28.5; 7, 37.5.

oxides is 60–70%, which is two to three times that obtained from the degradation of unfilled polymer (Fig. 4.18). In the degradation of polyorganosiloxane filled with SiO_2, TiO_2, Fe_2O_3 and Al_2O_3, benzene is the sole volatile product. The major effects of these oxides on the degradation mechanism are displayed even on the introduction of very small quantities [2–4% (mass)].

Thus, in the series of oxides Co_2O_3, MgO, ZnO, NiO, CuO, Bi_2O_3, CdO, PbO, SiO_2, TiO_2, Fe_2O_3, Al_2O_3 the following tendencies are revealed concerning their influence on the degradation of polyorganosiloxane synthesized in their presence during the polycondensation of diphenylsilane diol

   (i) a decrease in the initiation temperature of degradation and in the rate of the mass loss of polymer,

  (ii) an increase in the half-life temperature and the amount of solid residue,

 (iii) an increase in the proportion of benzene in the total quantity of volatiles.

The sequence is generalized and tentative, since some changes in this sequence are possible as regards certain characteristics within each of the groups studied.

    It is known [41, 81] that on heating unfilled polysiloxane synthesized by the polycondensation of diphenylsilane diol up to 770 K, only hexaphenylcyclotrisiloxane is released as a volatile product of the degradation. At higher temperatures benzene is also formed owing to cleavage of the $Si-C_6H_5$ and $SiO-H$ bonds. If the degradation proceeds via the siloxane bonds with the formation of cyclosiloxanes to promote the complete decomposition of the polymer with a high rate and minimal solid residue, then decomposition of the polymer via the silicon–carbon bonds leads to structurization and, consequently, to a decrease in the rate of mass loss and to an increase in the solid residue of the polymer following degradation. Unbound or physically adsorbed water does not influence the polymer degradation.

    The above data indicate that the nature of the disperse oxide fillers may play a key role in determining the relative importance of the processes of polyorganosiloxane degradation via $Si-C_6H_5$ and siloxane bonds. The influence of the oxides on polyorganosiloxane degradation is determined according to their position in the sequence of the donor–acceptor properties of the surface. The electron-acceptor and proton-donor ability of metal oxides increases in the series from Co_2O_3 to Al_2O_3 [58–62]. The oxides at the beginning of a series (Co_2O_3, MgO, ZnO, CuO) possess basic properties and, owing to their nucleophilic interaction with siloxane groups, promote chain cleavage to form cyclic decomposition products. As a result the initiation temperatures of degradation and the temperature of the maximal rate of decomposition become lower, and the solid polymer residue becomes smaller.

    The oxides Fe_2O_3, TiO_2, SiO_2 and Al_2O_3, being strong solid acids of aprotic and protic types [58], are able to undergo donor–acceptor interaction with the C_6H_5 groups of the polymer that have a negative charge, which causes a weakening of the $Si-C_6H_5$ bond, its splitting and hence additional grafting and structurization of the polymer. As a result of these processes, the rate and the extent of mass loss by the polymer decrease.

    The effective donor–acceptor interaction of polyorganosiloxane with the surface of the oxides Fe_2O_3, TiO_2, SiO_2 and Al_2O_3 leads to a shift of the initiation temperature of degradation towards the low-temperature range, benzene being released as a volatile decomposition product. However, owing to the subsequent grafting and structurization of the polymer, the temperature of the maximal rate of mass loss shifts by 100–120 K towards higher temperatures, and the temperature of the polymer half-life reaches 1070 K.

    The introduction of iron, titanium and silicon oxides into the polymer substantially increases its thermal stability, in agreement with data on their influence on the thermal stability of PDMS [312,313]. However, aluminium oxide, having the highest electron-acceptor and considerable proton-donor ability [58–62], promotes intense degradation of the polymer. In this case only benzene is released at a comparatively low temperature (470–520 K) [41,81] at which the organic groups (50–70%) are removed. With subsequent increasing temperature, the process is practically complete below 670 K by formation of a structurized inorganic polymer of the aluminosilicate type.

Data on the structurization process at different temperatures and concentrations of the filler, which are obtained on extracting polymer samples by solvents, confirm the conclusions on the pattern of the influence of the oxide on the mechanism of degradation of polydiphenylsiloxane.

Thus, disperse metal oxides promote the structurization of polyorganosiloxane, especially as a result of the surface aprotic and Brönsted acid sites. After degradation, which proceeds intensively over a narrow temperature range (20–30 K) with scission of the $Si-C_6H_5$ and $SiO-H$ bonds and the release of benzene, the structurization process predominates. The endopeak clearly displayed on the DTA curves and the narrow minimum on the DTGA curves (Fig. 4.19) at 933 K for the polymer and, for the filled samples (depending on the nature and concentration of the filler), in the temperature range 823–853 K, are consistent with this process.

The activation energy of the thermal–oxidative degradation of polyorganosiloxane synthesized from diphenylsilane diol filled with metal oxides shows turning values in its dependence on the filler concentration at low (10–15% (mass)) filler contents. Such a complex dependence is most probably caused by the competing

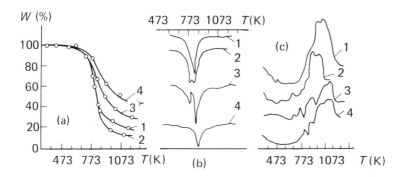

Fig. 4.19 — TGA (a), DTGA (b) and DTA (c) curves of polyorganosiloxane without filler (1) and containing 9.1% (mass) of CuO (2), PbO (3) and Fe_2O_3 (4) [325].

processes of structurization and degradation of the polymer chains [458–467] under the catalytic influence of the solid oxide surface, which features acid sites of various types. Simultaneously there exists a uniform field factor which determines the value of E_a, the polarizating action of the ions of the metal oxides (ξ) [313]. According to the data obtained (Fig. 4.20), there is a clear correlation between E_a and ξ: the greater the value of ξ of the metal ion, the lower the value of the activation energy for the thermal–oxidative degradation of the filled polymer. These results are in good

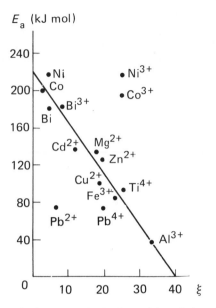

Fig. 4.20 — Correlation of activation energy for the thermal degradation of polyorganosiloxane with the polarizing action of metals.

agreement with the dependence of the polyorganosiloxane degradation mechanism on the donor–acceptor properties of the oxide surface [58–62,314–323]. The presence of such a correlation makes it possible to propose that the deviation of the Ni^{3+}, Co^{3+}, Pb^{2+} points is not random since, in the process of polymer degradation (according to radiographic data) one may observe the reductions of Ni_2O_3 and Co_2O_3 to Ni and Co, and the subsequent oxidation of Pb. The points corresponding to Ni, Co, and Pb^{4+} are situated satisfactorily on the curve for the dependence of E_a on ξ. Thus, there is a satisfactory correlation between the influence of the nature of the surface oxides and the polarizing action of their metal ions, on the one hand, and the mechanism of the degradation and its activation energy, on the other.

TGA studies of the degradation of filled PDMS and polyorganosiloxane obtained from the anionic polymerization of octamethylcyclotetrasiloxane and the thermal polycondensation of diphenylsilane diol respectively [41,81] in the presence of disperse $(20–50 \, m^2 \, g^{-1})$ metals (Fe, Co, Ni, Cu, Cd, Pb, Bi) and oxides $(Fe_2O_3, Co_2O_3, NiO, CuO, CdO, PbO, Bi_2O_3, ZnO, MgO, TiO_2, SiO_2, Al_2O_3)$ introduced at levels of 2–30% (mass) made it possible to determine the dependence between E_a and the pre-exponential factor A under non-isothermal conditions of the degradation of filled polymers. The activation energy of the thermal–oxidative degradation of polymers was calculated according to David and Zelenyanszki [339].

The degradation under non-isothermal conditions is known to be subject to the following equation:

$$f'(\alpha) = A \exp(-E_a/RT)f(a) \, , \qquad (4.7)$$

where α is the degree of conversion of the material during degradation, $f'(\alpha)$ is the rate of conversion, $f(\alpha)$ is a function reflecting the mechanism of conversion, A is the pre-exponential factor and E_a is the effective activation energy of the thermal degradation.

After the transformation, equation (4.7) takes the form

$$\log A = E_a/2.3RT + \log[f'(\alpha)/f(\alpha)] \qquad (4.8)$$

The existence of such a linear dependence points to the correctness of the studies on the polymer degradation.

The slope of the curves presented in Fig. 4.21 is individual to each polymer and does not depend on the nature, concentration or method of introduction of filler. It follows from equation (4.8) that the angle of slope is determined by the value of $1/T$;

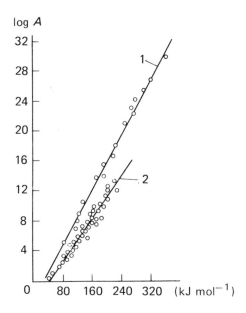

Fig. 4.21 — Dependence of the activation energy of the thermal degradation of polymers on log A (1, PDMS; 2, diphenylsilane diol-based polyorganosiloxane) filled with metals and metal oxides.

therefore, one may propose that the corresponding value of the temperature may be a quantitative criterion of the thermal stability and typical of each polymer. The values found of these temperatures for PDMS and diphenylsilane diol-based polyorganosiloxane are 593 ± 10 K and 153 ± 10 K respectively. These results are in agreement with data [39] on the thermal stability of organosilicon polymers.

Studies on the influence of disperse clay minerals on the degradation of filled polyorganosiloxanes [339–344] indicate a substantial role for the surface chemistry of minerals, in particular their acid–base properties, in the thermal stability of composites. The available data on the influence of muscovite, vermiculite, kaolin and montmorillonite, as well as of chrysotile asbestos, on the thermal degradation of polymethylphenylsiloxane, PDMS and polyphenylsiloxane indicate that the disperse minerals shift the temperatures of the maximal rate of mass loss towards the high-temperature region. It is found that, similar to oxides, disperse metals promote the structurization of organosilicon polymers at the expense of the functional groups of the polymers and also the surface OH groups of the minerals. The formation of a rigid polymer network increases the thermal stability of the composite.

However, the depolymerization of polyorganosiloxanes, especially of PDMS, competes with this process under the influence of strongly Brönsted-acid surface sites [41,81].

A clear dependence has been shown to exist between the quantity of water bound to the acid exchange sites (Al^{3+}, Mg^{2+}, Ca^{2+}, Ni^{2+}, Cu^{2+}) of kaolin and montmorillonite surfaces and their influence on the thermal degradation (depolymerization) of PDMS. The rate of polymerization of PDMS is reduced at the preset temperature of the filled system, with a decrease in the quantity of water bound to the exchanging ions of minerals. In the case of the H^+-form of minerals in which the exchanging protons preserve their high mobility and reactivity, and in the complete absence of water, the PDMS decomposition processes proceed with a higher rate at comparatively low temperatures (420–470 K) [41,81]. For minerals possessing a weak exchange capacity, or containing potassium, sodium or lithium ions at the exchange positions, the exchangable ions play a negligible role in the degradation of polyorganosiloxanes.

Thus, studies of the degradation processes of filled organosiloxanes has shown that the acid–base properties of the surface of oxides, silicates, aluminosilicates and clay minerals play a key role in the mechanism of the thermal behaviour of the filled systems.

During the degradation of polyorganosiloxanes filled with disperse metals it is normally possible to observe their stabilizing action towards the decomposition of the polymer, which is associated with the blockage of the terminal silanol groups and macroradicals on the metal surface, as well as with the non-chain inhibition of the thermal–oxidative degradation. It is emphasized that the polarizing action of metals plays a significant role in the degradation processes of polyorganosiloxanes, especially in the presence of C_6H_5 groups in the polymers.

References

[1] Korshak V. V. *Thermostable polymers.* Moscow, Nauka, 1969. 410 pp. (in Russian).

[2] Voigt J. *Stabilization of plastics against light and heat* (Monographs on Chemistry, Physics and Technology of Plastics, No. 10). Springer-Verlag, Berlin 1966.

[3] Madorsky S. L. *Polymer Reviews.* Vol. 7. *Thermal degradation of organic polymers.* New York. Wiley-Interscience. 1964. 315 pp.

[4] Grassie N. *Chemistry of high polymer degradation processes.* Interscience Publishers, New York, 1956, 350 pp.

[5] Neiman M. B. *Progress in chemistry of polymers.* Moscow, Nauka, 1969. pp. 396–448. (in Russian).

[6] Emanuel N. M. & Knorre D. G. *A course of chemical kinetics.* 2nd edition. Moscow, Vysshaya shkola, 1972. 563 pp. (in Russian).

[7] White B. *J. Appl. Polym. Sci.* 1959. **2** 281–288.

[8] Kostov G. & Bakalova El. *Neft. i khim.* 1985. **19** 14–18.

[9] Korshak V. V. *Chemical structure and temperature characteristics of polymers.* Moscow, Nauka, 1970. 420 pp. (in Russian).

[10] Rapport N. Ya., Shibryaeva, L. S., Zaikov, G. E., Iring, M., Tudes, F., & Fodor Z. *Vysokomol. Soed. Ser. A.* 1986. **28** 842–849.

[11] Costa L., Camino G., Guyot A., Bert M., Clouet G., & Brossas J. *Polym. Degrad. Stab.* 1986 **14** 85–93.

[12] McCallum J. R. & Wright W. W., *Macromol. Chem.* 1984. **3** 331–350.

[13] Radtsig V. A., Tolparov Yu. N., & Firsov E. I. *Vysokomol. Soed. Ser. B.* 1986. **28** 111–114.

[14] Andreeva V. A., Tolparov Yu. N., & Firsov E. I. *Vysokomol. Soed. Ser. B.* 1986. **28** 111–114.

[15] Minsker K. S., Kolesov S. V., & Zaikov G. E. *Ageing and stabilization of vinyl chloride based polymers.* Moscow, Nauka, 1982. 272 pp. (In Russian).

[16] Gladyshev G. P., Ershov Yu. A., & Shustova O. A. *Stabilization of thermostable polymers.* Moscow, Khimiya, 1979. 272 pp. (In Russian).

[17] Salovey R., & Luongo J. P. *J. Polylm. Sci.* 1970. Pt. *Al.* **8** 209–214.

[18] Kovarskaya B. M., Blyumenfeld A. B., & Levantovskaya Sh. I. *Thermal stability of heterochain polymers.* Moscow, Khimiya, 1977. 264 pp. (in Russian).

[19] Pavlova S. P., Zhuravleva I. V., & Tolchinsky Yu. I. *Thermal analysis of organic and high molecular weight compounds.* Moscow, Khimiya, 1983. 118 pp. (in Russian)

[20] Levantovskaya I. I., Klapovskaya O. A., Andrianova N. V., & Kovarskaya B. M. *Plast. Massy*, 1971. 46–48 (in Russian).

[21] Shnell G. *Chemistry and physics of polycarbonates.* Moscow, Khimiya, 1967. 229 pp. (in Russian)

[22] Zhuravleva I. V. & Rode V. V. *Vysokomol. Soed. Ser. A.* 1968. **10** 569–573.

[23] Korshak V. V., Vinogradova S. V., Salazkin S. N., & Komarova L. I. *Europ. Polym. J.* 1974. **10** 967–973.

[24] Zhuravleva I. V. & Rode V. V. *Vysokomol. Soed. Ser. A.* 1968. **10** 1362–1371.

[25] Danilina L. I., Muromtsev V. I., & Pravednikov A. N. *Vysokomol. Soed Ser. A.* 1975. **17** 2592–2596.

[26] Dashevskaya S. S., Akutin M. S., & Shlyapnikov Yu. A. *Vysokomol. Soed. Ser. B.* 1974. **16** 761–763.

[27] Bessonov M. I., Koton M. M., Kudryavtsev V. V., & Laius L. A. Polyimides — a class of thermostable polymers. Leningrad, Nauka, 1983. 308 pp. (in Russian).

[28] Katorzhnov N. D., & Strepikheev A. S. *Zh. Prikl. Khim.* 1959. **32** 625–628 (in Russian).

[29] Katorzhnov N. D. & Strepikheev A. S. *Zh. Prikl. Khim.* 1959. **32** 1363–1368 (in Russian).

[30] Sokolov L. B., Gerasimov V. D., Savinov V. M., & Belakov V. K. *Thermostable aromatic polyamides.* Moscow, Khimiya, 1975. 254 pp. (in Russian).

[31] Krasnov E. P., Aksenova V. P., & Kharkov S. N. Fibres made of synthetic polymers. Moscow, Khimiya, 1970. 246 pp. (in Russian).

[32] Rode V. V., Gribkova P. N., Vygodskii Ya. S. Vinogradova, S. V., & Korshak, V. V. *Izv. Akad. Nauk SSSR. Ser. Khim.* 1969. 85–88

[33] Saunders J. H., & Frisch K. C. *Polyurethanes: chemistry and technology. Pt. 1. Chemistry.* New York, Interscience, 1962.

[34] Rumyantsev L. Yu., Golovko L. I., & Omelchenko S. I. *Plast. Massy.* 1986. 19–20.

[35] Gribkova P. N., Rode V. V., Vygodskii S. Ya. Vinogradova S. V., & Korshak V. V. *Vysokomol. Soed. Ser. A.* 1970. **12** 220–228.

[36] Teleshova A. S., Teleshov E. N., & Pravednikov A. N. *Vysokomol. Soed. Ser. A.* 1971. **31** 2309–2315

[37] Blyumenfeld A. B., Kovarskaya B. M., Popov V. A., & Puzeev A. I. *Plast. Massy.* 1975. 75–76.

[38] Laius L. A., Dergacheva E. N., Zhukova T. I., & Bessonov M. I. *Vysokomol. Soed. Ser. B.* 1986. **28** 39–42.

[39] Kharitonov N. P. & Ostrovsky V. V. *Thermal and thermal–oxidative degradation of polyorganosiloxanes.* Leningrad, Nauka, 1982. 808 pp. (in Russian).

[40] Osipchik V. S., Akutin M. S., Lebedeva E. D., Dudin V. V., & Frolov V. G. *Plast. Massy.* 1973. 13–16.

[41] Bryk M. T. *Polymerization on the solid surface of inorganic substances.* Kiev, Naukova Dumka, 1981. 288 pp. (in Russian).

[42] Natanson E. M. & Ulberg, Z. R. *Colloid metals and metal polymers.* Kiev, Naukova Dumka. 1971. 348 pp. (in Russian).

[43] Hughes A. E. & Jain S. C. *Adv. Phys.* 1979. **28** 717–828.

[44] Balakina M. N., Serpuchenko E. A., & Kurilenko O. D. *Ukr. Khim. Zhurn.* 1983. **49** 945–948.

[45] Zhigotsky A. G., Shvets T. M., & Mikhailik V. A. *Poroshkovaya Metallurgiya*, 1981. **219** 69–72.

[46] Pisarenko O. I., Artemov A. V., Plachinda A. S., & Lunina M. A. *Russ. J. Phys. Chem.* **56** 47–48.

[47] Korsaks U. A., Filimonov V. N., Lokenbakh A. K., Lepin L. K. *Dokl. Akad. Nauk. SSSR* 1977. **237** 874–876.

[48] Erkelens J., & Eggink-du Burck, S. H. *J. Catal.* 1969. **15** 62–67.

[49] Mikhailovsky Yu. N., Maslovskaya P. S., & Pavlinova T. N. *Protection of metals.* 1972 **8** 481–484. (in Russian).

[50] Oranskaya O. M., Semenskaya I. V., Shmulyakovskii, Ya. E., & Filimonov V. N. *Kinet. Katal.* 1975. **16** 814–815.

[51] Maslovskaya R. S., Pavlinova T. N., Mikhailovskii Yu. N., & Zubov P. I. *Russ. J. Phys. Chem.* 1972. **46** 657–660.

[52] Maslovskaya P. S., Pavlinova T. N., Mikhailovsky Yu. N., & Zubov P. I. *Colloid. Zh.* 1972. **34** 940–943.

[53] Bryk M. T., Iliina Z. T., Chernova V. I., Drozdenko V. A., & Ognev R. K. *Metal polymer composites based on disperse titanium.* Kiev, Naukova Dumka. 1980. 166 pp. (in Russian).

[54] Bryk M. T. Chemistry of the surface of dispersed solid substances and its effect on the synthesis of filled polymers. *Fiz-Khim. Mokh. i Liofil'nost. Dispers. Sistem., Kiev.* 1982. **14** 64–73. C.A. 98: 34965g (in Russian).

[55] Fillers for polymeric composite materials. Milevski J., Kats G., & Ferrignu, T. H. *et al.* Moscow, Khimya, 1981 736 pp. Translated from English.

[56] Borovikov V. Yu. & Butyagin Yu. P. *Doklady Akad. Nauk SSSR.* 1971. **198** 618–621.

[57] Ivanchev S. S. *Radical polymerization.* Leningrad, Khimiya, 1985. 280 pp. (in Russian).

[58] Filimonov V. N. *Spectroscopy of photoconversions in molecules.* Leningrad University 1977. pp. 213–228. (in Russian).

[59] Tsyganenko A. A., Komenya A. V., & Filimonov V. N. *Adsorbtsiya i adsorbenty.* 1976. 86–91.

[60] Kiselev A. V. & Lygin V. I. *IR spectra of surface compounds.* Moscow, Nauka, 1972. 460 pp. (in Russian).

[61] Tretyakov N. E. & Filimonov V. N. *Kinet. Katal.* 1972. **13** 815–817.

[62] Tretyakov N. E. & Filimonov V. N. *Kinet. Katal.* 1973. **14** 803–805.

[63] Shvartsman L. A. & Tomilin I. A. *Usp. Khimii.* 1957. **23** 554–567.

[64] Batsanov S. S. *Electronegativity of elements and chemical bonding.*

Novosibirsk: Izd-vo SO Akad. Nauk SSSR, 1962. 195 pp. (in Russian).

[65] Chuiko, A. A., Kruglitskii N. N., Shumanskii A. P., Mashchenko, V. M. Russ. J. Phys. Chem. 1975 **49** 253–255.

[66] Kruglitskii N. N., Chuiko A. A., Shumanskii A. P., & Mashchenko V. M. *Ukr. Khim. Zh. (Russ. Ed.)* 1975 **41** 828–833. (in Russian).

[67] Sebkart P. O. & Rouzhet P. G. *J. Colloid Interface Sci.* 1982. **86** 96–104.

[68] Goworek, J., Jaroniec M., Kusak R., & Dabrowski A. *Przem. Chem.* 1983. **62** 148–152 (in Polish).

[69] Tretyakov N. E. & Filimonov V. N. *Kinet. Katal.* 1970. **11** 989–991.

[70] Morishige K., Kitaka S., & Moriyasu T. *J. Chem. Soc., Faraday Trans. 1.* 1980. **76** 728–745.

[71] Tsyganenko A. A. & Filimonov V. N. *Dokl. Akad. Nauk SSSR.* 1972 **203** 636–639.

[72] Tsyganenko A. A. & Filimonov V. N. *Usp. Fotoniki.* 1974. **4.** 51–74.

[73] Flaig Baumann, R., Neuwinger, H. D., & Boehm H. P. *Fortschr. Kolloide u. Polym.* 1971. **55** 7–15.

[74] Esumi K. & Megura K. *Sikidzaj Kyokajsi.* 1975 **48** 544–546. (in Russian).

[75] Isiryikyan A. A., Mikhailova S. S., Polunina, I. A., Tolstaya S. N., & Taubman A. B. *Kolloidn. Zh.* 1978. **40** 349–350.

[76] Parfitt G. D., Ramsbotham J., & Rochester C. H. *Trans. Faraday Soc.* 1971. **67** 1500–1506.

[77] Micale F. J., Kiernan D., & Zettlemoyer A. C. *J. Colloid Interface Sci.* 1985. **105** 570–576.

[78] Samuilova O. K. & Yagodovskii V. D. *Russ. J. Phys. Chem.* 1980. **54** 917–918.

[79] Zhimbal E. P., Smahlyaer, S. I., & Orobei, V. G. *Tr. Krasnodarskogo Politekhn. in-ta.* 1971 **40** 61–66 (in Russian).

[80] Davydov A. A., Rubens N. A., & Shchekochikhin Yu. M. *Adsorbtsiya i Adsorbenty.* 1976. **40** 61–66 (in Russian).

[81] Bryk M. T. & Lipatova T. E. *Physicochemistry of multicomponent polymer systems.* Kiev, Naukova Dumka, 1986. pp. 9–82, 324–345 (in Russian).

[82] Vlasova M. V. & Kakazei N. G. *Electron-paramagnetic resonance in mechanically damaged bodies.* Kiev, Naukova Dumka, 1979. 198 pp. (in Russian).

[83] Streletsky A. N. & Butyagin P. Yu. *Kinet. Katal.* 1980. **21** 770–775.

[84] Kochanovskaya L. D., Ovcharenko F. D., & Vasiliev N. G. *Dokl. Akad. Nauk SSSR.* 1980. **250** 1178–1180.

[85] Kiselev A. V., Lygin V. I. & Shchepalin K. L. *Kolloidn. Zh.* 1976. **38** 163–164.

[86] Tarasevich Yu. I. & Ovcharenko F. D. *Adsorption at clay minerals.* Kiev, Naukova Dumka, 1976. 352 pp. (in Russian).

[87] Goikhman A. Sh. & Solomko V. P. *Polymeric inclusion compounds*, Kiev, Naukova Dumka. 1982. 192 pp. (in Russian).

[88] Vasilev N. G. & Ovcharenko F. D. *Russ. Chem. Rev.* 1977. **46** 775–788.

[89] Telechkum V. P., & Tarasevich Yu. I., & Goncharuk V. V. *Teoret. eksp. khim.* 1977. **13** 131–134.

[90] Sivalov E. G., Vasiliev N. G., & Ovcharenko F. D. *Kinet. Katal.* 1981. **22** 1590–1594.

[91] Sivalov E. G., Vasiliev N. G., & Ovcharenko F. D. *Dokl. Akad. Nauk SSR.* 1980. **253** 1176–1179.

[92] Mank V. V. *Ukr. Khim. Zh.* 1976. **42** 1248–1251.

[93] Lahaye J. & Prado G. P. Part. Carbon: Form. Combust. Proc. Int. Symp. 1980. Ed. Siegla, D. C. & Smith, G. W. Plenum, New York, London, 1981, pp. 33–55.

[94] Kiselev A. V., Kovaleva N. V., Kosheleva L. S., & Titova T. I. *Kolloidn. Zh.* 1982. **44** 684–689.

[95] Arytyunyan R. K. *Kauchuk i rezina.* 1982. 29–31. (in Russian).

[96] Failkov A. S., Tyan L. S., Sibgatullina R. N. *Dokl. Akad. Nauk. SSSR.* 1982. **267** 422–426.

[97] Nikitina O. V., Kiselev V. F. & Lezhnev N. N. *Mekhanoemissiya i mekhano-khimiya tverdykh tel.* Frunze: Ilim, 1974. 146–149 (in Russian).

[98] Nikitina O. V., Lezhnev N. N., & Kiselev V. F. *Nauch. tr. VNII sazhevoy prom-ti.* 1972. **1** 70–95 (in Russian).

[99] Smirnov E. P., Godeev S. K., Koltsov S. I., & Aleskovsky V. B. *Zh. Prikl. Khim.* 1978. **51** 2572–2578.

[100] Gordeev S. K., Smirnov E. P., Koltsov S. I., & Aleskovsky V. B. *Zh. Prikl. Khim.* 1980. **53** 94–97.

[101] Bryk M. T., Baglei, N. N., Smirnov E. P., Gordeev, S. K., Burban, A. F., & Aleskovskii V. B. *Dokl. Akad. Nauk SSSR.* 1983. 1399–1402.

[102] Bryk M. T., Burban A. F., Gordeev S. K. Smirnov E. P., & Baglei, N. N. *Ukr. Khim. Zh.* (Russ. Ed.) 1984. **50** 1054–1060.

[103] Bryk M. T. & Burban A. F. *Polymer composites.* Berlin, Walter de Gruyter, 1986. pp. 269–274.

[104] Kouzov P. A. *Principles of the analysis of disperse composition of industrial dusts and ground materials.* Leningrad, Khimiya, 1974, 280 pp. (in Russian).

[105] Gregg, S. J. & Sing, K. S. W. *Adsorption, surface area, and porosity.* New York, Academic Press, 1967, 371 pp.

[106] Bryk M. T., Goikham A. Sh., Skobets I. E., & Ovcharenko F. D. *Kolloidn. Zh.* 1983. **45** 1043–1052.

[107] Chubar T. V., Ovcharenko F. D., Khimchenko Yu. I., & Vysotskaya V. N. *Carbon adsorbents and their application in industry.* Moscow, Nauka, 1983. pp. 92–99 (in Russian).

[108] Natanson E. M. & Bryk M. T. *Russ. Chem. Rev.* 1972. **41** 671–686.

[109] Solomko V. P. *Filled crystallizable polymers.* Naukova Dumka, Kiev 1980. 264 pp. (in Russian).

[110] Il'ina Z. T., Bryk M. T., Chernova V. I. Rybchinskii M. I., & Ognev R. K. *Fiz.-Khim. Mokh. Liofil'nost Dispersnykh Sist.* 1977. 9. 49–54 (in Russian). *C.A.* 1978, **89**, 6993k).

[111] Pakharenko V. A., Zverlin V. G., & Kirienko E. M. *Filled thermoplasts.* Handbook. Tekhnika, Kiev. 1986. 232 pp. (in Russian).

[112] Abramova I. M., Bunina L. O., Vasil'eva V. A. Zezina L. A., Kazaryan L. G., Kornienko G. N., & Sergeer V. I. *Plast. Massy.* 1986. 8–9.

[113] Ivanova, S. R., Ponedelkina I. Yu., Romanko, T. V., Karpasas, M. M. & Minsker, K. S., *Vysokomol. Soedin. Ser. A.* 1986. **28** 1217–1221.

[114] Possart W., Yudin V. S., Redkov B. P., Ziegler H., Pozdnaykov O. F. & Bischof G. *Acta Pol.* 1985 **36** 631–636.

[115] Tsvetkov N. S., Markovskaya R. F., & Ostapovich B. B. *Ukr. Khim. Zh.* (Russ. Ed.) 1986. **52** 434–439.

[116] Kovalev Ya. N., Pokonova Yu. V., Busel, A. V., & Meleshko V. N. *Izv. Vymzov. Str-vo i Arkhit.* 1986. 53–56 (in Russian).

[117] Magrupov M. A., Yusupov B. D., Akrarov M. K. Gafurov I., & Abdurakhumanov U. *Vysokomol. Soedin. Ser. A.* 1976. **18** 2203–2207.

[118] Ivan G. & Giurginica M. *IUPAC Macro'83*, Bucharest, 1983. Sec. 2–3, Sec. 5. Sp. 148–157.

[119] Kalnin' M. M. & Karlivan V. P. *Vysokomol. Soedin. Ser. A.* 1968. **10** 2335–2340.

[120] Malers Yu. Ya. & Kalnin' M. M. *Modification of polymeric materials.* **3**. 1972. p. 53–57 (in Russian).

[121] El'son V. G., Semchikov Yu. D., Khvatov N. L. *et al. Vysokomol. Soedin.* Ser. B. **22** 494–497.

[122] Kachan A. A., & Chervyatsova L. L. *Advances in chemistry of polyurethanes.* Kiev, Naukova Dumka, 1972. pp. 258–269. (in Russian).

[123] Egorenkov N. I., Lin D. G., & Sokolov E. N. *Vestsi Akad. Nauk BSSR. Ser. fiz.-tekhn. nauki.* 1975. 113–116.

[124] Gladyshev G. P., Mashukov N. I., Mikitaev A. K., & El'tsin S. A. *Vysokomol. Soedin. Ser. B.* 1986. **28** 62–65.

[125] Sizova M. D., Rakova V. G., Valiotti N. N., Sergeev V. I., Goroderskaya N. N., Karmilova L. V., *et al. Vysokomol. Soedin. Ser. B.* 1986. **28** 406–408.

[126] Nishzaki H., & Iosida K. *J. Appl. Polym. Sci.* 1980. **25** 2869–2877.

[127] Bouster C., Comel, C., Vermande P., & Veron J., *J. Therm. Anal.* 1981. **20** 115–123.

[128] Dickens B. *Amer. Chem. Soc. Polym. Prep.* 1981 **22** pp. 316–317.

[129] Shlensky O. F. *Thermal properties of glass reinforced plastics.* Moscow, Khimya, 1973, 221 pp. (in Russian).

[130] Shlensky O. F. & Afanasiev N. V. Results of science and engineering. Chemistry and production of high molecular weight compounds. *VINITI and Akad. Nauk. SSSR.* 1982. **17** 84–143.

[131] Di Giovine S. J. *Proc. Roy. Austral. Chem. Inst.* 1975. **42** p. 20–25.

[132] Chiu Jen *Amer. Chem. Soc. Polym. Prepr.* 1973. **14** 486–491.

[133] Petrova O. M., Komarova T. V., & Fedoseev S. D. *Chemistry of solid fuel.* 1982. p. 62–66.

[134] Paulik F. & Paulik J. *J. Therm. Anal.* 1973. **5** 253–270.

[135] Sickfield J., & Burhard H. *Farbe und Lack.* 1975. **81** 99–106.

[136] Grassie N. *J. Appl. Polym. Sci.: Appl. Polym. Symp.* 1979. 105–121.

[137] Zlatkevich L. *Antec 84. Plast. World Econ. 42nd Techn. Conf. and Exhib., New Orleans*, 1984. p. 253–256.

[138] Yartsev V. P., Istomin V. I., & Stretelkov Yu. V. *Nauch. Tr. Mosk. In-ta Mashinostr.* 1975. **68** 76–79.

[139] Komarova T. V., Fedoseev S. D., Petrova O. M. Seleznev A. N. & Polevaya, L. V. *Zh. Prikl. Khim.* 1977. 50 p. 1666–1669.

[140] Galchenko A. G., Khalturinsky N. A., & Berlin A. A. *Vysokomol. Soedin. Ser A.* 1980. **22** 56–59.

[141] Shlensky O. F. & Vishnevsky G. E. *Dokl. Akad. Nauk. SSSR* 1979. **246** 151–153.

[142] Egorenkov N. I., Kuzavkov A. I., & Lin D. G. *Kompozits. Polimern. Mater.* 1982. **13** 46–53.

[143] Wagner H., Sack S., & Steger E. *Acta Polym.* 1982. **34** 65–66.

[144] Sack S., Wagner, H., & Steger E. *Acta Polym.* 1985. **36** 305–310.

[145] Brodskii E. S., Lukashenko I. M., Morozova T. P., Sklemin, N. K., Kalinkevich, G. A., Stroiteleva R. G., & Khmel'mitskil, R. A. *Izv. Timiryazevsk. Selkhoz. Akad.* 1981. 150–153.

[146] Bellobono I. R., Rebora G., & Tagliavini M. *Poliplasti e plast. rinforz.* 1982. **30** 29–32, 47.

[147] Lum R., Wilkins C. W., Robbins M., Lyons A. M., & Jones R. P. *Carbon.* 1983 **21** 111–116.

[148] Andreichenko G. I. *Thermal degradation of solidified epoxy polymers*, 7 p. Dep. in ONIITEKHim, Cherkassay city. 03.04.86. N 447 khp.

[149] Firsov V. A., Lomov Yu. M., Andreev A. P., & Shologon O. I. *Effect of oxides of metals on thermal–oxidative degradation of epoxy polymers*, 7 p. Dep. in ONIITEKHim, Cherkassy city. 21.01.86. N 105 khp.,

[150] Lichtenstein N. & Ouellmalz K., *Staub-Reinhalt. Luft.* 1986. **46** 11–13.

[151] Antonov P. G., Kotegov K. V., Antonova A. V., Tsubina K. R. V., & Al'shits I. M. *Vysokomol. Soedin. Ser. A.* 1975. **17** 1252–1256.

[152] Razmerova M. V., Ronova I. A., Pavlova S. S. A., & Zhuravleva I. V. *Vysokomol. Soedin. Ser. A.* 1983 **25** 1332–1333.

[153] Styskin E. L., Itsikson L. B., & Braude E. V. *Practical high performance liquid chromatography.* Moscow, Khimiya, 1986. 288 pp. (in Russian).

[154] Berezkin V. G., Aslishoev V. R., Nemirovskaya I. B. *Gas chromatography in chemistry of polymers.* Moscow, Nauka, 1972. 287 pp. (in Russian).

[155] Vasile C., Onu P., Barboiu V., Sabliovschi M., & Moroi G. *Acta Polym.* 1985. **36** 543–550.

[156] Chaigneau M. *C. R. Acad. Sci. Ser. C.*, 1973 **276** 1625–1627.

[157] Iida T., Nakanishi M., & Goto K. *Osaka Inst. Technol.* 1972. **17A**. 53–66.

[158] Volokhonskaya M. M., Kopylov V. B., & Sorokin O. S. *Zh. Prikl. Khim.* 1983. **56** 1198–1200.

[159] Ostrovskii V. V., Starodubtseva N. N., & Kharitonov, N. P. *Zh. Prikl. Khim.* 1975. **48** 925–927.

[160] Carlson S. J. & Semlyen J. A. *Polymer.* 1986. **27** 91–95.

[161] Kovarskii A. L., Mezhikovskii S. M., Aseeva R. M. Vasserman A. M., & Berlin A. A. *Vysokomol. Soedin. Ser. B.* 1973. **15** 658–662.

[162] Bibik E. E., Vvedenskaya N. B., & Lukin Yu. N. *Studies in thermal degradation of PVA at a zirconium oxide surface.* 7 s. Dep. in VINITI. 28. 01. 85. N 7460-c (in Russian).

[163] Kirichenko E. A., Markov B. A., & Damaeva A. D. *Tr. Mosk. Khim.-Tekhnol. Inst.* 1973. **74** 108–109.

[164] Reich L. & Levi D. W. *Makronol. Rev.* 1967, **1**, 173–275.

[165] Behnish J., Schaaf E., & Zimmermann H. *Thermochim. Acta* 1980 **42** 65–73.

[166] Petrenko S. D. & Mikhailov Yu. A. *Khim. Teknologiya.* 1983. 29–30.

[167] Balakhonov E. G., Isakov G. N., Nekhoroshev V. P., Aksenenko I. V., & Ivanchev S. S. *Plast. Massy.* 1985. 47–48.

[168] Venger A. E. & Fraiman Yu. E. *Inzh.-Fiz. Zh.* 1981. **40** 278–287.

[169] Kovarskaya L. B. & Sanzharovsky A. T. *Plast. Massy.* 1971 37–40.

[170] Isakov G. N. *Methodology of a kinetic experiment in thermal analysis of polymeric materials and composites produced from them.* Deposited Doc. 1980, VINITI 4207–80 21 pp. (in Russian).; *C.A.* 1982, **96** 69867n.

[171] Pielichowski J., Wolff A., & Trebacz E., *Proc. Eur. Symp. Thermal Anal.*, Aberdeen, 1981, 2nd 123–126; (*C.A.* 1982, **96**, 36593s).

[172] Zakharov V. Yu. *Russ. J. Phys. Chem.* 1981. **55** 1538–1539.

[173] Ballauff M. & Wolf B. A. *Macromolecules.* 1981 **14** 654–658.

[174] Borham B. M. & Olson F. A. *Thermochim. Acta* 1973. **6** 345–351.

[175] Schultze D. *J. Therm. Anal.* 1973 **5** 353–354.

[176] Horowitz H. H. & Metzger, G. *Anal. Chem.* 1963. **35** 1464–1468.

[177] Venger, A. E. & Fraiman Yu. E. *Determination of kinetic parameters of the thermal decomposition of materials by the thermogravimetric analysis data.* Deposited Doc. 1976 VINITI. 1270–1276 11 p. (in Russian).

[178] Tochin V. A., Shlyakhov R. A., & Sapozhnikov D. N. *Vysokomol. Soedin. Ser. A.* 1980. **22** 752–758.

[179] Krylov, O. V. *Catalysis by nonmetals.* Leningrad, Khimiya, 1967, (in Russian).

[180] Wendlandt, W. W. & Collins L. W., *Thermal analysis*, Chichester, Wiley, 1977, 352 pp.

[181] Isakov G. N. *Fizika Goreniya i Vzryva.* 1979. **15** 11–19.

[182] Isakov G. N., Mamontov G. Ya., & Nesmelov V. V. *Thermal analysis. Part 2.* Riga, Zinatne, 1979. pp. 12–14, (in Russian).

[183] Isakov G. N. *Gas dynamics.* Tomsk, Izd-vo TGU. 1977. pp. 65–70, (in Russian).

[184] Daumantiene V. I., Andryulaitiene R. I., & Zabukas V. K. V sb. Primenie Polimer. Materialov V. Nar. Kh-ve. 1975 (**1**) 81–87 (in Russian). C.A. 85: 63592v.

[185] Malers Yu. Ya. & Kalinin M. M. *Modifik. Polimer. Materialov* (Riga), 1980. **9** 5–13.

[186] Pleshanov V. P., Berlyant S. M., & Burukhina G. A. *Vysokomol. Soedin. Ser. A.* 1982. **24** 1290–1294.

[187] Lipatov Yu. S. *Physical chemistry of filled polymers.* Moscow, Khimya, 1977. 304 pp. (in Russian).

[188] Egorenkov N. I., Lin D. G., & Belyi V. A. *Dokl. Akad. Nauk. BSSR.* 1972. **16** 1012–1014.

[189] Belokoneva G. I., Demchenko S. S., Red'ko L. A., Kachan, A. A., & Chervyatsova L. L. *Plast. Massy.* 1975. 57–58.

[190] Khanlarov T. G. *Katalit. Prevrashcheniya Organ. Soedin., Baku*, 1981 87–90 (in Russian). C.A. 98: 54644a.

[191] Kachan A. A., Chervyatsova L. L., Bryk M. T., & Red'ko L. A. *Synthesis and physicochemistry of polymers.* 1974 **13** p. 131–135, (in Russian).

[192] Emanual N. M. & Buchachenko A. L. *Chemical physics of ageing and stabilization of polymers.* Moscow, Nauka, 1982. 359 pp. (in Russian).

[193] Kalins M. M., Karlivane V. P., & Tiltinya I. *Modif. Polim. Mater.* 1969, **2** 14–19.

[194] Kalnins M. M., Karlivane V., Brakere R., & Metniece E. *Vysokomol. Soedin. Ser. A.* 1967. **9** 2178–2184.

[195] Kalnins M. M., Karlivane V. P., Brakere R., & Metniece E. *Vysokomol. Soedin. Ser. A.* 1967 **9** 2676–2680.

[196] Vainshtein A. B., Kutners E., Karlivans V., Kelner, E. I., Karp, M. B., & Ruran D. V. *Modif. Polim.* 1972. **3** 25–31.

[197] Malers L. Ya. & Miranovich A. A. *Modification of polymer materials* (Riga), 1980, **9** 23–29, (in Russian).

[198] Malers Ya., & Kalninya M. M. *Modification of polymer materials* (Riga), 1980. **9** 5–13, (in Russian).

[199] Schneider H. J., Reicherdt W., & Thinius K., *Plast und Kautsch.* 1970. **17** 310–317.

[200] Belyi V. A., Egorenkov N. I., & Lin D. G. *Vysokomol. Soedin. Ser. B.* 1972. **14**.

[201] Belyi V. A., Egorenkov N. I., & Lin D. G. *Plast. Massy.* 1973. 44–46.

[202] Egorenkov N. I., Lin D. G., & Belyi V. A. *J. Polym. Sci: Polym. Chem. Ed. 1975.* **13** 1493–1498.

[203] Egorenkov N. I., Lin D. G., & Kuzavkov A. I. *Vysokomol. Soedin. Ser. A.* 1975. **17** 1858–1861.

[204] Egorenkov N. I., Lin D. G., & Belyi, V. A. *J. Adhes.* 1976. **7** 269–277.

[205] Allara D. L., White C. W., Meck R. L., & Briggs T. H. *J. Polym. Sci.: Polym. Chem. Ed.* 1976. **14** 93–104.

[206] Malers, Yu. Ya., Kalnin' M. M., Labrentse B. O. *Modif. Polim. Mater,* 1980, **9**, 14–22.

[207] Egorenkov N. I., Lin D. G., & Belyi, V. A. *Dokl. Akad. Nauk. SSSR.* 1972. **207** 397–400.

[208] Belyi V. A., Egorenkov N. I., & Pleskachevsky Yu. M. *Vysokomol. Soedin. Ser. B.* 1970. **12** 643–644.

[209] Malers L. Ya. & Kalnin' M. M. *Modif. Polim. Mater.,* 1976. **6** 32–46.

[210] Chan M. G. & Allara D. L. *J. Colloid Interface Sci.* 1974. **47** 697–704.

[211] Allara D. L. & Chan M. G. *J. Polym. Sci.: Polym. Chem. Ed.* 1976. 1857–1876.

[212] Allera D. L. & White C. W. *Amer. Chem. Soc.: Polym. Prepr.* 1977. **18** 482–487.

[213] Egorenkov N. I., Kuzavkov A. I., & Lin D. G. *Modif. Polym. Mater.* 1985, 41–48.

[214] Egorenkov N. M., Kuzavkov, A. I., & Doktorova V. A. *Vysokomol. Soedin. Ser. A.* 1986 **28** 1525–1530.

[215] Egorenkov N. I., Lin D. G., & Belyi V. A. *Dokl. Akad. Nauk. BSSR.* 1971. **15** 710–712.

[216] Magrupov M. A., Yusupov B. D., & Atadzhanov M. R. *Uzb. Khim. Zh.* 1971. 34–36.

[217] Magrupov M. A., Yusupov B. D., Saidkhadzhaeva K. Sh., & Akhmedov M. M. *Uzb. Khim. Zh.* 1973. 41–43.

[218] Revyako M. M., Sokolov, A. N., & Razenkov V. I. *Inhibition of thermal–oxidative degradation of polyethylene filled with asbestos.* Deposited Doc. 1976, in ONIITEKHim (Cherkassy) N 30/73 (11p).

[219] Kozorezov Yu. I. *Plast Massy.* 1985. 50–51.

[220] Sizova M. D., Karmilova L. V., Vol'fson S. A., & Enikolopyan N. S. *Kompleks Metallo org. Katalizatory Polimeriz. Olefinov. (Chernoglovka)*, 1986, 93–99 (C.A. 106, 1987, 85608j).

[221] Burukhina G. A., Berlyant S. M. & Pleshanov V. P. *Plast. Massy.* 1985. 23–24.

[222] Kurukhina G. A., Pleshanov V. P., & Berlyant S. M. *Plast Massy.* 1981. 61.

[223] Lipatov Yu. S. *Physical chemistry of polymers.* Kiev, Naukova Dumka, 1967. 234 pp. (in Russian).

[224] Hawkins L. W. *Polym. News.* 1977. **4** 132–140.

[225] Uemichi Y., Kashiwaya Y., Tsukidate M., Ayame, A., & Kanoh, H. *Bull. Chem. Soc. Jpn.* 1983. **56** 2768–2773.

[226] Jellinek H. H., Kachi H., Czanderna A., & Miller A. C. *J. Polym. Sci.: Polym. Chem. Ed.* 1979. **17** 1493–1522.

[227] Hansen R.H., Benedicts T. & de Martin W. M. *J. Polym. Sci. Pt. 1.* 1964. 5897–609.

[228] Kodaira I. & Odzava D. *Gosej dsyusi.* 1975. **21** 18–22.

[229] Kiryushkin S. G., Kovalev I. B., Panchenkov G. M., Chebotarevskii A. E., & Schlyapnikov, Yu. A. *Plast. Massy.* 1982. 55–56.

[230] Murakami K., Tamura S., Kusano T. *Rep. Progr. Polym. Phys. Jpn.* 1969. **12** 282–288.

[231] Murakami K. & Tomura S., *Koge kagaki dzassi.* 1970. **73.** 574–580.

[232] Murakami K. *Sikidzaj kyekajsi.* 1972 **45** 2–9.

[233] Cullis C. F. & Laver H. S. *Eur. Polym. J.* 1978 **14** 575–580.

[234] Eliseeva I. M., Sviridenko V. G., & Lin D. G. *Vysokomol. Soedin. Ser. A.* 1986. **28** 1551–1553.

[235] Eliseeva I. M., Lin D. G., & Sviridenko V. G. *Contact oxidation and structurization of isoprene rubber on metals.* Deposited Docum. VINITI. 1986 N. 5283-C.

[236] Simpson M. B. *Kautsch. und Gummi, Kunstsoff.* 1980 **33** 83–85.

[237] Lvov Yu. A., Piotrovsky K. B., & Avdeevich T. A. *Kauchuk i rezina.* 1972 **9** 18–20.

[238] Kuzminsky A. S. *Vysokomol. Soedin. Ser. A.* 1977. **19** 2191–2203 (in Russian).

[239] Ide S., Nambu Kh., Kuroki T., & Ikemura T. *Nikhon kagaku kajsi.* 1983 1657–1663.

[240] Hirschler M. M. & Thevaranjan T. R. *Eur. Polym. J.* 1985. **21** 371–375.

[241] Burban A. F. Bryk M. T. *Plast. Massy.* 1987. 26–28.

[242] Litsov N. I., Neievich L. A., & Kachan A. A. *Dokl. Akad. Nauk. Ukr. SSR. Ser. B.* 1974. 626–628.

[243] Litsov N. I., Red'ko L. A., Negievich L. A., & Kachan A. A. *Vysokomol. Soedin. Ser A.* 1974. **16** 2700–2705.

[244] Shanks R. A. *Brit. Polym. J.* 1986. **18** 75–78.

[245] Nikolaeva T. A., Revyako M. M., Yatsenko V. V., Paushkin Ya. M. *Dokl. Akad. Nauk. BSSR.* 1982. **26** 50–52.

[246] Konovalova G. I., Pacharzhanov D. N., Kalontarov I. Ya., & Naumov V. N., *Plast. Massy.* 1970. 42–44.

[247] Nag N. K., Mukhopadhyay R., De, S. K., & Basu S., *J. Therm. Anal.* 1976. **9** 359–400.

[248] Kopylova N. A., Semchikov Yu. D., & Terman L. M. *Vysokomol. Soedin. Ser. B.* 1976. **18** 198–201.

[249] Logvinenko P. N. & Gorokhovskii G. A. *Vysokomol. Soedin Ser. A.* 1980. **22** 812–819.

[250] Logvinenko P. N., Kucher, V. G., & Gorokhovskii, G. A. Sint. *Fiz.-Khim. Polim.* 1978. **22** 47–50.

[251] Pogorelko V. Z., Karetnikova N. A., Roslyakova V. N., & Nistratova L. N. *Tr. Khim. Khim. Tekhnol.* , 1973. **1** 116–117.

[252] Semichikov Yu. D., Gitman I. P., & Kopylova N. A. *Tr. Khim. Khim. Tekhnol.*, 1973. **1** 113–115.

[253] Gronowski A. & Wojtczak Z. *J. Therm. Anal.* 1985. **30.** 345–351.

[254] Dzhardimalieva G. I., Selenova B. S., Pnonomareva, T. I., Skachkova V. K., & Pomogailo A. D. *Kompleks. Metaloorgan. Katalizatory Polimeriz. Olefinov. Chernogolovka*, 1986, 55–63 (in Russian).; *C.A.* 1987, 106, 103207j.

[255] Millan J., Martinez G., & Mijangos C. *Rev. plast. mod.* 1986 **37** 179–192, 208.

[256] Michell E. W. J. *J. Mater Sci.* 1985. **20** 3816–3830.

[257] Dasgupta A. & Bhattachrya S. K. *Indian J. Technol.* 1982. **20** 68–70.

[258] Iida, T. & Goto K. *J. Polym. Sci.: Polym Chem. Ed.* 1977. **15** 2435–2440.

[259] Iida T. & Goto K. *J. Polym. Sci.: Polym. Chem. Ed.* 1977. **15** 2427–2433.

[260] Iida, T., Nakanisi M., & Goto K. *Osaka kogye daigaku tyuo kenkyu syekho.* 1974. 1–5.

[261] Ballistreri A., Foti, A., Maravigna P., Montaudo, G., & Scamporrino, E. *J. Polym. Sci.: Polym. Chem. Ed.* 1980. **18** 3101–3110.

[262] Okazaki K., Watanabe K., & Apakava Kh. *Nikhon kagaku kajsi.* 1975. 607–610.

[263] Gubanov V. A., Zavakin I. A., Veretnnikov N. V., Sherman M. A., & Ryabinin N. A. *Vysokomol. Soedin. Ser. B.* 1982. **24** 723–727.

[264] Butyrin G. M. High-molecular-weight carbon materials. Moscow, Khimiya, 1976. 192 pp. (in Russian).

[265] Vershavskii V. Ya. Results of science and engineering. *Chemistry and production of high-molecular-weight compounds. 1976.* 67–120, (in Russian).

[266] Smirnov B. N., Tyan L. S., Fialkov A. S. Galkina T. U., & Galeev G. S. *Russ. Chem. Rev.* 1976. **45** 884–895.

[267] Chubar' T. V., Khvorov M. M., & Vysotskaya V. N. *Ukr. Khim. Zh.* (Russ. Ed.) 1980. **46** 403–405.

[268] Oya A. & Otani S. *High Temper. High Press.* 1980 **12** 663–674.

[269] Marović V. & Marinković S. *Carbon.* 1980. **18** 329–335.

[270] Goncharov G. S. & Kutina E. D. *Scientific Notes of the Leningrad State Pedagogical Institute. Chemistry and Methodology of Teaching Chemistry in Pedagogical Institute.* 1970. **433** 162–168 (in Russian).

[271] Goncharov G. S., & Kutina E. D. *Transactions of the Leningrad State Pedagogical Institute. Chemistry and Methodology of Teaching Chemistry in Pedagogical Institute.* 1970. **433** 162–168. (in Russian).

[272] Iliina Z. T., Brysk M. T., Kardanov V. K., & Kurilenko, O. D. *Ukr. Khim. Zh.* (Russ. Ed.) 1974. **40** 1180–1183.

[273] Low M. J. D. & Morterra C. *Carbon.* 1985. **23** 311–316.

[274] Kurnevich G. I., Loiko E. M., Gert E. V. Skoropanov A. S., Buyanova V. K., & Gridina U. F. *Thermochim. Acta* 1985. **90** 335–338.

[275] Gavrilov M. Z., Ermolenko I. N., Volosyuk T. P., & Borisenko E. M. *Vestsi Akad. Nauk. BSSR. Ser. Khim. Nauki.* 1979. 41–45.

[276] Ermolenko I. N., Safonova A. M., & Maleashkevich Zh. V. *Vesti Akad. Nauk. BSSR. Ser. Khim. Nauki.* 1979. 41–45.

[277] Ermolenko I. N., Gavrilov M. Z., Safonova A. M., & Malashkevich Zh. V. *Khimiya Drevesiny.* 1980. 27–33.

[278] Ermolenko I. N. & Safonova A. M. *Vesti Akad. Nauk. BSSR Ser. Khim. Nauki.* 1979. 25–29.

[279] Ermolenko I. N., Safonova A. M., Malashkevich Zh. V., Penenzhik M. A. & Kolokokina N. V. *Vestsi Akad Nauk BSSR. Ser. Khim Nauki.* 1979. 36–41.

[280] Ermolenko I. N., Safonova A. M., & Malashkevich Zh. V. *Vestsi Akad Nauk. BSSR. Ser. Khim. Nauki.* 1972. 60–66.

[281] Ermolenko I. N., Safonova A. M., & Malashkevich Zh. V. *Vestsi Akad. Nauk. BSSR. Ser. Khim. Nauki.* 1981. 63–67.

[282] Chervyatsova L. L., Motryuk G. I., & Kachan A. A. *Surface phenomena in polymers.* Kiev, Naukova Dumka, 1972. pp. 161–165, (in Russian).

[283] Korshak V. V., Gribova I. A., Pavlova S. A., Zhuravleva V., Vinogradov, A. V., & Rusakova I. O., *Vysokomol. Soedin. Ser. A.* 1977. **19** 2009–2017.

[284] Korshak V. V., Gribova I. A., Pavlova S. A., Zhuravleva I. V., Vinogradov A. V., & Namatsashvili G. V., *et al. Vysokomol. Soedin. Ser. B.* 1981 **23** 26–30.

[285] Mayatsky V. A., Sokolov L. B., Soldatov E. S. *Plast. Massy. 1982.* 31–36.

[286] Zinatullin R. F., Egorov A. E., Aminiev Kh. F., & Nigmatullin R. G. *Theses of Reports of Conference of Young Scientists.* Ufa, 1986, p. 87 (in Rusian).

[287] Korshak V. V., Sergeev V. A., Gribova I. A., Pavlova S. A., Zhuravleva I. V., Kolosova, T. A., *et al. Vysokomol. Soed. Ser. A.* 1980. **22** 1228–1232.

[288] Pesetskii S. S., Kaplan M. B., Starzhinskii V. E., *et al. Vestsi Akad. Nauk. BSSR. Ser. Fiz.-Tekhn. Nauk.* 1986. 35–38.

[289] Damyanov N., Kartalov P., & Damyanov S. *Transactions of Plovdiv Univ. Phys.* **13** 1975. 117–123.

[290] Onda, O. F., Kutiina L. V., Kogerman A. O., & Kharitinych N. E. *Ukr. Khim. Zh.* (Russ. Ed.) 1978. **44** 526–528.

[291] Korshak, V. V., Gribova I. A., Nekrasov Yu. S., Pavlova S. A., Gubkova P. N., & Avetisyan Yu. L. *Vysokomol. Soedin. Ser. B.* 1978. **20** 271–275.

[292] Volokhonskaya M. M., Kopylov V. B., & Sorokin O. S. *Zh. Prikl. Khim.* 1983. **56** 1198–1200.

[293] Baglej N. N. & Bryk M. T. *Ukr. Khim. Zh.* (Russ. Ed). 1974 **40** 827–829.

[294] Baglej N. N. & Bryk M. T. Ukr. Khim. Zh. (Russ. Ed). 1976. 42 41–45 (in Russian).

[295] Chervyatsova L. L., Belokoneva G. I., Demchenko S. S., Kachan A. A., Vonsyatskii, V. A., & Mamunya E. P., *et al. Sin. Fiz-Khim. Polim.* 1971. **8** 140–143.

[296] Chervyatsova L. L., Kachan A. A., Belokoneva G. I., Kurgan N. P., Kulik N. V., Smetankina N. P., & Oprya V. Ya. *Makromol. Granitsy Razdela Faz.* 1971, 198–202.

[297] Shcherbakova T. S., Igonin L. A., Chernova A. G., Gushchina E. I., Rodionov V. V., & Grishova A. I. *Plast. Massy.* 1976. 75–76.

[298] Flom D. G., Speece A. L., & Schmidt G. A. *Amer. Chem. Soc. Polym. Prepr.* 1967. **8** 1190–1202.

[299] Gladyshev G. P. *Methods for stabilization of thermally resistant polymers.* Preprint M., 1972. 42 p. (in Russian).

[300] Goldovsky E. A. & Dontsov A. A. *Kauchuk i rezina.* 1980. 42–46.

[301] Willis, R. F. & Shaw R. F. *J.; Colloid Interface Sci.* 1969. **31** 397–408.

[302] Metkin I. A. & Piotrovsky K. B. *Kauchuk i rezina. 1974.* 15–17.

[303] Gladyshev G. P. *Dokl. Akad. Nauk. SSSR.* 1976. **216** 585–588.

[304] Gumargalieva K. Z., Kamzolkina E. V., Kitaeva D. Kh., & Gladyshev G. P. *Vysokomol. Soedin. Ser. B.* 1974. **16** 310–311.

[305] Shustova O. A. & Gladyshev G. P. *Dokl. Akad. Nauk. SSSR.* 1975. **221** 399–402.

[306] Gladyshev G. P., Gumargalieva K. Z., & Ovcharenko E. N. *Vysokomol. Soedin. Ser. B.* 1975 **17** 775–778.

[307] Gladyshev G. P., Gumargalieva K. Z., Sevastyanov V. I., & Shustova O. A. *Vysokomol. Soedin. Ser. B.* 1975. **17** 862–863.

[308] Ovcharenko E. N. & Shustova O. A. *Vysokomol. Soedin. Ser. B.* 1975. **17** 864–866.

[309] Gladyshev G. P. *Vysokomol. Soedin. Ser. A.* 1975 **17** 1257–1262.

[310] Sevostyanov V. I., Ovcharenko E. N., & Lyashchik T. V. *Vysokomol. Soedin. Ser. B* 1976 **18** 790–793.

[311] Shustova O. A. & Gladyshev G. P. *Russ. Chem. Rev.* 1976. **45** 865–882.

[312] Nikitina T. S., Khodzhemirova L. K., Aleksandrova Yu. A., & Pravednikov A. N. *Vysokomol. Soedin. Ser. A.* 1968. **10** 2783–2794.

[313] Kirichenko E. A., Markov B. A., Ermakov A. I., & Damaeva A. D. *Russ. J. Phys. Chem.* 1973. **47** 1576–1578.

[314] Bryk M. T., Chubar T. V., & Kardanov V. K. *Itogi Nauki. Tech. Ser.: Khim. Technol. Vyskomol. Soedin.* 1982. **17** 225–249.

[315] Bryk M. T. & Kardanov V. K. *Visn. Akad. Nauk. URSR* 1979 31–40 (in Ukrainian).

[316] Natanson E. M., & Bryk M. T. *Visn. Akad. Nauk. URSR.* 1971 34–47 (in Ukrainian).

[317] Bryk M. T., Fil' T. I., Kardanov V. K. *Heterogeneous polymer materials.* Kiev, Naukova Dumka, 1973. pp. 88–93.

[318] Bryk M. T., Kompaniets V. A., & Kardanov V. K. *Sin. Fiz.-Khim. Polim.* 1974. **13** 135–140.

[319] Kardanov V. K. & Bryk M. T. *Ukr. Khim. Zh.* (Russ. Ed.) 1978. **44** 543–545.

[320] Bryk M. T., Kardanov V. K., Kompaniets V. A., & Pavlova I. A. *Sint. Fiz-Khim. Polim.* 1978. **22** pp. 54–58.

[321] Bryk M. T., Kardanov V. K., & Kurilenko O. D. *Ukr. Khim. Zh* (Russ. Ed.) 1975. **41** 685–689.

[322] Kardanov V. K. & Bryk M. T. *Fiz.-Khim. Mekh. i. Liofil'nost' Dispersn. Sistem Resp. Mezhved. Sb.*, 1975, 51–54 (*C.A.* 1976, **74**, 180987t).

[323] Bryk M. T., Kardanov V. K., Kompaniets V. A., & Pavlova I. A. *Bull. Bismuth Inst.* **1980.** 1–3.

[324] Sobolevsky M. V., Kaplan Sh. G., & Aleksandrova V. F. *Plast. Massy.* 1982. 26–28.

[325] Bryk M. T. & Kardanov V. K. *Zh. Prikl. Khim.* 1978, **51** 981–985.

[326] Bryk M. T., Sazkina O. N., Varavko I. A., & Mel'nik, L. A. *Kolloidn. Zh.* 1978. **40** 755–760.

[327] Chuiko O. O., Tiortykh V. A., & Petrova L. F. *Dokl. Akad. Nauk. URSR. Ser. B.* 1974. 817–820 (in Ukrainian).

[328] Goldovsky E. A., Fatkulina R. K., Kuzminsky A. S., & Dontsov A. A. *Kauchuk i rezina.* 1978. 17–21.

[329] Henry A. W. *Rubber Chem. Technol.* 1983. **56** 83–93.

[330] Smirnova M. *Mekh. i tekhnol. na kompoz. mater. Mater. ot 1-1a nats. konf.* Varna, 1976. Sofia, 1977 pp. 489–495.

[331] Krotikov V. A., Kharitonov N. P., & Kuznetsova L. K. *Zh. Prikl. Khim.* 1981. **54** 1785–1789.

[332] Petrova O. M. & Komarova T. V. *Plast. Massy.* 1983. 8–12.

[333] Zaikov G. E. *Problems of ageing and stabilization of polymers.* Dushanbe, Donish, 1986. p. 3–6, (in Russian).

[334] Verkhotin M. A. & Rode V. V. *Synthesis and studies in efficient chemicals, additives for polymer materials* (Tambov). 1969. **2**. 162–169, (in Russian).

[335] Skorik Yu. I., Kuchaeva S. K. *Zh. Prikl. Khim.* 1974. **47** 2621–2625.

[336] Kuzminova N. M. & Kusov A. B. *Trans. Lensovet Leningrad Inst. Techn. Inst.* 1973. **3** 91–94.

[337] Sazykina O. N., Karp L. S., & Gridunova E. B. *Kauchuk i rezina.* 1972. 9–10.

[338] Kashurkin N. A., Klochkov V. I., & Kesarev O. V. *Kauchuk i rezina.* 1978. 13–14.

[339] David P. K. & Zelenyanski E. *J. Therm. Anal.* 1973. **15** 337–340.

[340] Gorbachev V. M. *Russ. J. Phys. Chem.* 1977. **51** 292–294.

[341] Stepanov K. N., Ostrovsky V. V., Glebova I. B., & Kharitonov N. P. *Studies in the field of physics and chemistry of caoutchoucs and rubbers (Leningrad).* 1975. 215–217 (in Russian) (*C.A.* 1976, **84**, 181046x).

[342] Ostrovsky V. V., Glebova I. B., & Kharitonov N. P. *Zh. Prikl. Khim.* 1976. **49** 1402–1403.

[343] Skorik Yu. I., Khainike H., Henning H.-P., & Kuchaeva S. K. *Zh. Prikl. Khim.* 1981. **51** 124–128.

[344] Terlikovsky E. V., Simurov V. V., & Kruglitsky N. N. *Ukr. Khim. Zh.* (Russ. Ed). 1981 **47** 1243–1249.

Index

_BC_